THE OLD

New Crops Research Branch

The Yearbook of Agriculture 1970

CONTOURS OF CHANGE

UNITED STATES DEPARTMENT
OF AGRICULTURE

The helicopter and the horse
typify change in rural America.
Copter downdraft spreads pollen
in seed corn field, to establish
new hybrids. The horse is about
gone as a farm work animal,
except in rare scenes like below
in Appalachia. Grain combines
and other machines have done
away with much manual labor, but
man with a grain scoop still is
needed.

Sweet corn, left, starts trip to cannery. Herbicide test plots, right, dot ricefield at University of Arkansas branch experiment station. Effective herbicides have increased rice-growing efficiency. Right, sunflowers, an oilseed crop, provide beauty and income.

tton production is now almost
ally mechanized, with about a
llion fewer workers needed.
ft, harvesting cotton; top left,
tton awaits ginning in Missis-
ppi. On this page: Top, baled
tton in California. Center, bales
 cotton linters, short fibers
th wide industrial uses. Right,
Maid of Cotton models garment.

Above, terraces in Great Plains Conservation Program help to prevent water erosion and conserve rainfall in onetime Dust Bowl. Right, irrigating a crop with siphon tubes. Upper right, grama grass; and flood control dam pays extra dividends in recreation, scenic beauty.

Animal and mechanical research
have increased efficiency in beef
production. With a bale thrower,
one man can now bale and load
hay. Left, riding the range at a
USDA cattle research station.
Right, Omaha stockyard; steer
at feed firm research farm.

Research is vital too in dairying, along with recordkeeping. Left, USDA technician milks cow in basic research project. Lower right, data processing of dairy herd improvement records. Below, registered Jersey herd. Top right, dairy farmer.

White turkeys contrast with a
stockyard river of hogs and with
Rambouillet sheep at breeding
laboratory.

Processing and transportation are key parts of today's agricultural marketing system. Left page, cans are filled with pear halves while oranges are sized automatically and packed for fresh market. This page, women inspect peach halves for defects, and cut flowers are unloaded from a jet freighter.

Food programs of USDA bring
better nutrition to millions. Food
stamps, for instance, boost the
buying power of needy families.
Above, father pays for groceries
with food stamps, later carves
and serves. On right page, child
relaxes with spoon at a day care
center where USDA supplies food;
first graders enjoy school lunch.

City and country are growing closer, as illustrated above. Yet poverty is proportionally greater in rural areas. School facilities too often are inadequate, living conditions bad. Loans by USDA enabled the farmer at top right to rise from sharecropper and acquire a new home.

Despite rural shortcomings, the
countryside can offer beauty,
and space to breathe and enjoy
life, as contrasted here with
the sign-burdened ugliness of
a suburban county.

Exports are vital for farm income and U.S. trade balance. Lake freighter loads corn, a grain export. At Japan trade fairs, doughnuts made with flour from U.S. wheat are fried in oil from U.S. soybeans; and a man tries American lemonade. Top right, Tokyo children eat school lunch doughnuts made with U.S. products. Japan is one of our major markets.

American know-how helps the developing nations. Left, bagging corn in El Salvador corn improvement program. Right, soybean drinks fortified to offset protein deficiency. U.S. firms sell Vitasoy in Hong Kong and Saci in Brazil. Below, Vietnamese extension workers on U.S. study trip listen at a USDA exhibit.

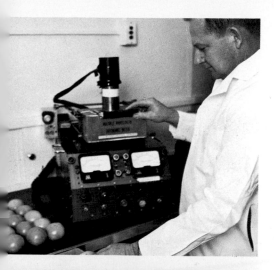

Futuristic techniques include
egg-in-round operation with
rotating tiers of hens, and
difference meter for sorting
tomatoes by stage of maturity.
On far page, green tomatoes
were sorted by eye, giving
uneven results after tomatoes
ripened for seven days. Photo
under meter shows effectiveness
of scientific sorting.

The look of tomorrow—infrared photo of Lower Rio Grande Valley. Bare fields and bare soil through sparse vegetation are green. Vegetation is pink, rose, or red, and reservoir is blue. Remote sensing planes or satellites gather infrared and other data for super-fast information on crops, soil, water.

Foreword

CLIFFORD M. HARDIN

Secretary of Agriculture

Contours of Change, the Yearbook of Agriculture for 1970, is a book about Rural America and the forces—some obvious, some subtle—that are constantly reshaping it.

The book looks not only at the technological revolution in agriculture, the changing face of Rural America, and the growing importance of America's role in world agriculture; it peers also into the 1970's and, to some extent, into the long-term future.

The 1970 Yearbook provides stimulating reading. This is evidenced by such titles as: "Are They Making a Living Down on the Farm?"—"A 20,000 Mile Train Full of Corn"—"Food for All in Need Gets Top Priority"—"Tomorrow's Vision Saves Many of Today's Rural Communities"—"Who Should Pay for Conservation?"—"Technologies for Tomorrow"—"A Sinlge Chariot with 2 Horses: The Population and Food Race."

The reader will find here the response of American agriculture—a technological revolution that has enabled the individual farmer to increase his productivity at a much faster rate than that of the industrial worker.

Using a modern feeding system for broilers, one man can now take care of 60,000 to 75,000 chickens. One man in a modern feedlot can handle upwards of 5,000 head of cattle. One man, with a mechanized system, can operate a dairy enterprise of 50 to 60 milk cows.

Agriculture, in short, does an amazingly efficient job of producing food for an ever larger number of people. Yet the farmer is not realizing a rate of return for his labor and capital investment that is commensurate with the rest of the economy.

The reader will find that the "contours of change" in Rural America stem from the past and extend into the future.

● Almost 15 million acres have been shifted from farming to nonfarming uses in the past decade. Much of this land now serves urban and urban-related purposes and a considerable portion has made way for the Nation's great highway network.

● There are now about 900,000 fewer operating farms than in 1960—largely the result of consolidations into bigger units to achieve maximum benefits of mechanization. Despite their increased size, *most farms are still family operated.* While these considerations helped many farmers, others were left without adequate economic opportunity. Those without means of livelihood joined large numbers of rural people in migratory movements to urban areas. Most found city employment; some did not; and lack of experience in industrial and urban types of work often made the adjustment difficult.

● Some communities in Rural America have become virtual ghost towns because the need for the services they once supplied declined with the drop in rural population.

● Poverty and poor housing are proportionately greater in Rural America than in our cities.

● Many community facilities that urban Americans take for granted are lacking or deficient in Rural America. In 1968, out of approximately 57,000 rural communities, some 33,000 lacked a public water system and 43,000 did not have adequate sewerage systems.

Facts such as these suggest the dimensions and importance of the task that lies ahead in creating a new, promising environment of opportunity—economic, educational, cultural, recreational—as America continues to grow. Within the coming 30 years this country's population is expected to increase by 100 million. In the decade of the seventies alone, a half-trillion-dollar expansion in economic activity is foreseen.

Much of this increase needs to take place outside the great metropolitan areas. Expansion of present towns and small cities will be required, with new centers of growth in America's heartland. It is imperative that the people of Rural America start making plans and decisions to assure that this development comes about in an orderly, healthy manner. City dwellers have an equal interest, since a sound pattern of national growth can alleviate many of today's urban problems.

Agriculture will be deeply involved in the growth process because, as this book indicates, farmers, ranchers and foresters have stewardship over much of the Nation's land and water resources. Farmers are at work every day on voluntary, cooperative programs to protect and improve America's environmental assets.

Also, agriculture is taking a leading role in attaining the goal set forth by President Nixon to "put an end to hunger in America . . . for all time." Some 10 million persons in needy families are receiving assistance through the Food Stamp and Commodity Distribution programs of the Department of Agriculture. While much remains to be done, America has turned the corner in its drive to eliminate hunger and malnutrition.

What happens beyond our national boundaries will also be of concern. For example, what will be the effect of new technology on mankind's ability to feed itself? What can we expect from higher protein in cereal grains? What are the prospects for the use of world resources?

These are some of the many subjects explored in *Contours of Change*. This is a book for all Americans. It reflects the broad functions of the Department of Agriculture.

We hope it will contribute to a better understanding of agriculture and Rural America by the American people; we hope also that it will engender in farmers and other rural Americans a fuller appreciation of their importance to the Nation and the world today; and finally we hope that it will contribute in a forceful and constructive way toward a balanced growth for the Nation and to the quality of life for all Americans.

Preface

JACK HAYES
Yearbook Editor

Everyone talks about "relevance" these days, but many of us don't realize just how relevant Rural America is to our Nation's hopes and aspirations. For one in every three Americans lives beyond the city line, in Rural America.

This Yearbook is a situation report on that often neglected third of all Americans. It is also a report on agriculture, which is sometimes taken for granted despite its role in providing us with food for life and growth, cotton and wool for our clothing, timber for our homes, and wood pulp for paper.

Here again, what could be more relevant than agriculture—which puts food on our tables every day. Agriculture is the Nation's largest industry. It provides jobs for millions of Americans on the farm, in the supermarkets and food processing plants, in the factories that make tractors and farm trucks and combines, and in the giant transportation networks that bring food to our market baskets and help deliver our farm exports overseas. Three of every 10 jobs in private employment are related to agriculture.

Contours of Change is about people, farming, rural areas, conservation and environment, food marketing and processing, developments in technology, and world food problems. This book looks back to the recent past—in some cases the more distant past. It attempts to tell where we are today, and it looks to the future.

Change is always with us, and yet sometimes we should take stock. A certain nostalgia inevitably accompanies a recording of change, as we see old ways fade and new ways take over. There is pride, too, in what has been accomplished. Pride, for instance, in USDA conservation programs of the last 35 years which, in the words of a Yearbook author, have "healed the gullies and eroded clay hills of much of the Southland, helped the amazing recovery of the Dust Bowl of the thirties, and literally changed the face of the American landscape from coast to coast." Air travelers rarely make a trip without seeing the flash of some of the nearly 2 million water-conserving farm ponds that dot the countryside today.

Contours of Change is a pictorial record, as well as a written report. The photographs bring statistics to life, show the great range of our magnificent country, depict people and places and dreams fulfilled and dreams unrealized. A poet must have written the caption for the first color photograph in this book, a scene picture on a page by itself of a Maryland dairy farm. The caption could not be used with the photograph, but it reads in part: "Across these rolling fields soldiers marched and counter-marched to Antietam, Harper's Ferry, Gettysburg. Their guns still echo in a summer thundershower."

Similarly, on a misty morning we might look across the countryside of America and see a pioneer with ax and horse and wooden plow, where today the machine has taken over—and in some ways man has lost out. But perhaps if we look again we may see through the mist a better time ahead, where progress and people go hand in hand. The past was hard, and the present is not easy. This Yearbook, hopefully, points some of the roads we can take to a brighter future.

The Yearbook Committee that planned *Contours of Change* consisted of Wayne D. Rasmussen of the Economic Research Service, who was chairman, and the following members:

Robert J. Anderson (ret.), Agricultural Research Service.
Warren R. Bailey, Economic Research Service.
John C. Blum, Consumer and Marketing Service.
Jean Brand, Extension Service.
Michael F. Brewer, Resources for the Future, Inc.
T. C. Byerly, Assistant Director for Science and Education.
Cora Cronemeyer, U.S. Department of Labor.
Lynn M. Daft, Office of the Secretary.
Wayne V. Dexter, Office of Management Services.
William A. Faught, Economic Research Service.
Ruben M. Heermann, Cooperative State Research Service.
Elizabeth S. Hight, Food and Nutrition Service.
Paul J. Jehlik, Cooperative State Research Service.
J. Don Looper, Foreign Agricultural Service.
Lloyd E. Partain, Soil Conservation Service.
C. Kyle Randall, Economic Research Service.
Phillip K. Reiss, U.S. Department of Commerce.
Lyle P. Schertz, Foreign Economic Development Service.
L. T. Wallace, University of California.
Lowell H. Watts, Colorado Extension Service.
Joseph W. Willett, Economic Research Service.

Advisers were Don Páarlberg, Director of Agricultural Economics; and M. L. Upchurch, Administrator, Economic Research Service.

Contents

THE AGRICULTURAL REVOLUTIONS

COUNTRY AND CITY—ONE NATION

AMERICA'S NEW ROLE IN WORLD AGRICULTURE

A LOOK INTO THE FUTURE

The Agricultural Revolutions

WHAT'S HAPPENED TO FARMING

A HUNDRED YEARS AGO most of the Nation's population were farmers. Anyone could go west, claim his 160 acres, and become a farmer. With farming predominant it naturally was largely subsistent—the family consumed much of what it produced, and sold or bartered a small surplus to fill out other living needs.

Farming was also largely self-sufficient. Tools were simple—a plow, a cultivator, a reaper, a scythe, and a hoe. Farmers built houses, barns, and fences out of trees felled in clearing the land for crops . . . Raised work animals for power and grew the "fuel" to feed them . . . Saved as seed stock the biggest corn ears and the best calves . . . Raised sons to till the fields, daughters to cook and weave.

Farming was truly a "way of life."

As the frontier marched westward, farming continued to expand in number of farms, acres in cultivation, and workers employed until about the period 1920–1930. Since then, the number of farms and workers has declined except briefly during the economic depression of the 1930's. Acres of cropland continued constant from the 1920's until the 1950's before declining. We now harvest crops from about the same acreage as at the beginning of this century—roughly 60 million fewer acres than at the peak.

Up to about 1920 the nature of farming had not really changed very much in 100 years. Most farmers were still largely self-sufficient with respect to what they needed for production. Horses and mules were the chief source of power except for threshing, which was done with the aid of steam engines. Soil fertility was supplied by rotating row crops with close-grown crops, grasses, and legumes.

Crop yields were about the same—corn, 26 bushels; wheat, 14 bushels; and cotton, 170 pounds—as the early 19th century. Production technology had changed hardly at all. Farming practices represented family skills, and consisted chiefly of conventional wisdom handed down from father to son.

Some folks imagine farming is still like that. They do not realize that since the mid-1920's we have seen three fullscale revolutions in U.S. agriculture—mechanical, technological, and business management—which together are changing the nature of farming.

The real beginning of the mechanical revolution in farming was marked by the advent in the late 1920's of the general purpose type tractor—soon to be mounted on rubber-tired wheels. Horse-drawn farm machines were quickly adapted to its use.

With this tractor you could plow, disk, harrow, cultivate the rows of corn and cotton, mow and bale hay, stack the bales, pull a grain harvester or a corn picker, haul trailer loads, and dozens of other jobs. This tractor essentially emancipated farming from its dependency upon animal power.

In 1930, we had over 19 million horses and mules on farms, and less than a million tractors. Today we have so few farm horses and mules that we stopped counting them in the 1959 Census of Agriculture. But we now have nearly 6 million farm tractors and their size and adaptability continually amaze.

After the general purpose type tractor, in quick succession came the self-propelled grain combine, the rice harvester, the corn picker, and the cotton picker.

We now have mechanical harvesters for almost every crop . . . Field for-

✦

AUTHORS DONALD D. DUROST and WARREN R. BAILEY are Economists with the Farm Production Economics Division, Economic Research Service.

Six-horse team was still being used to drill wheat during 1922, in Sheridan County, Mont.

age harvesters and powered silo fillers . . . Machines that dig and load potatoes, pick canning tomatoes (not the fresh), strip tobacco leaves, shake the nuts from walnut and almond trees . . . And we have a seemingly endless list of materials handling machines—bale loaders, hydraulic scoops, and so on. Imagine, we have self-propelled ladders on which the fruit picker or pruner can stand and move himself from tree to tree.

The mechanical revolution is continuing—tractors with power steering and power brakes, automatic transmissions and other automative adaptations, plus hydraulic lifts.

With all of these new tractors and machines, total manhours required in farming have declined from 23 billion in 1930, to 15 billion in 1950, 7 billion in 1968. Consequently, output per manhour doubled in the two decades between 1930 and 1950, and almost tripled in the 20 years since 1950.

The mechanical revolution has permitted each worker to grow more acres of corn or cotton and to perform each task more precisely and more timely.

The second revolution—the technological—had its real beginning with the advent of corn hybrids soon after 1930. Up to that time crop improvement had consisted largely of plant and seed selection rather than plant breeding as such.

Hybridization combines "hybrid vigor" with the heavier yielding habit of one parent variety and the sturdier plant structure of another. Associated with other practices of that era, hybridization increased the expected yields of corn by 20 to 25 percent. Eventually, the impact was even greater because of the potential it gave for combining other technologies such as fertilizer, increased plant populations, narrow row spacing, and chemical herbicides.

Up to World War II, corn typically was grown in a 3-year rotation of corn-oats-clover, without fertilizer, in 40-inch rows, planted 10,000 seeds to the acre, and the Corn Belt yield was about 38 bushels an acre.

Today, corn seldom is rotated. Leading growers typically fertilize with 150 pounds of nitrogen, plant 25,000 seeds to the acre in 20-inch rows, control weeds with herbicides, and get yields of 130 to 150 bushels an acre. The average Corn Belt yield is now 90 to 100 bushels.

The impact is two dimensional on total corn production—where we once planted 33 acres of each 100 and got 1,250 bushels, we now plant the whole 100 and get 9,000 to 10,000 bushels.

3

Above, wheat combine in 1968, Wasco County, Oreg. Below, cutting wheat with tractor-drawn binder near Fargo, N. Dak., in 1945.

Date harvesting.

We converted our grain sorghum to hybrids in a span of 4 years, about 10 years ago. The direct impact was a 25 percent increase in yield.

The U.S. acre yield of wheat has doubled since 1930—from 14 to 28 bushels—without assistance from hybridization. The gain resulted from improved natural varieties, better and more timely tillage, more effective pest control, and heavier soil fertilization. The technical problem of wheat hybridization is now solved. Hybrids are appearing in parts of the wheat region. Again, they too promise 25 percent higher yields.

Cotton lint yields have increased threefold since 1930, now average 515 pounds an acre. Part of the increase is due to a shift of acreage out of the lower-yielding southern Piedmont to the Mississippi Delta and the irrigated Southwest, where yields average 650 pounds and 1,000 pounds respectively. Again, the gain was due to improved technology—varieties, pesticides, herbicides, soil fertilization, and so on.

Other crop yield increases per acre since 1930: rice, 2,100 to 4,500 pounds; tobacco, 775 to 2,000 pounds; peanuts, 700 to 1,750 pounds; soybeans, 13 to 26 bushels; potatoes, 65 to 215 hundredweight.

Nothing equalling the spectacular new technologies in crop production has occurred in livestock—except the feed conversion ratios in broilers and turkeys.

By 1950 we were producing broilers commercially with a feed efficiency of about 3 pounds of grain ration per 1 pound of broiler live weight, and that was a gain of 40 percent over conventional farm performance. Now the ratio has been reduced to 1.8 pounds of ration per pound live weight, and it will go still lower.

Nothing like that gain in feed-conversion efficiency has occurred with hogs or beef cattle. The ratio for hogs is 3.5 to 4 pounds of grain (feed concentrates) per pound of live weight gain. But in cattle feeding the ratio is 6 to 9 pounds of grain per pound of live weight gain. These differences in feed-conversion ratios largely explain why chicken is priced so much lower than pork and beef in the supermarket.

The substantial increases in pork and beef output have resulted directly from the huge increase in feed output plus a corresponding increase in number of animals.

The mechanical and scientific revolutions have both directly and indirectly changed the nature of farming.

Understandably, farming today is highly commercial, thoroughly market oriented. From production largely for home use, it has shifted to production for sale. Today, nearly all farm output—except some feed and crop seed—goes through commercial channels.

It is true for part-time as well as full-time farms. Even in low income areas farmers supply only a part of their meat, chicken, eggs, and milk needs, and not much else. Most farm families buy their food from the supermarket because it saves work in preparation, is handier, and more sanitary.

In fact the term "commercial farmer" no longer serves to distinguish a group who are market oriented because all are thus oriented.

The greater degree of market orientation means that farmers are now highly conscious of their commodity prices, whereas formerly they were more concerned about their production costs.

Today's farming is also market oriented in another way, that of product specification and quality. Each farmer once produced the type, size, and quality of product he individually thought best, only to find that when he got there the market wanted something different. Actually, farmers often had little control of the quality they produced.

Today's farmer knows what is wanted, produces commodities according to specification—formula-fed broilers of a specified age and weight, hennery eggs, cattle fed to an exact weight and finish, wheat with a minimum protein. Product specification often is part of a production contract between the farmer and the buyer-processor.

Farmers no longer need rely on their conventional wisdom, as to what the market wants. And, today's farmer has far more control over the quality and specifications of what he produces. He uses a known, specified technique and process. Much of the guesswork on quality is gone.

It follows that the new farm production technologies are now more standardized, more widely known and accepted. Thus, we know the amount of fertilizer (element by element), the row spacing, and the plant population for top yields of corn; the feed ration for a meaty broiler; and how to produce fine head lettuce. Our producers do not skimp or take chances on the production mix—they simply cannot afford to.

Just as today's farming is more market oriented, so is much of the food processing migrating off the farm.

Remember when a farmer sold and delivered fresh, raw milk to the final household consumers? Now his milk is picked up daily at the farm, taken to a plant for pasteurization, homogenization, vitamin D irradiation, and bottling for delivery to food store or

Applying nitrogen to corn on the contour, Harrison County, Ind.

home. Likewise, the separation of cream from milk is now done almost entirely off the farm.

Cattle feeding (grain fattening) formerly was done entirely by farmers on farms, particularly those in the Corn Belt. Now much of the cattle feeding is done in huge specialized lots where fattening rations are carefully formulated, feed ingredients mixed and metered out to each feeding pen. Animals are fattened to the exact degree of finish desired.

Broilers, eggs, and turkeys were once predominantly farm enterprises, often a sideline managed by the farmer's wife. Now these products are produced mainly in specialized facilities, not associated with a "farm," where feed rations are carefully formulated, and environment is carefully controlled. Only in some local areas are "farm" or "ranch" eggs, chickens, and turkeys still available directly to consumers.

Many other products were sold directly to consumers from a roadside stand or an open air "farmer's market"—an area with individual sales booths. Farmers brought their apples, pumpkins, potatoes, fresh apple cider, eggs, live chickens, hams, and dressed beef and pork.

The traditional "farmer's market" has all but disappeared. Fruit and vegetables are now harvested, sold, and delivered in truckload lots directly to wholesalers. Poultry and meat animals are sold alive, directly to slaughtering plants, country auctions, country buyers, or are consigned to commission selling houses.

Thus many functions formerly done by farmers on their farms have moved to off-farm processing plants. The employment and wages have migrated too, although often both farm and nonfarm people work in the off-farm plants.

Farmers themselves now chiefly produce just the primary ingredients of food and fiber. Thus, the term "farming" does not embrace all that it once did 100 or even 50 years ago.

Product specialization has taken a regional dimension, and in some instances is shifting between regions.

Corn production continues to be concentrated in the Corn Belt, where climate and soils are suited to the corn plant. In the Southeast corn, traditionally used as human food and feed for work animals, has always been secondary to cotton, peanuts, and tobacco.

Milo (grain sorghum) production is concentrated in the Great Plains where it has replaced some of the corn acreage in recent decades. In fact, milo has entered the western Corn Belt. To a lesser extent milo is grown in the irrigated valleys of the Southwest. In 10 years the crop has expanded from 550 million to 750 million bushels, due mainly to the higher yielding hybrids and to more acres irrigated.

Soybeans—traditionally a Corn Belt crop—have recently entered the Mississippi Delta. In 10 years the crop has expanded from 500 million to a billion bushels.

Cotton acreage and production have declined in the lower yielding area.

Soybeans.

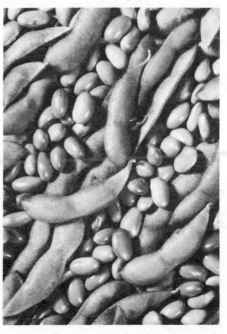

7

the Southeast, and have increased in the better adapted, higher yielding areas of the Mississippi Delta and the irrigated Southern Plains and Southwest (including California).

Both fresh and processing type vegetable production has increased in the Southwest, in Texas, and in Florida. Winter crop head lettuce is grown in southern California. Fall and spring crop lettuce is produced in Texas and Florida.

Staked vine-ripened and green-picked tomatoes are available to consumer markets are expanding. In these new areas, the fattening is done in huge specialized feedlots of up to 100,000 head capacity, quite unlike the on-farm feeding which still predominates in the Corn Belt.

Traditionally, we associate cattle raising with the range country of the Plains and the West. That is where the calves and steers came from to be fattened on Corn Belt farms.

In recent decades cattle "ranching" has expanded in the Southeast on land no longer used for cotton; to be

Feedlot in the High Plains.

sumers throughout the country all seasons of the year. The green-picked are shipped to warehouses near population centers for ripening in controlled temperature holding rooms until they are red ripe.

Cattle feeding (grain fattening) originated in the Corn Belt, where range steers were brought to be fattened by the farmer on corn he grew himself. That activity has continued to expand along with the expansion of corn grain supplies, U.S. population, and consumer demand.

More recently, beef fattening has moved into the Southern Plains, the Southwest, the Central Valley of California, and the Pacific Northwest, where milo grain or barley are indigenous or accessible, and where con-

more accurate, it has "come back." For it was in the Coastal Plains of the Carolinas that cattle ranching—in the American tradition of cowboys, branding, and roundups—got its start, long before the Civil War. Carolinians carried the art and folklore West.

Some surplus cattle from the Southeast is now finding its way to Corn Belt feedlots.

We now have about 900,000 fewer operating farms than in 1960! But essentially all the land is still in production, because of farm consolidation.

All the net decrease in number of farms has come in the smaller farm operations, those whose product sales are under $10,000 a year. In fact, we now have 184,000 more farms whose product sales are above $10,000. And the percentage increase is greatest among those farms whose sales are above $40,000. We had 194,000 such farms in 1968, their annual product sales averaging above $100,000.

More than 4 out of each 5 dollars worth of farm products are produced on farms with sales over $10,000.

Large farms are feasible today because modern machines permit each man to till more land. Greater output per farm unit means a larger volume of business, larger gross, and larger net income.

Contrary to common belief, the larger farms do not have much lower unit costs of production than fully mechanized one-man or two-man farms. The reason is that technical economies pertain to size of plant rather than size of business. And in farming, the "plant" is the man and his complement of machines.

We will continue to have small and part-time farms for various reasons. The income supplements the earnings from a nonfarm job of the operator, his wife, a son, or a daughter.

Many continue to farm because they own the land, and they can custom-hire the more exacting production operations like harvesting. Modern technology is available to them.

Often the small or part-time farm has been inherited and is being operated "on the side." Small farms have great staying power. At worst, the small farmer with a nonfarm job may field rent his cropland to a neighbor.

Though fewer and larger, most of our farms are still the family type. They differ not in number of workers or in business organization, but only in acres, resources used, and total output.

The dwindling number of small farms raises a fear that huge corporations may take over the business of farming, as they have in automaking, retail food sales, and so on. Such fears are greatly magnified.

Interestingly, we have always had some corporation farms—the XIT ranch in Texas, the Dalrymple Farms in North Dakota, the Campbell wheat ranch in Montana, and so on. These have operated side by side with conventional ranches and farms for decades.

A recent nationwide survey shows a rising number of corporations farming. But most are family type corporations—a form of business organization that is useful under some circumstances.

Farms today are more specialized.

Years ago farms were highly diversified, with many individual enterprises. Feed crops were carefully balanced against livestock enterprises, and a high degree of complementarity existed between enterprises and in the use of land and labor.

Today, farmers are concentrating on fewer but much larger crop or livestock enterprises. For example, we now see many one-enterprise and two-enterprise farms where formerly there were three to five enterprises. Specialization is aided, of course, by the availability of purchased production needs and custom services. Consequently there is less reason to diversify, and fewer problems of resource use within the farm business.

Farmers are now purchasing way more production goods and services, as they must if they are to have today's modern technology.

Even 40 years ago they were still providing most of their production needs—horsepower (and its feed), soil fertility (clover rotations), livestock feeds, crop seeds, and workers. Each farmer owned the machines to perform almost every farming operation.

Today's farmer buys prodigious amounts of production needs—fertilizer, formula feed, hybrid seeds, insecticides, herbicides, tractor fuel—and employs a myriad of custom services such as machine harvesting, fertilizing, pesticide spraying, and airplane crop dusting. Almost any production operation or harvesting can be custom hired.

This availability of custom services means that anyone can engage in farming. Anyone who owns or rents land can become an "instant" farmer and achieve essentially the same unit-cost efficiencies as other farmers. Likewise, a person can continue in farming beyond the usual retirement age.

Purchasable inputs and services also permit the small or part-time producer of commercial crops to use most of the same production techniques and technology as the "commercial" farmer, because the technology in the form of material and custom services is broadly available to anyone.

Farming is also changing in its life style.

Once it was easy to define and clear to see the distinction between farm and nonfarm, between rural and urban. Those who lived in the open country could surely be farmers; those who lived in town were nonfarmers. Today, many farmers live in town and many urban workers live in the country. When either group engages in both farming and another occupation, are they farmers or nonfarmers?

Many farmers are combining a farm enterprise—such as corn production— with a nonfarm "enterprise" such as working in a country bank, whereas formerly they combined only farm enterprises. This is "diversification" of a different sort.

Raising broilers or producing table eggs is a "moonlighting" activity of many otherwise full-time nonfarm workers. Thus, off-farm income is increasingly important to farm people everywhere.

For example, when in 1968 the average income of farm-operator families was $9,627, about $4,841 of it was net income from farming and $4,786 came from nonfarm sources—wages, rent, dividends, business earnings.

During the 1950's and 1960's a third revolution has appeared in U.S. farming, the revolution in business methods and financial management. With it, the farmer has now taken his place with other businessmen as a user of production credit, a contractor of production services, an employer of workers, and a user of systematic accounts and records. This revolution is discussed in the next chapter.

THE NEW FRONTIER OF FINANCE

SO MUCH HAS BEEN SAID about the scientific and technological revolutions in farming that another revolution has gone unnoticed. This is the revolution in farm financial management and in who finances farm production. While changes in the technology of farm crop and livestock production have been spectacular, the revolution in managerial style, in use of business methods, and in financing of production is equally important.

Dig into this matter and you discover two things. One is that the revolution in financial management was made possible by the mechanical and technological revolutions, and has closely followed them. The other discovery is that changes in financial management are having a great impact on farming. And the main impact may be yet to come.

Our pre-1930 farming, self-sufficient as it was, had little need for outside capital funds. About the only debt farmers had was a land mortgage. Farmers, being self-sufficient, bought hardly any production goods except occasional small hardware items and petroleum.

Production goods expenditures for all farms now exceed $25 billion annually, nearly four times greater than in 1930. A 400-acre Illinois corn farmer works with land and machinery assets probably worth in excess of a

✦

AUTHOR WARREN R. BAILEY is Deputy Director, Farm Production Economics Division, Economic Research Service.

COAUTHOR JOHN E. LEE, JR., is Chief, Agricultural Finance Branch, Farm Production Economics Division.

quarter million dollars. His annual production expenses may run from $20,000 to $30,000. How are such financing needs met? Who is doing the financing?

We can explain what we mean by farm financial management by contrasting it with production management, the essential content of the traditional term "farm management."

Production management deals with what production resources—land, materials, labor—and what production methods—row spacing, rate of fertilizing—will be used. Thus production management concerns the economic efficiency of the production process, like factory plant efficiency in manufacturing.

Farm financial management on the other hand takes the production plan as given, and concerns itself only with what financial method the farmer uses to obtain his production resources (goods and services), somewhat like corporate finance.

The new financial methods and strategies that today's farmers use to obtain production goods and services are what this chapter is about.

First, we need to distinguish between four kinds of goods and services used in farm production because they differ in how they may be obtained by farmers. The four are land, machines, breeding livestock, and those expendable items used directly (seed, fertilizer, etc.) in producing a crop or livestock.

U.S. farmers traditionally have owned their farms, owned land—whether they homesteaded it, bought it, or inherited it. Owning land gave you status, lent stability. Renting land gave inferior status, was considered an expedient until you could become an owner. Yet there has always been land for rent. Even on the frontier, land homesteaded by those who did not intend to become farmers was available to settlers for rent.

The point is that in ownership one has purchased the production services for all time, not just for the year ahead. Thus ownership ties up investment

funds. In renting you pay for your land service one year at a time.

Today, renting land is an accepted practice, widely used by the modern farmer.

In fact, a large part of the corn land in the central Corn Belt, the wheat land in the Plains, and the cotton land in California and Arizona is not owned by the operating farmers. Renting land enables them to operate on a much larger scale than they otherwise could.

Here are some interesting examples:

Rice growers in the Sacramento Valley of California typically specialize in rice production. They own the tractors, tillage tools, and harvesters, and they have a rice acre allotment, yet they own no land. (Rice allotments there are assigned to growers, not to land). So the growers rent land from owners who have no rice allotment, with the rent exceeding the owner's profit from any other crop.

The growers prepare the ground and irrigate it with water supplied by the landowner. Then they custom hire the airplane application of seed and fertilizer. When the crop is ripe, the growers harvest the rice with their own combines, and haul the rice to a warehouse for custom drying and storage.

ROTATING FARMERS

In upland areas of the valley, other growers typically specialize in tomatoes they grow under contract for a soup canner, yet they own no land. They field-rent land from general-crop farmers who grow the sugarbeets and alfalfa in the rotation, but not the tomatoes. Thus, farmers rotate as well as the crops.

The rice growers and the tomato growers have one thing in common. Both are bona fide farmers. While their mode of operation does not fit our traditional image, farm operators in the West have long rented their land, leased their machinery, and hired migrant labor crews. Now these patterns of acquiring production goods and services, once considered unique to the West and to specialized crops, are emerging elsewhere.

11

Chisel planter in Ida County, Iowa, is example of increasing complexity of farm machinery.

For example, in central Illinois you can now custom hire in a package deal all the field operations required in growing an excellent crop of corn. Thus anyone who owns or can rent land may function as a "farmer" though employed fulltime otherwise.

These examples also illustrate how the technological revolution has permitted separation of the functions and operations involved in farming into separate activities which can be performed by different specialists.

Whereas it was once assumed that the farm operator would own his own land, supply his own labor, grow his own feed, fuel, and horsepower, and finance his few cash expenses out of his own savings, today's farmer can choose which functions he wants to perform and which way he will acquire and finance the goods and service he needs.

Not only land for crops but land for grazing is widely rented. Often it is the forage, not the land, that is being rented. Take the foothill cattleman who brings his herd down to graze a field after the sugarbeets are harvested. He pays by the animal-day, not by the acre. Or take the western rancher with permits to graze the public range. He pays by the animal-unit-month.

Sheep raising in the Southwest is migratory year long—from the high mountain range in summer to the desert range in winter.

As with land, our rural tradition once said that each farmer should own the power and machines to perform every cropping operation. "Be self-reliant because things need to be done on time and you cannot always depend upon others." This admonition had its place on the frontier but it eventually became imbedded in our traditions where it persisted long after it was no longer relevant.

Today's farming machines are far more complex, more specialized, and more expensive than the simple tools we once used. And being specialized, most of today's machines are needed only a few days on any one farm each year. Hence, farmers today try to avoid tying up their own funds in the ownership of specialized machines, and seek other ways of obtaining the services of such machines.

Today's farmer owns chiefly just the tractors, plows, seeding and tillage tools which are adapted to the cultural operations for a variety of crops. These machines are used again and again during the crop season. Even this restricted group of machines can mean a total outlay of $20,000 to $30,000 on a Corn Belt or a cotton farm.

Tractors, trucks, and other farm equipment are typically financed by banks, PCA's (farmer-owned Production Credit Associations), and equipment dealers. If dealer financed, the dealer must in turn be financed, usually by a commercial bank or by the parent equipment manufacturer. When the manufacturer provides financing it in turn must be financed, usually by a bank.

Typically, loans for machinery and equipment are extended through a collateral mortgage. Terms for such loans vary with the life of the item purchased.

Tractor payments may extend over a 3 to 5 year period, with 3 years the most common. A glass silo may be financed over a 10 year period. Default on payment by the purchaser may result in the item's being repossessed by the lender.

Banks usually prefer not to get involved in repossessing machinery since they are not prepared to deal with the repossessed items. For this reason they often prefer that the machinery dealer set up the collateral loan with the purchaser. The bank can then purchase the loan.

This works to the bank's advantage not only because it is freed from getting involved in owning machinery, but also because the dealer serves as a cosigner of the loan.

Harvesting tomatoes in California.

The number of manufacturers setting up financing subsidiaries seems to be increasing. For the company, this may promote sales. For the farmer it is an alternative source of financing.

When it comes to the crop harvesting and other specialized machines, today's farmer often can obtain their services without owning them. The chief device is to custom hire the machine operation. When he does this, the farmer is functioning like a housebuilder who subcontracts the masonry work, the plumbing and wiring, the heating system, and the roofing.

And, of course, it is the custom operator—not the farmer—who must finance the investment in the machine.

Custom combine harvesting is available throughout the wheat growing regions, except in some minor inaccessible spots. Many custom operators begin the wheat harvest in Texas in May and follow the ripening of the crop into Canada in October.

Custom harvesting is also available in corn, grain sorghum, barley, cotton, rice, and many other crops. A good share of the alfalfa hay grown for sale or farm feeding in the San Joaquin Valley is custom baled—between 10 p.m. and 7 a.m., the dew hours, to avoid loss of leaves.

In rice growing the seeding, fertilizing, and weed spraying are all done from custom operated airplanes over fields that are continuously flooded with irrigation water.

Custom airplane crop dusting is widely used in orchard fruit and vegetable production.

Some orange grove owners in southern California subcontract (custom hire) all of the farming operations— cover crop seeding, irrigation, pruning, pesticide control, and fruit picking. This has been going on for decades.

Now we are told you can subcontract as a package the corn growing operations in the central Corn Belt.

In many areas the picking of vegetables, fruit, and nuts simply are no longer performed by farmers, but by the shipper-packer whose crews move from farm to farm—thus providing a scheduled flow of produce into the grading and packing sheds.

Livestock custom operations include sheep shearing, dehorning, branding, and artificial breeding.

Another device farmers are beginning to use to obtain the services of the more expensive machines is to rent them, like you would a floor sander or a chain saw.

A large machine dealer in the San Joaquin Valley rents out tractors and trucks by the month, like the rent-a-car business. He keeps the machines in running order—you buy the gas and oil. We can expect more of this.

We know a large multi-branch bank in the West that is now renting tractors and other major machines to farmers. This takes the place of mortgage lending as it allows a longer payback period.

Livestock breeding herds traditionally have been financed much like farm machinery, with short-term or intermediate-term collateral mortgage loans. The livestock and its "increase" represent the collateral. The lenders are local commercial banks and Production Credit Associations.

Though still small, the recent activity in renting livestock is attracting some public interest. In the Northeast dairy farmers can now lease milk cows under a standard rental contract. The owner of the cows may be a contracting firm, or a local bank, or an individual investor for whom the bank serves as an agent.

Leasing saves the dairyman from having his own funds tied up in cow equities. The scheme is useful to older farmers who have small herds and wish to retire, but could use the income from leasing their cows out. The scheme could be useful to young dairymen with limited capital who need to expand. Whether dairy cow renting expands remains to be seen.

Rental of beef cows has expanded in parts of the West. Private companies, acting as brokers, invest the funds of high salaried clients in the ownership of beef cows to be rented to ranchers. This scheme allows the rancher to stock his land without a major financial commitment. It permits the new cattle owner to gain tax advantages via the capital gains treatment of earnings from breeding stock—lets him convert wage earnings to capital gains.

Another kind of production goods and services are the expendables—the seed, feed, fertilizer, labor, and so on—used up directly in each production cycle.

Someone might ask why these direct production expenses have to be financed. Why aren't they paid directly out of last year's sales or savings?

There are several reasons.

In farming (with only a few exceptions) the production process itself takes considerable time—roughly 6 months to a year. It takes 6 months from land breaking to harvest to grow a crop of corn . . . 4 months to grow spring seeded wheat and 8 to 11 months to grow the fall seeded . . . 6 months to grow out a litter of pigs. Expenses are incurred throughout the production process.

Basic crop production operations are land preparation (plowing, etc.), planting the seed, cultivating weeds, and harvesting. Additional operations may be side-dress fertilizing, irrigation, insect spraying or dusting, and herbicide control.

Crop production expenses include seed, fertilizer, chemicals, tractor fuel and lubrication, mechanical repairs, hired labor, custom hired operations, and (as applicable) irrigation water.

These expenses can be met basically in four ways: the operator's bank reserves from a previous crop, borrowing, dealer's credit, and advances or credit via a producer's contract.

Farmers find it uneconomical to use the proceeds of one year's crop to cover production expenses of the next because the money may lay idle for months. So they put their crop sales to work and borrow other money when the time comes to meet operating expenses, except in dairying where sales occur the year around.

A common way of financing through borrowing is by a crop mortgage—a lien against the prospective crop. Let us see how it is done with cotton growing in the West.

The farmer must have his cotton ginned (separate the seeds, and bale the lint fiber) before he can sell his crop. Cotton gins are owned and operated by companies who merchandise cotton lint fiber and cottonseed oil. Ginning the farmer's cotton (for a service charge) and providing a buying service assure the company a steady source of supply.

The company advances production funds to the grower and takes a crop mortgage to be repaid when the grower sells his crop. Then the company in turn "sells" the crop mortgage to a commercial bank. Banks like this kind of lending, because the

Custom operator stands on his hay grinding machine while rancher A. C. Smith on tractor feeds oats and barley hay into the "tub" grinder, in Corson County, S. Dak. Grinder's capacity is up to 15 tons of hay an hour.

cotton company serves as an agent of the bank and an endorser of the mortgage. Lending losses are minimized since cotton prices are supported by the Government.

Crop mortgage lending applies to any other crop having a ready market: corn, wheat, rice, soybeans, barley.

Collateral mortgages may be used instead of or in addition to crop mortgages to secure production credit. For example, the cotton companies discussed above may "list" the farmer's machines even though these may not be actually mortgaged along with the crop itself.

Collateral for securing production credit may include all tractors, trucks, and other major machines owned by the farmer. It could also include stock securities and other assets. Real estate is not usually included, though it could be.

The collateral mortgage becomes a second mortgage on any items already mortgaged. With collateral mortgages it is not expected that the collateral will actually be sold, should foreclosure become necessary. Actually the collateral serves to satisfy the rules and legal requirements of banks.

Dealer credit as a means of financing production goods and services came into its own with the technological revolution. The reason: manufacturers and vendors of the new wares have sought ways of helping the farmer obtain, use, and finance them. This help is in the self-interest of both the vendor and the manufacturer.

For example, the vendor of chemical fertilizers, insecticides, and herbicides will deliver the material to the farm but may choose not to collect until after the crop is harvested and sold. This extension of "dealer credit" is a tool of financial management that the modern farmer can use in obtaining production goods and services.

The vendor may go further and for a modest charge agree to apply the materials to the crop field, using his own machines. In fact, the vendor may prefer to do this to assure proper application and greater success. The

vendor will have useful technical information based on the manufacturer's lab tests or field trials. The big chemical companies experiment extensively.

Thus, along with the production goods the farmer buys technical services from the vendor who may know more about one aspect of farming than does the farmer.

There are other advantages to the farmer.

He need not own or invest in a spreader or spraying machine. Vendor application greatly aids the crop use of liquid and gaseous fertilizers, as they require expensive machines.

Similarly, farmers use dealer credit to obtain seed, feed, pesticides, tractor fuel, machine parts and repair service, baling twine, and other materials used in the production process, under various delayed billing arrangements.

Credit supplied by merchants and dealers reduces the farmer's need to borrow money to cover production costs. In the interim the production items still have to be financed, and someone has to pay the costs of that financing.

In some cases the merchant himself finances the delayed billing from his own reserves or by borrowing from a bank. The merchant covers the cost of that financing indirectly through the price of the production items he sells or directly by levying an interest or carrying charge for the billing period.

Sometimes the fertilizer manufacturer or chemical company that supplies the dealer may delay billing the dealer. In such cases the manufacturers—who in turn must cover their costs with a bank loan—provide the financing for the farmer's production needs.

In dairying, financing production costs through dealer credit presents no problem because the biweekly milk checks provide a steady flow of income to the farmer. His feed bills are usually due in 30 days with a cash discount allowed for payment within 10 days.

Another form of production credit is the advance that a contract farmer may get from the shipper-packer or processor with whom he has the contract.

Many farm products—including eggs, broilers, vegetables for canning and freezing, oranges for frozen juice concentrate, and cucumbers for pickling—are produced under contract for a shipper or processor. In a real sense the farmer acts as a subcontractor to the shipper or processor—the general contractor. The shipper or processor may finance the production wholly or in part by advancing part or all of the production costs to the farmer.

A common approach is illustrated by the pickle processor who works through a local "farm supply" dealer. The dealer parcels out "allotments" and sets up the contracts with local farmers. He provides the farmers with seeds or plants of a variety designated by the pickle company. He also furnishes fertilizers and chemicals along with recommendations on how to use these materials and how to plant, space, cultivate, and harvest the cucumbers.

When the farmer delivers the cucumbers to the dealer for grading, he is paid at the contracted rate after the costs of the materials furnished have been deducted. Financing for the local dealer is usually provided by a bank and, in part, by the processor.

In a similar way, plants, fertilizer, insecticides, feed, and baby chicks are supplied to farmers producing other farm products under contract.

Fresh vegetables for shipment to distant markets are typically produced under contract. The grower is responsible only for bringing the crop to harvest. The shipper does the harvesting of such crops as head lettuce, carrots, broccoli, celery, and snap beans. The crop, as it is harvested, is hauled to a packing shed where it is trimmed, graded, and packed in shipping cartons which are loaded in refrigerated or iced rail cars or trucks.

In the case of fresh vegetables, several basic contracts are common:

• $125 minimum to grower (costs) plus half of the profit.

• Like above but also cash rent to the grower plus a third of the profit that is made.

In both these cases the grower buys all the inputs, but he can finance them out of the guarantee—whether it is paid in advance or is used as collateral for a bank loan.

• The grower is paid a flat sum per acre, a sum covering all the usual costs—machine work, materials, labor—plus a profit. Part or all is paid in advance. The grower buys his own inputs. Efficient growers can reduce the cost and increase what is left as profit, but they dare not neglect good farming.

Canning tomatoes are usually produced under a written contract between the grower and a vegetable processor.

The contractor or the processor agrees to pay a specified price for all of the tomatoes which meet a specified size and grade, from an agreed upon acreage.

Again the written contract is useful to the grower when he asks the bank for a production loan.

For flower seeds and other special crops, farmers with irrigated, fertile soils in a sunlit desert valley stand ready to grow any crop a seed company may wish.

The farmer as a custom grower of broilers is another example of financing through producer contracts. Usually there is a written contract between the grower and a poultry processor and merchandiser, a feed manufacturer, or a retail food chain. The basic contracts specify the number of broilers to be produced by breed and weight as well as the kind and formula of feed to be fed.

Under one version of a broiler contract, the grower stands all costs and gets a guaranteed price per pound of liveweight bird.

Under other versions of the basic contract, the grower is furnished baby chicks and feed and custom grows the birds for so much, say 5 cents, a pound liveweight of birds delivered.

Let us reflect a bit.

Above, oranges flow into a plant for processing into frozen concentrated juice, at Auburndale, Fla. Below, harvesting cucumbers in Midland County, Mich.

The mechanical and technological revolutions have brought a fantastic array of production goods and services . . . plus technical information and instructions . . . to modern farming. These aids sought after by today's farmer are obtainable because of a third revolution—farm financial management.

Because farming processes are composed of separable operations—fertilizing, crop dusting, harvesting—which are specialized, today's farmer has the freedom to choose which operations he will do and which ones he will subcontract to others.

Because production goods and services can be purchased on an annual basis, today's farmer can play whatever role he chooses . . . an entrepreneur who uses other people's land and machines, for the profit . . . a resource owner whose earnings are rent . . . an equity investor whose return is money interest.

Did the traditional farmer have any more freedom than that?

ARE THEY MAKING
A LIVING DOWN
ON THE FARM?

FARMERS AND THEIR FARMS in our 50 States are not all alike, not by a long shot. Operators of farms differ in age, educational attainment, management skills, whether they are full-time or part-time farmers, and in many other ways. Their farms range from under 10 acres to thousands of acres in size, they may raise livestock or grow crops, they may be specialized in one type of farm enterprise or be diversified, and their sales may range annually from under $2,500 to well over $100,000.

But, despite their many differences, our farmers do have one important thing in common. They are all businessmen just like the man who operates the corner drug store or the local lumber mill. And, like businessmen, they are in farming to make a living. So, in the final analysis, it all boils down to farm income—what are our farmers getting for their labor (including unpaid family labor), for their management, and for their capital, after allowing for farm production expenses.

Most farm income is from marketings of livestock and livestock products and crops. Some 150 different farm products are produced on 3 million farms in this vast country.

Our farmers sell products we are all familiar with such as cattle, milk, eggs, honey, wheat, corn, cotton, tobacco, potatoes, lettuce, oranges, and apples. But, did you know that our farmers also market products like mink, goats, rabbits, guavas, bananas, coffee, passion fruit, Austrian winter peas, and buffalo meat? Of course these little known products are minor in the farm income picture, but for some individual producers they may be quite important.

Cash receipts from farm marketings in 1969 totaled around $47 billion, of which $28 billion came from livestock and livestock products and $19 billion from crops. This total was only $28 billion in 1950. The increase since 1950 stems almost entirely from a substantially larger volume of farm products marketed, since prices received by farmers in 1969 averaged just slightly higher than 20 years earlier.

The 10 most important farm products in terms of cash receipts from farm marketings are in order of importance—cattle and calves, milk, hogs,

✦

AUTHOR C. KYLE RANDALL is Chief of the Farm Income Branch, Economic Research Service.

COAUTHOR MARDY MYERS is Head of the Farm Income Estimates Section, Economic Research Service.

corn, soybeans, eggs, wheat, broilers, tobacco, and cotton. Other important products are greenhouse and nursery, grain sorghum, hay, tomatoes, potatoes, rice, turkeys, oranges, sugar beets, apples, sheep and lambs, peanuts, barley, sugarcane, and grapes.

Some idea of the cash income range for these important money crops is seen in the $12 billion received annually from cattle and calf marketings down to about $200 million from grape marketings.

And, of course, the $47 billion received from marketings is not spread out evenly among the regions or States of the Nation. The West North Central States from Minnesota to Kansas lead the way in receipts from farming followed by the Western Region, the South Central States, and the East North Central States. As some of you might guess, the South Atlantic and the North Atlantic areas bring up the rear in farm income.

What kind of farming predominates in the various regions? In the important West North Central States, you will find income from cattle and calves way out in front in all States, except North Dakota where wheat is king. This region also gets a lot of income from hogs, dairy products, corn, and soybeans. In the West, cattle and calves also lead the way in farm receipts, with dairy products second in many Western States.

The South Central area presents more of a mixed picture, with cattle in the forefront in Texas and Oklahoma, while other leaders are tobacco, broilers, cotton, rice, and soybeans. In the East North Central area from Ohio to Wisconsin, dairy products lead the way followed by income from hogs, corn, and cattle.

South Atlantic farms are characterized by receipts from broilers, dairy products, and tobacco; however, citrus products are the most important cash crop in Florida. In the North Atlantic area, farm marketings of milk and eggs are tops except in Maine where potatoes are still the No. 1 source of gross farm income.

Surprising to many may be the fact that California is the leading State in cash receipts from farm marketings. Farmers in the Golden State receive over $4 billion a year from sales of farm products. After California, leading States in the cash farm income picture are Iowa, Texas, Illinois, Minnesota, Nebraska, Kansas, Wisconsin, Missouri, and Indiana. At the bottom of the scale is Alaska where farm receipts run just over $4 million a year.

California is tops in receipts from eggs, greenhouse and nursery products, hay, tomatoes, turkeys, sugar beets, barley, and grapes. Iowa leads the way in cash income from cattle and calves and hogs. Texas is way out in front in receipts from sales of cotton, sorghum grain, and rice, while Illinois is tops in income from corn and soybeans. Wisconsin is the Dairy State, while Kansas leads the way in cash income from farm marketings of wheat.

Direct Government payments to farmers totaled $3.8 billion in 1969. These payments have increased sharply since 1960, due to the start of voluntary programs designed to hold down output of feed grains, wheat, and cotton.

Farmers also add to their incomes in the form of home consumption of farm products and gross rental value of farm dwellings. These have moved in opposite directions since 1950.

Farm families consumed $700 million worth of home-grown farm products in their households in 1969. This was only about a third the value in 1950. There are many reasons for this decline. Foremost is the steady drop in the number of farms and farm people. Also, as farms become more specialized, there is less opportunity and reason to consume their own products.

Gross rental value of farm dwellings was estimated at $2.6 billion in 1969, up 76 percent from 1950. There are far fewer farm dwellings, but this decrease has been more than offset by an increase in the average value of dwellings remaining on farms.

Left, farmer Edward L. Garris displays part of his tobacco crop in Halifax County, N.C. Below, grapes are laid out to dry into raisins, in California.

Above, sugarcane fields in La Fourche Parish, La. Below, pigs at self-feeders in Indiana.

As yet, however, we have been talking about gross farm income. Farmers have a whopping big expense bill to pay before they can even begin to think about their own income. The bill for farm production expenses added up to $38.6 billion in 1969, about double that of 1950. In 1969, production expenses were eating up 71 cents of each gross income dollar.

What accounts for this sharp upward leap in farm production expenses? As you might have guessed, they are paying higher prices just like everyone else. In 1969, the index of prices paid by farmers for items used for production purposes, interest, taxes, and farm wage rates was more than 40 percent higher than in 1950.

Farmers also bought more of the items needed to make the farm go, the other important factor contributing to the increase in farm production expenses. In 1969, farmers used a 45 percent larger total of goods and services than in 1950. The same changes in farm technology, including increased specialization, that helped boost farm output since the end of World War II also required buying larger amounts of items such as feed, livestock, seed, and fertilizer.

All this discussion of farm income so far has been in terms of current dollars. There are occasions when it is useful to talk about income in dollars of constant purchasing power.

This may sound like some fancy economic or statistical jargon, but the underlying idea is simple. We are trying to compare the buying power of the $16.0 billion of realized net farm income in 1969 with the buying power of the $12.9 billion in 1950. To make the comparison, all we have to do is adjust for the change in prices paid by farmers for family living items. From 1950 to 1969 these prices increased 42 percent. This is about double the increase in realized net farm income.

This means that although realized net farm income in current dollars was 23 percent higher in 1969 than in 1950, the bigger stack of dollars in 1969 would actually buy about 20 percent less of the same goods and services because of the adverse effect of higher prices.

We have been talking thus far in

French fried potatoes roll off a machine in a processing plant at Presque Isle, Maine.

terms of the combined income of all farmers and treating American agriculture as though it were one big farm, but much of the talk about farm income is in terms of average income per farm.

In 1969, realized net income per farm was $5,401, more than double the 1950 figure. This number should be labeled "USE WITH CAUTION." It is influenced by the number of farms as well as the aggregate amount of realized net farm income. And, the number of farms has been declining rapidly and steadily.

There were about 3 million farms in 1969, down almost 50 percent from the number in 1950. Furthermore, much of the decline in farm numbers has been in the smaller farms while the number of larger farms has increased in recent years. From 1960 to 1968 the total number of farms declined 908,000, or 22 percent. But the larger farms, those with value-of-sales of $20,000 or more, increased about 50 percent from 340,000 to 526,000.

Farms with value-of-sales from $10,000 to $19,999 stayed about the same in number, just under a half million, while smaller farms declined from 3.1 million in 1960 to 2 million in 1968.

In 1968 there were still twice as many farms with sales of less than $10,000 as there were with sales of more than $10,000. Many of these small farms are part-time or part-retirement farms which, although meeting the Census definition of a farm, can hardly be considered farming units in terms of dependence on farming for a living.

When we turn our attention to how farm income is spread among these farms, we find a vastly different distribution.

For instance, the larger farms in 1960 made up 21 percent of all farms, got more than 70 percent of total cash receipts from farming (including government payments), paid more than 70 percent of farm production expenses, and retained nearly 60 percent of realized net farm income. By 1968,

this group made up a third of all farms, but their share of cash receipts and production expenses had climbed above 85 percent, while their share of realized net income was 76 percent.

In 1960, average realized net farm income ranged from a high of $18,955 for farms with value-of-sales of $40,000 or more to a low of $850 for farms with value-of-sales of less than $2,500. Keep in mind that even with this wide range, the average for all farms in 1960 was only $2,962. In 1968, the range extended from $24,083 to $1,059 while the all-farm average was $4,851.

We would like to reemphasize our "USE WITH CAUTION" label regarding average income for all farms. Also, estimates of class averages are sometimes misleading and should be used cautiously. Basic information for number of farms and their characteristics by sales class do not provide information about individual farms. We do not intend to give anyone the idea that every farm in a specific group experiences income and expenses that change along with the indicated group average.

So far we have talked about the income from farming as an industry, but there is also much interest in the income of farmers, their families, and other farm residents as members of the farm population. Here the significant factor has been a sharp increase since 1960 in the income of farm people from nonfarm sources.

In 1968, the farm population received $11.8 billion in income from nonfarm sources such as wages and salaries, nonfarm business and professional income, rents from nonfarm real estate, dividends, interest, royalties, unemployment compensation, veterans' benefits, and social security payments. This was nearly double the $6.3 billion farm people received from nonfarm sources in 1950 and substantially higher than the $7.2 billion received in 1960.

Now let's look at the income from farming of people who live on farms. In 1968, it was $13.1 billion, down 7 percent from 1950. Combining the income of farm people from farming with their income from nonfarm sources, and deducting personal taxes and nontax payments, the disposable personal income of the farm population from all sources was $22.7 billion in 1968, up 17 percent from 1950.

The farm population, like the number of farms, has been declining rapidly. In 1968, there were 10½ million people living on farms, less than half of the 23 million on farms in 1950. Some idea of the dramatic drop in the farm population can be seen when you realize that one out of every four Americans lived on a farm in the mid-thirties while today only about one out of every 20 resides on a farm.

This sharp decline in farm population together with the increase in aggregate disposable income of the farm population explains the sharp rise in per capita disposable income of the farm population. In 1950, the per capita amount was $841; in 1968, $2,163. In 1950, nearly a third of the per capita personal income of farm people came from nonfarm sources; in 1968 it was approaching a half.

Despite the sharp rise in per capita disposable income of farm people, there is still a wide gap between their average incomes and that of nonfarm people. In 1968, the per capita disposable income of the farm population was almost three-fourths that of the nonfarm population. This was considerably better than the 58 percent ratio in 1950, but it indicates that on the average, farm people are at a disadvantage in terms of income.

Contrary to what you might think, income from off-farm sources is not limited to the smaller farms. Operator families on all size classes of farms receive sizable amounts of income from off-farm sources, and the average amount per family increased sharply from 1960 to 1968 for each size class. However, it is true that the relative importance of off-farm income is greatest for the smaller farms.

The importance of off-farm income for the smallest size farm operation—less than $2,500 in sales—can be appreciated when you see that this group averaged $6,241 in off-farm income in 1968, or 6 times the average net amount they realized from their farm operation.

Even the largest farms—those with value-of-sales of $40,000 or more—averaged $5,108 in off-farm income in 1968. In this case, however, off-farm income was only about a fifth as much as realized net farm income.

The agricultural revolution is not over yet by any means. The number of farms and farm people will continue to decline. Farms will get bigger and become more dependent on capital.

Whether the changes in American agriculture will be as drastic as those of the past 20 years is open to question, but undoubtedly there will be further change in the American farm income structure. Hopefully, the changes now occurring and to come in the future will enable farm operators and their families to obtain a fuller share of the national income than is true today.

THE FARMER SPEAKS FOR A WAY OF LIFE

FARMERS TODAY cherish traditional rural values, yet feel they are victims of the economic system. The cardinal points of the agrarian creed—independence, the belief that agriculture is man's fundamental employment upon which other economic activities depend, and the conviction that farming is a natural life and therefore a good life—are held by many farm people, and, as a 1969 study shows, by many city dwellers as well.

Farmers stress freedom of action;

freedom from the crime, noise, and traffic of the cities; a healthier environment, and the farm way of life as reasons why they want their children to stay in the country. But, they say, large capital requirements, low farm prices, high prices for everything needed for production, and long hours and hard work are discouraging young people from staying in farming.

The idea that agriculture has a basic value of itself was strongly expressed by a farmwoman of Briscoe County, Tex., on September 18, 1969, at a "listening conference" held by the Secretary of Agriculture. She said: "I only want to remind you that when the farmer falls, the Nation falls!"

Another farmwoman, Mrs. E. C. Goza of Mayesville, S.C., spoke at a similar conference of the difficulties faced by the farmer: "I think that farmers are more or less called to the profession or they would never be able to withstand the strain and 'wear and tear'—and it seems as though this strain has grown greater each year for the past decade due to the ever-increasing price squeeze and labor shortage in farming."

The belief that agriculture is the base upon which the Nation's economy rests was expressed by S. J. Grahmann, farmer of Hallettsville, Tex.: "With agriculture accounting for 75 percent of our nation's new creative wealth, consistently low agricultural prices will eventually reduce everyone to poverty."

Farmers today, for the most part, are convinced that they are adding to the wealth and well-being of the Nation. Yet they are just as convinced that their relative position in the economy is declining.

During the 1930's, parity prices—that is, fair prices for farm products in relation to the prices farmers paid for

✦

AUTHOR WAYNE D. RASMUSSEN is Chief, Agricultural History Branch, Economic Research Service.

COAUTHOR GLADYS L. BAKER is Head of the Historical Research Section, Agricultural History Branch.

S. J. Grahmann, who is quoted on this page, in his corn field at Hallettsville, Tex.

goods, looking back to the 1910–14 period—became a goal for farmers, farm organizations, and Congress. Parity prices were to be both the measuring rods and the means of securing for the farmers a fair share of national income and national wealth.

The present parity ratio, which is the ratio of the index of prices received to the index of prices paid, based upon 1910–14, is not an accurate measure of farm income because it does not reflect increases in productivity, returns on investment, or direct government payments. Farmers express concern both that the parity ratio is about 74 percent and that the income to each person in farming is only about 73 percent of what the nonfarmer receives. The parity index was at or above 100 from 1942 through 1952, but has been falling since.

Farmer after farmer at the "listening conferences" expressed dismay that in a period of general prosperity, their relative position as measured by parity was declining.

In 1953 and 1955, when extensive field hearings were held by agriculture committees of the Congress, farmers also expressed concern at how things were going.

Orville C. Russell of Muncie, Ind., called himself an "old fashioned dirt farmer." He spoke about the interdependence of agriculture, industry, and labor, and of the need for farmers to organize because of their minority status. In testimony of Oct. 19, 1953, he said:

"Agriculture today through organization should, and now is, recognized as a basic factor in our national economy. . . .

"In these United States there are three groups, indispensable to each other—agriculture, industry, and labor. Neither one can successfully survive without the others, and neither one should usurp power over the others. . . .

"I would like to speak of the place of agriculture in Government. Industry and labor are both organized. They put forth every effort to gain power in Government. Agriculture should be on an equal basis in Government, if Government by all people is for all people."

Three years of declining farm prices brought back disturbing questions concerning fundamental agrarian values. Were farmers being punished for producing abundantly? Instead of economic rewards, did hard work, efficiency, and technological progress bring lower farm prices and income? Could agriculture be considered the fundamental industry when farm prices were falling while other segments of the economy were relatively prosperous?

Kenneth Fridley, operator of a 640-acre Oregon farm, stated the dilemma:

". . . Late events have created doubts and a feeling of despair in the mind of the farmer. . . . It is a strange paradox that the American farmer should be treated as an economic delinquent

Nebraska Farmer Karl John Luther stops his tractor to chat in front of a corn crib.

when he has responded in every crisis in the past two decades to expand and produce to feed his countrymen and the rest of the free world."

Helge Nygren, President of the Morton County (N. Dak.) Farmers Union, stated that as a family farmer he was probably one of the most important men in America. He deplored what he considered unfair treatment given the family farmer "who founded the country." Was it just for those responsible for the American way of life to be blamed rather than rewarded for their efficiency, he asked.

"I am sure if we want to be honest, we must all admit that the family farm is the American way of life; this, I am sure, everyone knows. Still nearly every paper today has articles telling us that we must do something to do away with the inefficiency in agriculture and by that statement we all know that they mean the family farmer, and in the same article they holler about the burdensome surpluses.

"Let us check this for one moment. Does it make good sense to say to a man you are inefficient, but still you produce too much? . . .

"Are we willing to do away with our American family farmer because of this cry of efficiency? If we do, we must be willing to do away with not only the family farmer but also with the small towns and all small business, all our country schools and churches, and all social and civic functions in our rural and urban areas, and in its place what would we have?"

Other farmers discussed the unfairness of a system which failed to reward those who had provided the base for the economy and the country's most cherished institutions. One farmwoman asked how family farmers could "enjoy the beauties of nature with rumblings of a mortgage foreclosure overhead?" Farm people, she said, "were honest, kind, generous, hard working and long suffering." She felt if the farm way of life were to disappear the strength and security of the Nation would go with it.

In a 1955 statement, Lynn Bowe, owner of 400 acres of Minnesota land, who had started farming after World War II, discussed some of the difficulties and gave the following explanation of why he continued to farm:

"I suppose the reason why I farm, I farm because, well, with practically any other area I believe I could go into, I could with the same ability and energy make double the income, but I farm because I like the soil and I have fundamental respect for it, and I believe it clothes and feeds me, and that one day I will become a part of it.

"I enjoy working with growing crops and with livestock; and I believe I can understand why since time immemorial people have lived with that intimate contact with growing things, as an important asset and as an indispensable part of the heritage of man.

"Thirdly, and last but not least, I should say that farming offers a large amount of personal freedom in planning and operating, and under no conditions do I want to trade off this freedom of choice for anyone telling me what I can and cannot do on my own farm."

Farmers continue to enjoy farming as a way of life but surveys show they are becoming discouraged with farming as a way of making a living. A survey for the *Wisconsin Agriculturist* in 1966 found that 44 percent of those participating felt sure they would farm if they were starting over again while 14 percent were sure they would not, and another 17 percent doubted if they would choose farming. Those who were not sure or were undecided constituted 25 percent.

Of those who would not choose farming, 55 percent gave as one of their reasons that it required too much money for land and equipment. Too low income was given as a reason by 49 percent. Preference for town or city life was given by only 2 percent. Too long hours was given by 38 percent while 13 percent said the work was too hard. Six percent said people look down upon farmers.

A study of dryland grain farms in

Farmer Lawrence Bass packs tobacco for shipment in Wake County, N.C.

At that time, 38 percent indicated they wanted to farm. A followup study of the boys in 1962 showed that only 14.3 percent of them were actually farming. Studies in 1964 and 1966 indicated that 24 percent were in farming, but those working in nonfarm occupations had risen from around 35 percent in 1962 to 64 percent in 1966.

Some farmers' sons who preferred farming as a way of life as well as a way of making a living, were discouraged by what has been labeled the corporate invasion of American agriculture. Corporations, with their large economic resources, could afford to take a loss for a number of years, if necessary. They could use losses in farming to offset capital gains in other corporate operations. They could and did often bid up the price of land in their purchases of large tracts.

Corporations which weren't interested in accumulating farmland of their own could through contracts control the marketing of large segments of the industry, making "factories in the field." Farmers would lose their independence. Corporations, it was felt, were not interested in farming as a way of life. They had no ties to the rural community. Local communities and local government, as farmers had known them, would disappear and with them the basis for the democratic way of life.

Robert W. Scott, then Master of the North Carolina State Grange, in a May 31, 1963 letter to a Congressional Committee, stated the corporate threat to the family farm. He wrote:

"The family farm is in grave danger unless steps are taken to provide it with the same degrees of competitiveness enjoyed by corporate farming, contract farming, and other types of farming operations.

"Given the same tax advantages and the same opportunities to buy needed supplies and to market farm products and an access to adequate resources through credit, I am confident that the family farm system can prove its superiority as the most efficient, the most economic, and the most satisfy-

Montana published in 1963 indicated that most farmers would still choose farming if they were starting over again. They would continue to farm even if it meant a lower standard of living, but some of those interviewed would not recommend farm life for a son or daughter. Farming was preferred as an occupation because of the independence it provided.

An Iowa farmwoman, interviewed in 1969, said the only way a boy could become a farmer was to inherit his father's farm. She said there is "no chance for anyone to become a new farmer." A recent college graduate who was farming with his father said, "I like the farm but it costs too much to start farming."

Donald Kaldor, a professor of economics at Iowa State University, began in 1959 a study of the long range occupational plans of 870 Iowa farm boys in their senior year of high school.

ing operation in a prosperous agriculture. . . .

"If agriculture becomes centered in the hands of a few giant corporations vertically integrated from the field to the table and able to fix prices, then food costs would likely be greater, rural community life as we know it today would disappear, and the attitudes of self-reliance, social responsibility, individual incentive, and tolerance would be lost to America. . . ."

Farmers who are concerned over corporation farming favor legislation to bar or impede it. Twenty-seven United States Senators sponsored a bill in 1969 to prevent tax-loss farming. Bills were also introduced to ban feeding of livestock by packers with more than $1 million in annual gross sales.

A poll taken by *Wallaces Farmer* indicated that 78 percent of Iowa farmers favored national legislation to prevent packers and chain stores from operating feedlots. One farmer said, "We need legislation to prevent big chains from crushing the farmer."

However, farmers who marketed more than 500 hogs a year were less favorable to national legislation. One said, "Although I don't like large companies in competition with me, we live in a free country, anyone has a right to operate feedlots."

All farm organizations have not agreed on the need for federal regulation. The American Farm Bureau Federation called the idea of limiting the flow of a certain type of capital into farming and of demarcating who is and who is not a farmer "unacceptable."

Agrarian traditions have been called upon by farm people to support diverse positions on many issues. Even the perils of the nuclear age were mentioned in an agrarian context in a letter from an Alabama farmer published in the August 1968 issue of the *Progressive Farmer*. He wrote:

"This farm to city migration has got to be stopped and reversed if we are to survive as a nation in this nuclear age. With the ever menacing threat of nuclear war, what would be a better guarantee or defense than self-sustaining, self-supporting farm families as far back in the country away from towns and cities as possible.

"The morale and morals of the masses would be much improved if millions of our children were reared in the clean pure air where they could learn of God and Mother Nature."

The idea of encouraging a different distribution of population—encouraging more people to stay in or return to the country—is being studied by

Farmer William F. Morris examines young pig in his farrowing house in Roane County, Tenn.

American leaders as a means for improving the environment. Some of the arguments presently advanced by urban-oriented people for such a program go back to the point of the agrarian creed that the country provides a natural and therefore a good life.

A series of informal surveys made in the summer of 1969 showed that most commercial farmers and farm families now enjoy many of the amenities of city life—running water, electricity, telephones, television, radios, and access to shopping and cultural centers. At the same time, farmer after farmer cited traditional agrarian values as their reasons for staying in farming.

A successful commercial farmer in southwestern Iowa, Ernest Baker, stated that he had been discouraged, but really never dissatisfied, with farm life. He liked farming, and believed that a farm was a wonderful place to raise a family.

As far as basic satisfactions were concerned, he saw little difference between his father, himself, and his three sons. So far as farm life was concerned, it differed little from that in town, but crime, traffic, and particularly noise, would keep him from ever liking the city.

Commercial farmers, though, are still dependent upon weather, market prices, credit availability, increasing production expenses, and other things over which they have no control. An unfortunate series of disasters, combined with high costs of production and credit, led Willis Hansen to leave the farm in Solano County, Calif., that had been homesteaded by his great-grandmother in the 1860's.

He bought a trailer in town and sold his home place, which is no longer in commercial farm production. Yet Mr. Hansen still believes that farming is a good way of life. He prizes his independence, and likes the open spaces and the freedom from the traffic and dangers of city life.

The commercial farmer today is economically interdependent with the industrial city—the inevitable result of modern technology. His way of living, so far as physical conveniences and social and cultural life are concerned, is not obviously different from that of the city man. But he has made only minor modifications in the beliefs that have made up the agrarian tradition—independence, the importance of agriculture in the economy, and the value of farm life.

SYSTEMS COME, TRADITIONS GO

REVOLUTION HAS BEEN the order of business in agriculture, and it still is. During the past hundred years, output from farming has increased about six times, measured in constant dollars. During that same period, productive farm supplies of all types have increased less than three times. Thus efficiency of production, measured in dollars, has doubled.

Productivity, measured in terms of output per acre, per animal breeding unit, per man-hour, has increased steadily since the difficult days in the 1930's. Then, the land was tired and wearing out; drought beset the Plains and with it dust storms; and prices of farm and forest products hit the floor.

Through all our previous history, pioneers put new land to the plow as old lands wore out. Yields changed but little. Finally, in the thirties, the era of exploitation began to give place to the current era of conservation— of the land, water, air, and finally of our communities, of our whole environment.

Farm production now consists of the managed use of purchased materials, know-how, land, and livestock,

31

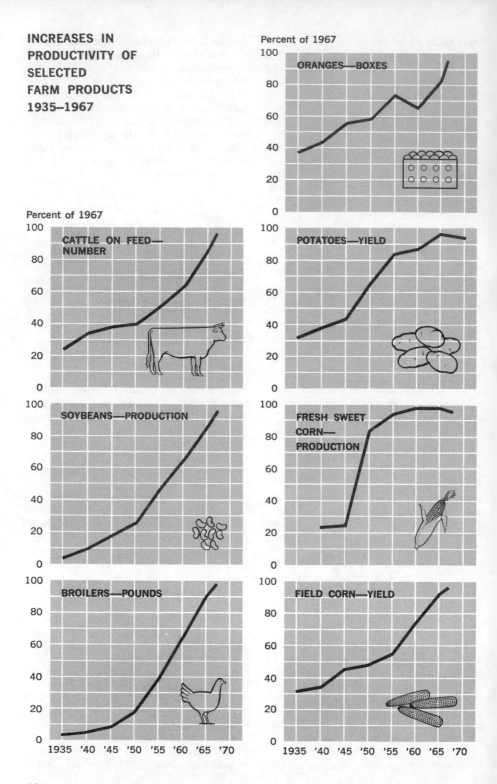

INCREASES IN PRODUCTIVITY OF SELECTED FARM PRODUCTS 1935–1967

Percent of 1967

ORANGES—BOXES

Percent of 1967

CATTLE ON FEED—NUMBER

POTATOES—YIELD

SOYBEANS—PRODUCTION

FRESH SWEET CORN—PRODUCTION

BROILERS—POUNDS

FIELD CORN—YIELD

1935 '40 '45 '50 '55 '60 '65 '70

1935 '40 '45 '50 '55 '60 '65 '70

32

Cotton stripper-harvester of type used on Texas High Plains. A two-row stripper-harvester replaces about 100 men doing handpicking. Trailer load of cotton is in foreground.

to obtain high yields of high quality plant and animal crops. Superior seed—superior breeding stock—protection against insects, diseases, parasites, and weeds—fertilization, reproduction, planting, tillage, and harvest aided by tireless machines—water management — formulated livestock feeds—are used in effective systems.

Some of the facts of the matter are indicated in the charts, which show the trend in productivity for selected farm commodities during the period 1935–1967, using 1967 values as 100 percent. The number of cattle fed increased four times during this period. Production of soybeans increased 20 times. Production of broilers increased more than 50 times. Production of oranges more than doubled. Potato yield per acre trebled. Production of sweet corn for the fresh market increased four times. Corn yield trebled.

How about the other side of the coin? Farm population has dropped from 32 million in 1935 to 11 million in 1967 while the total population

✦

AUTHOR T. C. BYERLY is Assistant Director for Science and Education.

increased from about 125 million to about 200 million. The equivalent of almost eight million full-time jobs in farming have disappeared.

People continue to leave the farm. More farm wage workers live off the farm than on the farm. Increasingly, farmers are moving to town.

Fewer farm families keep cows and chickens; and fewer nonfarm rural families, too. Many families that move to the city don't eat as well as they were able to do in the country—no garden, no cow, no pig. National food surveys in 1965 showed that more people were ill fed then than in years earlier; and rural-urban migration was a factor.

Mechanization is a basic component of the mechanical and scientific revolution. Tractor horsepower available on farms in 1967 was more than five times greater than in 1935. In 1935, about 2 to 3 horsepower from tractors was available to each farmworker; in 1967, more than 40 horsepower per farmworker was available. Expenditures for power and repairs increased about six times over the 1935 base during the 1935–67 period.

33

Why have these great changes occurred? Causes are diverse. Consider broilers and eggs here from the science standpoint. Genetic improvement, nutritional information, especially vitamin D and development of means for eradicating pullorum disease, made possible the shift from a small flock, highly seasonal type of enterprise to the industrialized, highly integrated, large scale enterprises we now have.

The change to ready-to-cook chilled or frozen broilers and the sharp change in price concomitant with production efficiency have kept volume increasing steadily.

Thousands of people contributed to the growth of the broiler industry. Processing technology provided the equipment for on-line picking, eviscerating, and inspection capability at a rate of thousands of broilers per hour. Successively, the market changed from live to New York dressed—head and feet on, guts in—to the present fresh, chilled, or quick-frozen, ready-to-cook product.

In the days of the live market, barred feathers were a mark of quality. As soon as the shift to dressed marketing got into full swing, the black pin feathers of barred birds became a blemish to appearance and caused increased processing costs.

Nutrition research during the 1930's and 1940's added one vitamin after another, knowledge of essential trace minerals, and amino acids. At the end of the 1940's vitamin B_{12} was discovered. It was the final link needed to complete the shift from meat, milk, and fish meals to soybeans as a principal source of protein to supplement corn for poultry and pigs—and people, too, for that matter. For B_{12} must be provided in the food of these one-stomach species while cows and sheep and other ruminants depend on bacterial production of B_{12} in their paunches.

White feathers became desirable—white feathers coupled with plump breasts and rapid growth and high feed efficiency. A great search took place in the late 1940's under the "Chicken of Tomorrow" slogan. Government, marketers, processors, and poultry breeders participated.

The search was successful. Breeding stock with the needed white feathers, plump breasts, hybrid vigor, and rapid growth and feed efficiency were found in California, in Connecticut, and other places. Commercial producers quickly changed to white feathered broilers.

Egg production has undergone changes almost as dramatic as those in the broiler industry, but by a somewhat different road. While hybrid corn was getting under way in the 1920's, a geneticist, L. C. Dunn, at the Storrs Agricultural Experiment Station in Connecticut tried inbreeding chickens.

He didn't have much luck. The stock went to pot pretty fast. So did stock in similar research in England under Michael Pease. But Morley Jull came to USDA's Agricultural Research Center in Beltsville, Md., in 1924 and started inbreeding afresh. That stock wasn't too good, either. C. W. Knox came to Beltsville in the thirties and he did some more work on inbreeding.

These and other early researches laid the foundation for production of commercial hybrids. At long last the possibility of chickens bred like corn took hold, first in the hands of hybrid seed corn companies with know-how in large-scale search and test and exploitation of superior hybrids. Now these incrossbreds compete with crossbreds, strains, and strain crosses.

The feed industry, marketing outlets, and poultry men have worked together to industrialize egg production. Confined flocks of many thousands of layers are commonplace, and egg production per hen at twice the rate of the 1930's are necessary for survival. Oh, yes, vitamin D, discovered by E. V. McCollum at the University of Wisconsin in the 1920's, is still an essential to winter egg production.

From grocery money for farm families to a business for a few thousand entrepreneurs, that's the story of poultry. So, too, from chicken on Sunday to an alternate to hamburger.

And as efficiency of the broiler industry increased, the margin per bird over production cost decreased and forced further efficiencies, increase in size of enterprise, or its abandonment.

Broiler production is highly integrated with the supply of feed, credit, and processing, and marketing of the finished product. There are, of course, analogous and older integrated systems, such as beet sugar, and fruits and vegetables for processing.

In these integrated systems, and in others now developing, computer technology will provide a new tool for greatly increasing efficiency of production, marketing, processing, and distribution.

The stress of the 1930's, necessity for increased efficiency, the search for new crops, and need for added income made farmers receptive to change. As broilers began in the thirties, soybeans started their change from a minor crop to a major one. During the 1935–67 period, soybeans have displaced oats in many Corn Belt farms and provided a new crop for acres no longer needed for cotton.

Science made adaptation of the soybean to a wide north-south range easier through the research on photoperiod to which H. A. Allard and W. W. Garner of the U.S. Department of Agriculture contributed so substantially. Breeders selected soybeans for day-length flowering suited to each latitude from Louisiana to Minnesota, and soybean production increased by 20 times from 1935-1967.

Orange production increased three times during the period. Helped by research to find virus-free stock, production has grown despite freezes and diseases. It could grow because research on better concentrates and better juices, in the Utilization Research Laboratories of the U.S. Department of Agriculture, kept the demand for orange products expanding.

Corn yield increase started in the 1930's when hybrid seed became available. The scientific demonstration of hybrid vigor in corn by E. M. East at Harvard, G. F. Shull at Princeton, and D. M. Jones at the Connecticut Agricultural Experiment Station before 1920 was not put to work until the 1930's. Traditional corn breeding methods based on selection of open pollinated corn stood in the way.

Since inbreds so obviously were inferior, it took bold, young breeders and seedmen to produce and demonstrate the superiority of hybrid corn seed.

Stress of the 1930's started adoption of hybrid seed on the way; it was complete by the middle 1950's as seed adapted to the various latitudes was developed. Adoption of hybrid seed was accompanied by about a 60 percent increase in acre yield.

Hybrid seeds alone are not enough. These plus fertilizer are not enough. Add pesticides and still the story is incomplete. The capability of the soil, estimated by a soil survey, with soil amendment by technology based on research of soil scientists and plant

USDA soil scientist Robert Hicks (left) helps Michigan farmer Wallace Swank plan use of his land according to its production capacity

physiologists, are needed, too. So saline and sodic soils are made productive because L. A. Richards and other scientists at the U.S. Salinity Laboratory at Riverside, Calif., taught us and the world how to do it.

Interaction, the theme song of Charles Kellogg of the Soil Conservation Service, is the road to sustained productivity. Good seed, sufficient, well-managed water, fertilizer, and pesticide chemicals as needed, planted at the right time—not by the phase of the moon but by soil temperature

There is some concern that excess nitrogen from fertilizer will contaminate our wells, lakes, and streams. Further technological improvements are needed so that nitrogen, whether from fertilizer, soil reserve, or manure, becomes available to crop plants as needed without excess which may be leached or volatilized from the soil.

The quadrupling of feedlot cattle is technologically based on engineering and management systems for delivering feed to large lots of cattle and establishing a continuous flow of

Sprinkler irrigation in a citrus grove, Highlands County, Fla.

and moisture in the right seedbed— and hope the rains come at the right time—all these are needed.

Corn yield has doubled since 1955, largely due to fertilizer nitrogen in the context of all the interacting factors just named—and more plants per acre, too. Basic discoveries on fixation of atmospheric nitrogen were made by the German chemist Fritz Haber and others before World War I.

Since that time the chemical industry has developed and adopted technology in the manufacture and delivery and application of anhydrous ammonia to the field that makes generous application of nitrogen profitable to the grower at current corn prices. Increased use for other crops including forest crops is also occurring.

slaughter cattle of uniform quality.

Because of its suitability for automated feeding systems, grain and other feed concentrates comprise an increasing portion of feedlot cattle diets. For the first 20 years of the 1935–67 period, beef cows replaced horses; since then, they have replaced dairy cows as milk production per cow increased through general use of tested, superior sires by artificial insemination.

Increased beef production parallels consumer income, because beef is a status meat. Increased production can bring lower prices to consumers only as technology—a higher percent calf crop and improved feed efficiency— makes it possible.

Large feedlots—especially those near cities, large dairy farms, egg, swine, turkey, and broiler enterprises bring problems of waste disposal paralleling the Augean stables. But there is no Hercules to turn an Alpheus river through them to disperse the filth, nor any river the public will long permit to be used for this purpose.

Indeed, it is our dependence on outmoded means of waste disposal, or our tendency to ignore the matter that comprises one of our most urgent problems in farm technology. A billion tons of animal wastes must be moved; hopefully to the land where their value as fertilizer and enhancing soil condition is large—but perhaps not large enough to cover handling and transportation costs to take a billion tons of wastes from feedlots, dairy, egg, and broiler facilities to croplands.

The increase in irrigated acreage is based on the wide adoption of pump irrigation in the Plains States and on the development and use of additional water supplies in the Western States. The very large increases in crop yields accomplished by irrigation and fertilization have made it profitable at current cotton, grain, and other crop prices, and at current water costs.

A dropping water table in the Texas High Plains makes future increase in water cost and ultimate decrease in supply inevitable there.

Irrigated acreage has more than doubled since 1935. Irrigated land, under proper management, yields far more than dryland. Kansas and Nebraska, which increased their irrigated acreage from about a half million acres to 3.5 million, trebled their acre yield of corn, much of which is now irrigated in these States.

As stress in the 1930's forced change, so the stress of World War II forced change. DDT was found to be a lifesaver for our troops in the tropics. It freed them of lice, fleas, mosquitoes, vectors of disease. At war's close, it became available for agricultural use. Since it was not protected by patent, chemical companies quickly came up with their own effective pesticides—the chlorinated hydrocarbons, carbamates, and organophosphates.

Weed killers that will destroy weeds without injury to crop plants came at the close of World War II and partly due to wartime research.

Dramatic increases in potato yields, and in production of sweet corn—available now year around without earworms, occurred between 1945–50. Other crops responded, too. But resistant pests soon renewed pressure for more effective pesticides.

Damage by pesticides to bees, other beneficial insects, and to fish, birds, and other wildlife have so challenged the use of chemical pesticides as to make urgent the need for new, more specific chemical pesticides, less toxic for birds and bees and fish—and people, too.

We must increase our efforts to find new and more effective cultural and biological control methods which may be integrated with minimal effective use of chemical pesticides.

Our present and prospective abundance of food, fiber, and forest products rests on the application of technology. We in the United States can look forward to vast areas of wooded lands and grassy ranges, teeming with wildlife, because technology has made our cultivated acres so productive. So, too, can all other developed countries.

Continuing development and application of technology in production of food, fiber, and forest products can supply the next generation abundantly. It can enable them to take the actions necessary to have clean air, sparkling water, and a green and pleasant world in which to live. Will the world's peoples take this course?

Assessment of the benefits of these great changes in agriculture, even in retrospect, is difficult. Assessment of current changes and those in prospect is even more difficult.

The first tests of new technology generally depend on the old, hard, questions: Will it work? Will it pay? Inherent in these questions, but seldom clear, is, Will the new technology benefit the user? the supplier of materials and equipment required? other

Waxed paper containing hundreds of corn borer eggs is cut into small disks as part of USDA research at Ankeny, Iowa, to develop corn genetically resistant to borer. Disks are distributed in corn plots to create artificial infestations and test the resistance of corn strains.

people in the same part of agriculture? the public?

The corollary, what damage will the technology do and to whom, has lately been emphasized—especially with respect to use of pesticides, hormones, antibiotics, and fertilizer.

There is an increasing trend to monoculture and specialization, away from "general" diversified farming.

Mechanization of some operations— land preparation, planting, cultivation, even harvesting—shortens the season when extra help is needed but does not eliminate it. We have a substantial migratory farm labor force. Mechanization has not eliminated it;

in fact, monoculture has aggravated the problem.

Technology is based on scientific discovery, chance discoveries, experience, invention, ingenuity, hard work, and motivation. Men seek profit; they seek recognition of their peers for their achievements; they seek opportunities for themselves, their families, their communities. They seek to reduce the burden of stoop labor. They seek the satisfaction of service.

And, finally, farmers, scientists, industrialists, everyone seeks to satisfy an insatiable curiosity. Jules Verne said, "What the mind of man can imagine, some man will do."

38

Technology is based on the exploitation and adaptation of discovery and invention in practice. Its application is assumed to convey benefits to the user; this is often the case. Technology is increasingly based upon a complex and systematic application of processes and equipment based on scientific information resulting from research in many scientific disciplines.

Our newly applied technology has brought indirect and sometimes unforeseen costs. Pesticides have been dispersed throughout our environment. Crop adjustments have left people without work or means of self support. Our abundance has cost the taxpayer in funds for supply management and the producer in depressed prices.

But these costs are small in comparison to the very large benefits in abundance of food, fiber, and forest products of land and other resources available for non-agricultural uses in moderate cost to consumers of products of the land, and the benefits to our friends in other lands from the materials and skills we share with them.

Migrant worker harvests beans in Oneida County, N.Y.

KING COTTON BLASTS OFF

IF YOU GREW UP before the mid-point of this century you may have the wrong image of cotton farming. Even if you are younger, you have probably seen paintings depicting scores of stooping laborers, women and children, picking cotton; or perhaps that of a tired man at the plow behind a tired mule.

This is not the picture today. The image of a planter on a horse overseeing scores of stooping laborers has given way to that of a hard-working businessman in a pickup truck, equipped with a two-way radio, supervising several well-paid operators of machines with power steering and air-conditioned cabs.

Although cotton is our last major field crop to approach full mechanization, the change has happened with space-age speed. The blast-off for "mission mechanization" occurred only 20 years ago—about the time we started to think about space travel.

Tractor power was used for some of the heavy plowing work prior to World War II, but during the mid-1940's most of the planting, cultivating, weeding, and harvesting was done by mules and men. By 1970, after two decades of research and development, most of the human drudgery of life on a cotton farm was gone.

In 1948, about 140 man-hours were required to produce a bale of cotton in the United States. In 1968, only about 25 man-hours were required. Most of this reduction was in the virtual elimination of the drudgery of stoop-labor for weeding and harvesting. The reduction in man-

39

hour requirements per bale, combined with acreage adjustments in recent years, reduced labor requirements in cotton production over the last two decades by as much as one million worker equivalents.

These very rapid adjustments were sparked, among other things, by three events: (1) the diminishing supply of farm labor during and after World War II, (2) introduction of a successful picker-type harvester in the early 1940's, and (3) introduction of chemicals for weed control in 1947.

Although the space-age cotton farmer does things differently from his grandfather's ways, he still does many things for the same reasons. His grandfather saved seed from the best-yielding field on his farm and stored it in a cool, dry bin in his barn. He tried to make sure the seed was pure and vigorous.

For the same reasons, most of today's farmers buy their seed from certified seed producers who grow it on productive soils; harvest, gin, delint, and handle it carefully to prevent damage; and store it under controlled conditions. In addition to delinting, seed is often graded to remove light, immature seeds, and is usually coated with one or more chemicals to combat seedling diseases.

Today's farmer prepares his seedbed with large tractors and carefully chosen equipment. He now has enough power to till his land deep or shallow, depending on the needs of his particular soil. Research has provided him with information and scientific equipment to determine his needs. However, land preparation is still a major power consumer, and over-tillage is a more frequent problem than under-tillage in most areas.

Instead of breaking the old stalks

✦

AUTHOR REX F. COLWICK is Leader of Cotton Harvesting Investigations, Agricultural Engineering Research Division, Agricultural Research Service, headquartered at State College, Miss.

COAUTHOR VERNON P. MOORE is Leader of Cotton Ginning Investigations in the same division, headquartered at Stoneville, Miss.

from the previous crop with a stick or a rolling cutter, powered high-speed cutters like giant lawnmowers now chop them into small pieces for easy covering. Solid or liquid fertilizer is often applied in the same trip with one of the seedbed preparation operations, and a preplanting herbicide may be incorporated in the soil to stop early weed growth.

Rows are bedded and shaped to provide smooth, uniformly-shaped surfaces for precision planting with multiple-row planters. Obtaining precision in the height, the shape, and the density of the seedbed is easier on fields that have been graded to a uniform slope. Land-forming, practiced for many years in irrigated areas, has been found essential in other areas for achieving uniform drainage, thus permitting timely scheduling of all operations.

Planting is becoming a science rather than an art. Scientists, engineers, and weather forecasters advise the farmer when to plant—based solely on soil and weather conditions rather than on the time of the moon.

The control panel of the planting tractor is beginning to resemble an airliner's cockpit, for in addition to planting seed, the operator is often controlling several operations. A planting tractor you may see in some of the larger cotton growing areas might have a seedbed conditioning or shaping tool mounted forward, and a rear-mounted planter equipped with fungicide, insecticide, and herbicide applicators.

The number of planting units per tractor may vary from 4 to 8 or even more rows.

Farmers used to plant at least twice as much seed as needed and then spend many hours thinning to the desired stand with a hoe. Now, they plant with precision either in spaced hills or in a continuous drill, and dispense with hand thinning. And some scientists and farmers are experimenting with narrow-row planting similar to planting grain. Their goal is to reduce production operations to essentially two steps—planting and harvesting.

But despite such advances, getting a good stand of cotton is still one of the farmer's major problems on which engineers and scientists are continuing to work for improvement.

Some of the greatest changes in cotton production technology have been in weed control. One of the first innovations departing from the old methods of hand hoeing and mechanical cultivation was flame cultivation. This occurred in the 1940's when equipment was developed using liquid petroleum gas to direct a hot blast of flame at the base of the cotton plant. Weeds smaller and more tender than the cotton were killed. Although flaming is still a good supplemental weed control practice in some areas, it has been largely replaced by chemicals.

Chemical weedkillers were first introduced for use in cotton in the late 1940's. They have been improved from year to year along with the equipment for applying them. It is now possible to virtually eliminate hand hoeing by using a combination of several herbicidal sprays.

A preplanting herbicide can be mixed into the seedbed to give control of most grasses several weeks past planting. Along with planting, a band of pre-emergence herbicide can be sprayed over the row to kill weeds escaping the preplanting spray. This also will kill any emerging weeds for several weeks.

When the cotton is several inches tall, a post-emergence chemical can be sprayed on small weeds under the cotton. This might be repeated once or twice, and then a "lay-by" herbicide can be applied for control through the remainder of the growing season.

Such a chemical control program is usually supplemented by mechanical cultivation between rows with conventional sweep-type plows—often

Eight-row cotton planter that can plant over 100 acres a day.

done in conjunction with the chemical application.

Although scientists are discovering promising ways to eradicate them, the common cotton insect pests including the infamous boll weevil are still with us. And in many areas, new insects are a recurring threat. But insect control is also becoming a science instead of an art. Many farmers hire professional insect scouts to advise them when and how to apply insecticides, and what kind to use. Then they have a choice of fast aerial application, or of spraying with a ground machine.

When insects pose a threat, today's farmer wages war against them instead of sitting back and hoping for the best. And he has many more weapons than formerly. He has a wide choice of insecticides for many insects as well as promising new experimental techniques such as sterile-male population control and boll weevil diapause control, where the weevils are poisoned in the fall just as they prepare to go into winter hibernation.

These mechanical and scientific developments have had a tremendous impact on yields. Better land preparation, better water control, better seed, better planting techniques, better use of fertilizer, and better pest control, coupled with improved varieties, have increased average yields of upland cotton from about 300 pounds of lint in 1948 to over 500 pounds in 1968.

Machines harvested at least 96 percent of our cotton crop in 1969 compared to less than 10 percent 20 years ago. Each two-row machine can do the work of four-score handpickers.

There are two types of machines in use—pickers and strippers. The picker-type machine uses hundreds of rotating spindles which enter the cotton plant and remove the cotton lint and seed from the bur, much like a handpicker. The burs, unopened bolls, and plants are left intact.

Mechanical stripping removes the burs, bolls, and some leaves and stems from the plant. Stripping is necessarily a once-over job and must be done after most of the crop is mature.

In 1969, about 68 percent of the U.S. crop was machine picked and about 28 percent was machine stripped. Stripping is a lower-cost operation than picking, but its use with present machines is limited in areas where the cotton plant grows taller than 3 or 4 feet.

Chemicals that defoliate the cotton plant of its leaves have helped make mechanical harvesting a success. Defoliation decreases the leaf trash harvested by a picker and exposes the lint for better contact with the picking spindles. For stripping, chemicals are sometimes used to kill or dry the leaves and plant. But where frost comes early, most farmers wait for nature to do it.

Like other technological revolutions, the rapid mechanization of cotton harvesting has created problems, foremost of which has been the maintenance of lint quality. Gins at first were not equipped to clean and gin the seed cotton containing more moisture and trash.

Gins have been improved to the point that grade losses are minimized, but the extra drying and cleaning necessary to do this often hurts the spinning quality of the lint. So the quality problem remains a challenge to engineers and scientists to reduce contamination in the harvesting and handling operations.

When grandfather used to take a bale of cotton to the gin, he could usually get it ginned and be home before dark. Now, with each harvester dumping a bale or two per hour in huge transport trailers, the rate of delivery to the gin increases many-fold. Instead of the harvesting season lasting three months, it may now be over in three weeks. The log jam at the gin creates problems for both producer and ginner.

It is well that this log jam was not created overnight. When experimental pickers were first put into the field the existing gins were hard pressed to process the cotton at all. The moisture which was added by the picker, together with the green leaf gathered with the cotton, caused chokages in the

Above, a high clearance sprayer being used for insect control in cotton. Below, plane drops sterile moths of pink cotton bollworm near Comanche Point, Calif., in a USDA biological control program against this cotton pest. The moths are sterilized by exposure to Cobalt-60 radiation and then released over infested areas. When they mate with nonsterile moths, there are no offspring. Right, larva of bollworm in cotton boll. They can destroy whole cotton fields.

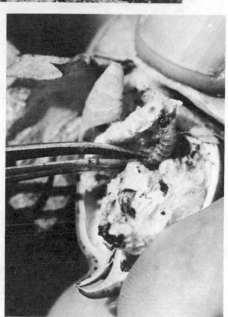

Above, spindle-type harvester which selects and picks the ripe cotton, leaving unopened bolls. Below, stripper type harvester that removes all the cotton from plant in a once-over operation.

gin machinery and yielded lint of "rough" preparation and low grade.

Due to the excessive moisture and foreign matter, bale value differences between hand and machine-picked cotton of $25 per bale were not uncommon. Ginners raised the temperature on their drying systems in an effort to dry the cotton sufficiently to reduce chokages and rough preparation. The drier cotton cleaned more easily but the excessive drying caused length shortening and corresponding reductions in use value.

The addition of a second drier made possible a longer exposure period and the use of lower temperatures to reduce the moisture content to a level low enough for efficient cleaning and smooth ginning without fiber degradation. Automatic controls were developed for cotton driers to hold temperature and fiber moisture content within predetermined limits.

Additional seed cotton cleaners were added to the system to remove more of the foreign matter, but there were still excessive discounts on machine-picked cotton due to the high foreign matter content of the lint.

The lint cleaner was developed to remove the fine "pin and pepper" trash which was the major cause of low grade and subsequent price discounts. This machine proved most successful and came into widespread use within a very short time, and grades obtained were almost comparable to those recorded from hand-picked cotton.

Some gins installed three stages of lint cleaning but tests showed that the weight loss from the third lint cleaner was greater than the increased bale value obtained by the additional trash removal.

Therefore, two lint cleaners have become the standard of the industry for both machine-picked and machine-stripped cotton. With the use of two lint cleaners, it was possible to remove some of the seed cotton cleaning machinery to minimize fiber damage and yet obtain acceptable grades.

Although sticks and green leaves continue to be something of a problem, the stick and green leaf machine was developed to remove this type of foreign matter. It was found much more efficient than the old bur machines and did not produce "pin and pepper" trash which had to be removed in subsequent processes.

Gin machinery manufacturers were quick to adopt the stick and green leaf machine principle and this too became a standard of the industry.

During the several years of developing machines and recommendations for handling machine-harvested cotton more and more mechanical harvesters were being employed and cotton was coming to the gin at an ever increasing rate.

In order to process the cotton more rapidly, gin machinery manufacturers furnished gin stands of 100 and 120 and even 140 saws each, where 80-saw stands had been the standard of the industry for a number of years. (A gin stand removes the lint from the seed.) This increase in the number of saws allowed gins to increase their processing rate from an average of about 4 bales per hour to 8 or 10, but this was still not sufficient to keep pace with the harvest.

It took development of the high capacity gin stand to accomplish a breakthrough. The average high capacity plants now are capable of processing some 18 to 20 bales per hour and the gin of the near future will probably have a capacity in excess of 30 bales per hour.

This breakthrough in development of the high capacity gin stand created bottlenecks throughout the ginning system. Seed cotton cleaners of up to 10 feet in width had to be developed, whereas 6-foot cleaners had been the standard of the industry for several years.

The conventional unloading system has proved inadequate for the high capacity plants, as has the packaging system. For many years cotton was unloaded by using a vacuum system which sucked the cotton from the farmer's conveyance into the gin plant.

This system was quite adequate at a ginning rate of less than 10 bales per hour. But as ginning rates increased, it required as many as 4 to 6 men to handle the cotton on the gin yard and feed the plant, making unloading an extremely costly operation.

To alleviate this problem, a new unloading system was developed by which the farmer's trailer could be dumped into a pit and the cotton fed from the pit to the gin plant mechanically. With this new system, one man can handle the cotton on the gin yard and feed a plant at a rate in excess of 30 bales per hour.

The packaging problem has been approached from numerous angles. The present bale packaging system has been automated to the extent that the bales are tied out automatically, but it is still an intermittent process, limited to a production rate of about 35 bales per hour. It requires 4 to 5 men to operate it.

Currently, a new packaging system is under development which, if successful, will require one or two men to operate it at a production rate of 30 to 40 bales per hour. It will have many advantages over the current American package, which has the dubious reputation of being the worst cotton bale package produced in the world.

Our present system is wasteful and expensive and requires many handlings and recompressions of the bale after it leaves the gin. This new experimental package will be sampled automatically at the gin, will move through the channels of trade with a minimum of handling, and will lend itself readily to modern high-speed mill operation.

Cotton ginning has evolved during the past 25 years from a rather crude farm operation to a highly technical, semi-automatic manufacturing operation.

The gin contains a device for metering the seed cotton into the plant, a drying system which is automatically controlled to give the proper amount of drying for adequate cleaning and quality preservation, a seed cotton cleaning system for removing large foreign matter, a high capacity gin stand for separating fibers from the seed at a rate unheard of just a few years ago, and a finishing-cleaning operation for the removal of small "pin and pepper" trash, combing fibers to give them a smooth appearance before they are conveyed to the packaging machinery.

Research has established standards for use of this equipment to provide the farmer with maximum bale value consistent with the preservation of fiber length and strength characteristics for optimum mill use.

Spinning quality is put into the fiber by the cotton breeder. The best that the cotton picker and gin can be expected to do is to preserve this quality.

As labor became increasingly scarce after World War II the slogan was "Mechanize to stay in the cotton business." Now that the farmer has mechanized, he finds costs have increased while the price of cotton has dropped. The cost-price squeeze has been drawn tighter by competition from synthetics, foreign production, and textile imports. Government assistance has helped keep production up to meet our domestic needs, but this obviously is not the ultimate answer.

The mechanization process continued rather slowly from the early 1940's until the latter 1950's. Increasing input prices (including labor) and rather constant lint prices were evident by the late 1950's. Producer efforts to reduce costs to cope with these problems led to rapid mechanization between 1958 and 1969. With this more complete mechanization several hundred thousand fewer workers were required to produce the U.S. cotton crop. A number of these people had limited skills and limited opportunities to obtain alternative employment in other economic sectors.

The cotton industry feels that research and promotion can solve cotton's problems by reducing production costs, finding new use for cotton, and promoting wider marketing.

MAKING A BETTER APPLE, OR PUZZLES AND POMOLOGY

APPLES ARE the most important of the deciduous (non-evergreen) tree fruits grown in this country and the world. Within the past 30 years more changes have occurred in the apple industry than in all its previous history. These changes were the result of modern technology.

From the beginning of apple culture up to 1940, efforts to improve production consisted largely of culture, variety testing, and selection. As a result, about 12 varieties emerged as leaders and these varieties now make up over 90 percent of the potential 150 million bushel crop produced annually in the commercial apple districts of the United States.

A great many diseases and insects attack the apple. In humid areas apple scab, a fungus disease, infects both foliage and fruit. Sprays for control of this disease are essential for production of acceptable fruits.

Copper compound sprays were used from 1890 to 1910 to control apple scab. Since these compounds made the fruits russet-colored, the apple industry changed to sulfur sprays for disease control, and these were used for the 40-year period 1910 to 1950.

In the early 1930's, it was shown that sulfur sprays, when employed as a fungicide, reduced the process of photosynthesis (food manufacture) by apple foliage in amounts ranging from 30 to 50 percent. Such an effect would be expected to reduce apple crop production in humid areas where control of apple scab was necessary.

With the introduction of newer, less toxic fungicides in the late 1940's, apple production began to increase. During the period 1939 to 1966, the apple tree population in New York State decreased 45 percent, while annual crops increased 8 percent. This means that production per tree or per unit of bearing surface doubled.

While emphasis on better varieties, better tree nutrition, and the limiting of plantings to the better soils and sites were contributing factors, the use of modern fungicides was certainly the most important change in obtaining significantly better yields of fruit.

When left to its natural bearing habit the apple is characteristically biennial; that is, a heavy crop is followed by a light crop. Flower buds which blossomed in the spring of 1970 were formed or differentiated in the young buds the previous summer, or about 6 to 7 weeks following the 1969 bloom and at a time when the 1969 apple crop was developing. Therefore, the potential for the 1970 crop was determined approximately 15 months

NEW YORK STATE APPLE PRODUCTION
1939 = 100

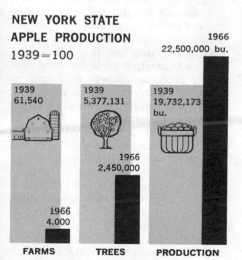

1966
22,500,000 bu.

1939
61,540

1939
5,377,131

1939
19,732,173 bu.

1966
2,450,000

1966
4,000

FARMS   TREES   PRODUCTION

1/15 Number Farms with 1/2 Number Trees = Greater Total Production

AUTHOR M. B. HOFFMAN is Head of the Department of Pomology, Cornell University, Ithaca, N.Y.

47

before it was harvested. A heavy or excessive set of fruit in 1969 has the effect of reducing or preventing flower bud formation and the trees have little or no bloom in 1970.

This phenomenon has been recognized since the beginning of apple culture. The problem has long concerned the apple grower and the pomologists who serve him. Biennial bearing creates marketing problems. There is a year-to-year irregular supply to the consumer. The grower is plagued with too many small sized fruits in the heavy crop year and too many oversized fruits in the light one.

While growing costs up to harvest time are approximately the same in the heavy crop year as in the light crop year, fruit prices are low when the crop is excessive and high when the crop is light. Biennial bearing is uneconomic.

There is now good evidence that the seeds in apple fruits are the guilty tissues which have some unexplained physiological effect in inhibiting flower bud formation. When there are too many fruits with too many seeds, the newly formed buds remain vegetative and fail to form flower parts. Also, leaves play an essential role in flower bud formation. An excessive set of fruit results in small sized leaves, while individual leaves are larger when fruit set is moderate.

Thinning or removal of excessive fruits is the only practical means of assuring annual bloom and annual apple cropping. The thinning must be accomplished within 4 weeks of bloom or else the new buds will have passed that stage in which they can be influenced to form flowers. Even if labor were available, hand thinning of commercial apple plantings sufficiently early to assure annual flowering would be impracticable.

Research on the possibility of spray thinning apples was started in 1940. The early work involved bloom sprays of dinitro-orthocresol which prevented fruit set by unpollinated flowers. Later on it was learned that the growth-regulating chemicals naphthalene-acetic acid and its amide, naphthaleneacetamide, would reduce fruit set when applied during the early post-bloom period. In 1960 1-naphthyl N-methyl carbamate was added to the list of the post-bloom apple thinning agents.

Early results varied from overthinning to no thinning. With continued effort a better understanding of those factors which influence results was obtained.

Spray thinning apples has now become a widely used commercial practice. During the 20-year period 1935 to 1955, the light year apple crops in New York State averaged 14 million bushels while production in heavy crop years was 23 to 24 million bushels. The extent of alternation amounted to approximately 35 percent.

With commercial use of thinning sprays, annual crops for the decade of the 1960's have ranged between 20 and 22 million bushels. This is a better situation for both the apple industry and the consumer.

In young plantings, trees of some apple varieties are characterized by much vigorous vegetative growth and delayed flowering and fruiting for many years after the planting is established. Delicious, the most important variety grown in the United States, is notorious for this behavior. Young trees of Delicious, growing under ideal conditions, may remain relatively unproductive their first 10 years.

This frustrating biological and economic problem has been overcome by spraying the trees in early summer with growth-regulating chemicals. Either 2,3,5-triiodobenzoic acid (TIBA) or succinic acid 2,2-dimethylhydrazide (ALAR), alone or in combination, will stimulate flower bud formation on young Delicious trees and bring them into bearing at 5 to 6 years of age or at that time when there is sufficient bearing surface on the young tree to justify cropping.

As they approach maturity, apples are subject to drop from the tree. This is due to formation of an abscission layer at the end of the stem where it is

Influence of thinning sprays on size of apples.

connected to the fruiting wood. A natural process associated with maturity and senescence, this is the same process responsible for autumn leaf fall by trees.

Apple varieties vary greatly in their susceptibility to fruit drop during harvest. McIntosh, an important variety in the New York and New England area, is noted for this fault. If 2 to 3 days of warm weather with temperatures in the upper 60's or low 70's occur during the latter half of the harvest period, unharvested McIntosh trees may drop 50 to 75 percent of their crop within a 2-day period.

Since drop apples with their bruises and skin breaks are unfit for storage and fresh fruit channels, the harvest drop problem has been a costly one. In 1939 it was found that a naphthalencacetic acid preharvest spray, at a concentration of only 10 parts per million (ppm), would delay fruit abscission and control the harvest drop of McIntosh for approximately 10 days.

Since that time, other growth-regulating chemicals have been found effective for this purpose when used as preharvest sprays. Adaptability of these chemicals varies with the variety. The grower has considerable choice and is now in a position to control fruit drop of his apple crop until the harvest is completed.

With an increasing shortage of seasonal labor for hand harvesting fruit crops, much effort is being put into development of mechanical harvesting. This practice is extensively used for fruits that are adapted, and progress has been made in mechanical harvesting of cherries and apple varieties which are processed immediately upon harvest.

Mechanical harvesting involves the shake and catch principle. Tree or limb shakers operated hydraulically are used. Vibrations from the shaker remove fruit which falls to catching frames from which it is conveyed on endless belts to field containers. Some fruits, in varying amounts, resist the shaker. These require more vigorous shaking for longer periods of time.

It would be helpful and minimize the amount of tree shaking, both in time and force, if all fruits on the trees were beginning to form an abscission layer. Such is never the case. The harvest of commercial fruit crops cannot be delayed until this natural process of abscission begins, because much of the fruit would be overripe, natural drop would have started, and loss from spoilage would be great. Therefore, a method of uniformly promoting abscission by all fruits just ahead of the shaking operation would be ideal.

Research on screening chemicals which would simultaneously initiate

Above, mechanical harvesting of apples for processing. Below, closeup of a tree shaker harvesting cherries.

the abscission process of all fruits has shown that 2-chloroethylphosphonic acid (Ethrel) is very effective for this purpose. (This use of Ethrel in apple production was not registered with the U.S. Department of Agriculture at the time of this writing.)

In orchard experiments, the fruit removal force for Montmorency cherries one week after spraying trees with Ethrel was reduced 33 percent.

The time required to harvest the sprayed trees with a shaker was less than half of that required for unsprayed trees. Furthermore, the fruit removal from the sprayed trees was complete while 3 to 5 percent of the cherry crop was frequently retained by unsprayed trees.

The Ethrel spray initiates the abscission layer between fruit and stem. Therefore, destemming many fruits during the processing operation is eliminated. Similar results have been obtained with Ethrel sprays on sweet cherries that were mechanically harvested for brining. The promotion of abscission and reduction in fruit removal force brought about by Ethrel results in a smoother separation of fruit from stem with a reduction in the proportion of fruits with torn flesh at the point of separation. This is a desirable factor in quality maintenance through post-harvest handling operations in the processing of both tart and sweet cherries.

The Rome Beauty apple is one of the principal varieties grown for processing. Rome Beauty fruits develop from flowers differentiated in terminal buds on lengthy shoots of the previous season's growth. These long willowy shoots do not sufficiently transmit the vibration force of the shaker for successful mechanical harvesting of Rome Beauty and other processing varieties having this fruiting habit. After vigorous shaking of Rome Beauty trees with maximum force, 20 percent or more of the crop has remained on the tree.

In contrast, Ethrel sprays resulted in a 50 percent reduction in fruit removal force. And following a 2-second shake, 98 percent of the crop was on the catching frame. These effects of an Ethrel spray are realized within 1 to 2 weeks following treatment. The time required depends on variety and prevailing temperature.

Chemical promotion of abscission will be a breakthrough for mechanical harvesting of cherries and apples produced for processing outlets. While there is a continuing need for delaying abscission and controlling harvest drop of those varieties of apples hand-harvested for storage and fresh fruit channels, the promotion of abscission is equally valuable in the mechanical harvesting of processing fruits.

Approximately 50 percent of the annual apple crop is stored immediately upon harvest and later moved into fresh fruit markets. The remainder of the crop is processed into sauce, frozen slices for pie stock, and juice. Two kinds of storage environment are used for fresh fruit apples: (1) Refrigerated rooms with normal atmosphere, and (2) refrigerated rooms with controlled atmosphere (CA.)

Many apple varieties reach the end of their storage life in normal atmosphere storage by mid-January. A few varieties such as Winesap and Rome Beauty will satisfactorily store longer in normal atmospheres.

CA storage atmospheres involve the use of lower than normal oxygen and higher than normal carbon dioxide levels in gas-tight refrigerated rooms. The low oxygen level and high carbon dioxide level retard fruit respiration, softening, change in ground color, quality change, breakdown, and the development of decay. The percent oxygen and percent carbon dioxide required for best keeping quality in the CA environment varies somewhat for the different varieties.

Basic principles of CA storage were discovered in England. Research on the application of these principles to American varieties was started in the 1930's.

The first commercial CA storage for apples in this country was constructed by a New York State apple grower in 1940. It had a capacity of 10,000 bushels. In 1969 there were 14.6 million bushels of CA apple storage space in the United States.

CA storage has extended the marketing season for fresh apples throughout the late winter, spring, and early summer months, or until early varieties of the following year's crop begin to mature. The consumer is never without the opportunity to obtain fresh apples.

During the storage period, the greatest losses to the apple industry, the individual grower, and the consumer have been due to a physiological disorder known as scald. This nonparasitic storage trouble causes the apple skin to become brown, and the fruit is unsalable in fresh fruit channels. In its late stages the disorder affects the flesh so deeply that it cannot be properly peeled for processing. One grower in a single storage season lost 80,000 bushels of Rome Beauty apples to scald.

Four decades of research have given no satisfactory explanation of the basic causes of scald. Susceptibility of apples varies from season to season. While climate during the growing season seems to play a part in susceptibility of stored fruit, all the factors responsible for a "bad scald year" have not as yet been defined.

Prior to 1955 the only means of scald control in significant amounts was the wrapping of individual fruits in paper treated with white mineral oil, or by mixing one-half pound of shredded oil paper per bushel of fruit. This method calls for grading, wrapping, and packing prior to storage rather than on removal of fruit from storage, when grading and packing for market could be more appropriately done.

In 1955 it was reported that diphenylamine (DPA) showed promise as a chemical treatment for scald control. Further research efforts on this approach indicated another chemical, 6-ethoxy-1,2-dihydro-2,2,4-trimethyl quinoline (ETHOXYQUIN), had similar effects. Developmental work with these two chemicals has shown that dipping the fruit is the most effective means of scald control with either DPA or Ethoxyquin. Dipping assures complete fruit coverage. Concentrations of 1,000 to 2,000 ppm of DPA or 1,800 to 2,700 ppm of Ethoxyquin depending on variety are called for.

Other methods of treatment such as spraying the fruit on trees just prior to harvest or spraying it after harvest in field containers or as it passes over grading machinery has given significant control of scald. But these methods are not as effective as dipping for complete coverage. The apple industry now has a chemical method of scald control which when properly used will avoid the heavy losses of former years.

Chemicals that are proving useful in apple production and storage offer no problems in environmental pollution or contamination of the edible fruits. Those used for spray thinning and control of harvest drop have relatively short lives. Ethrel which stimulates abscission does so by liberating ethylene upon breakdown. Ethylene occurs naturally in ripening fruits.

The commercial grower has a strong interest in meeting allowed tolerances of all chemicals used in overcoming production and storage problems.

During the prosperity of the mid-1920's, McIntosh apples frequently sold on the New York City wholesale market for $5 per bushel. This fruit was packed in the old apple barrel. In the depression years of the 1930's, the wholesale price of McIntosh packed in wooden boxes ranged from $2 to $3 per bushel. During the very prosperous years of the 1960's, the wholesale price of a one-bushel cell pack carton of McIntosh has ranged between $4.50 and $5.50.

Wholesale prices appear to be determined, in the main, by the Nation's economy and the supply of fruit. Despite recent increases in costs of growing, harvesting, storing, and other operations involved in production and marketing of fruit, wholesale prices of apples today do not vary greatly from those of the mid-1920's. Use of modern technology to increase yield, secure annual cropping, improve quality, prevent wastage, and extend the marketing season is what has made this possible.

WINNING THE RACE
TO GET THE HAY IN

HOT AND HEAVY WORK, done as rapidly as possible, with frequent glances toward an approaching rain cloud, was rather typical of hay harvesting in 1940. By the late 1960's, some of the anxiety and much of the heavy work associated with hay harvesting had been eliminated by machines.

Hay is a very perishable crop and, in order to retain feeding value, it must be cut at the right time and cured properly. Since the highly nutritious leaves of legume hay, such as alfalfa, are more susceptible to loss than the leaves of grass hay, legumes must be handled more carefully. Cutting at the proper stage of maturity is important with both types.

The farmer in the late 1960's was much better equipped for the race than the farmer of 1940. Then most of the hay harvested was cut with a two-wheeled, horse-drawn mower with a 5-foot cutterbar. Only a few tractor-powered mowers with cutterbars up to 7 feet long were used.

After the hay had cured sufficiently in the swath, it was raked into a windrow with either a side-delivery rake or a spring-tooth sulky rake. The more highly mechanized operations used a loader pulled behind the wagon to pick the loose hay up from the windrow and load it on the wagon. One man, using a pitchfork, placed the hay from the loader into the wagon bed for hauling it to the mow or barn loft. The hay was usually lifted into mow by either a harpoon or grapple fork operating on an overhead track. Final placing or stacking within the mow was again done by hand, using a pitchfork.

Field pickup balers did not become popular until after the self-tying or automatic baler was introduced in 1940. This made baling a one-man operation and began the rapid adoption of labor-saving forage handling machines.

Following World War II, changes in methods and equipment for hay handling began to take place rapidly and by the middle 1960's, the manpower required to produce a ton of hay had been reduced to one-third of that required 25 years earlier.

Faster and more uniform field drying of hay is made possible by the use of conditioners or crushers. These con-

✦

AUTHOR JAMES L. BUTLER is Leader, Forage and Oilseeds Harvesting and Processing Investigations, Agricultural Engineering Research Division of the Agricultural Research Service. He is stationed at the Georgia Coastal Plain Experiment Station, Tifton.

sist of a pair of rollers, held together by adjustable spring pressure and driven by the tractor power takeoff. The rollers may be attached directly behind the cutterbar or they may be attached to a unit to pick up a previously cut swath. In either instance, the cut hay is passed between the rolls to crush the stem and thicker parts and then dropped back on the stubble in cither a swath or a loosely formed windrow.

Virtually all mowers in use by 1969 had cutterbars 7 feet long or longer. A choice of either tractor-powered units or self-propelled units could be had. Some of the self-propelled units had 16-foot cutterbars with 12-foot cutterbars being common. The mowers, especially the self-propelled units, could be equipped with conditioning rolls and devices for bringing the hay into a narrow swath from which the hay could be baled, cubed, or chopped without additional raking.

While the mower-conditioner- windrower does all these in one operation, the side delivery rake was still being used in most operations. This type of rake, powered from either the power takeoff or ground drive, may be either tractor-mounted or trailed behind the tractor. This rake has the capability of moving the hay from the swath to the windrow very gently and in a short forward travel.

Up to the point of windrowing, the haymaking operation is essentially the same whether it is to be handled as loose hay, baled hay, cubes, sun-cured pellets, chopped hay, or haylage. From this point on, however, the physical form in which the hay is to be handled and stored dictates the equipment and method to be used.

Under conditions of low rainfall during the storing and feeding period, and where the hay will be cut, stored, and fed in or near the field where it is produced, stacks of long, loose hay can be used advantageously. These are formed by using tractor-mounted buck rakes, which are similar to a big pitchfork, to pick the hay up from the swath or windrow. When the rake is filled with hay, the tractor transports it to the stack. The fork is lifted by hydraulic cylinders, powered by the tractor's hydraulic system, and the hay dumped onto the stack.

Portable cages, which are used to help form the stack, are removed once the stack is settled. If the hay from these stacks must be moved short distances, a specially designed trailer which can load the stack onto itself can be used to transport and unload the stack.

By using these methods and machines, it is possible to handle long, loose hay without hand labor.

In the quarter century between 1940 and 1965, the number of tons of hay sold off the farm increased from 11 million tons to 22 million tons. The economics of handling and transporting require that the hay be made as compact as possible and that the form of the package be one which can be easily handled. To varying degrees, these requirements are met by bales, cubes, and pellets. Hay in these forms also has advantages for the producer-feeder.

Baled hay is by far the most popular of the forms of hay, accounting for over 80 percent of total production. The automatic baler, operated by one man, can package up to 20 tons of hay per hour. These balers, which use either twine or wire to tie the bales, can be adjusted to change either the length or density of the bale.

Bale throwers can be attached to the baler to throw bales into a wagon towed behind the baler. The use of these makes it possible for one man to bale and load in one operation. Since the bale is not dropped back onto the ground, and no separate pickup is required, the weather risk is reduced.

Self-unloading wagons, vertical elevators, and mow conveyors used in conjunction with bale throwers make it possible for one man to bale, haul, unload, and store hay with a minimum of effort. This system, which utilizes random stacking in the mow, does waste some storage space, but the cost of the additional space is more

than offset by time and labor saved.

Self-loading and self-stacking bale wagons, either tractor powered or self-propelled, became rather widely used in the late 1960's. These machines pick the bale up from the ground and, by means of cross-conveyors, longitudinal conveyors, and stacking arms, automatically load the bales on the wagon, which is then transported to the stack.

When properly positioned, the wagon bed is tilted to a vertical position with the bales which were on the back of the wagon resting on the ground. The wagon is then driven forward leaving the bales in a free-standing stack. Such stacks, naturally, are limited in height to approximately the length of the wagon bed.

Use of these wagons makes it possible for hay to be put into storage without any hand labor. Hand labor is required with this system only when feeding, or if additional transportation is required.

Cubing or wafering machines, which appeared during the 1960's, have a great potential for revolutionizing hay handling. These machines tightly compress hay into small units. The pressure applied is great enough so that the hay retains the compressed form after pressure is removed. Various sizes and shapes of these units, ranging from 4-inch diameter disks to ⅝-inch cubes, have been introduced. By 1969, cubes with a 1¼- x 1¼-inch cross-section and a length ranging from about ½ inch to about 3 inches appeared to be the most popular.

Cubing machines require that the moisture content be about 10 percent prior to cubing. These moistures cannot normally be reached by field drying except in the more arid hay producing areas. Thus, the field-going units are being operated primarily in the irrigated areas of the West. The physical characteristics of grass are such that grass hay is much more difficult to form into a cube than are the legumes. This has further restricted the use of cubing machines to legumes.

Hay is usually prepared for cubing by cutting with a self-propelled mower-

54

Left, a unit that combines mowing, conditioning, and windrowing the hay crop in one operation. Above, farmer Carl Anderson drives a rotary hay rake, in Grafton County, N.H. Below, this baler ejects bales into a trailing wagon.

conditioner-windrower and left in the field until the proper moisture content is reached. This may be as long as 8 to 10 days and results in the surface of the windrow appearing thoroughly bleached.

Since the windrow was formed from a 12- to 16-foot swath, however, the percent of material on the surface is very small. The cubing operation thoroughly mixes the hay and the finished cube usually has an attractive green color. The pickup attachment of the cuber gently lifts the hay from the windrow and, since no raking is normally done between cutting and cubing, a minimum of material is lost in harvesting.

Just prior to compressing, moisture is sprayed onto the surface of the hay to aid in bonding the particles together. The hay is then forced through openings in the die by rollers. The resistance to flow of hay through the die causes the roller to apply pressure which compresses the hay and causes it to stick together. As the hay is extruded from the die, curved plates break it into segments which approximate cubes.

Cubes have relatively free flowing characteristics, allowing them to be handled by a wide variety of devices. Density of the cubes plus the flow characteristics make them well suited for transporting, handling, storing, and self-feeding.

In more humid areas, the technology of the sixties did not make field-cubing feasible. Here, the pellet was the more popular form of self-contained unit of hay. In these areas, pelleting is always done in conjunction with some type of mechanical drier or dehydrator.

Dehydrators, which have tremendous capacity for evaporating water, can virtually eliminate the weather hazard in haymaking. Since from 3 to 4 tons of water must normally be evaporated to produce one ton of dry hay, dehydration is naturally more expensive than when the hay is left in the field to dry for 1 or 2 days. Normally, field drying for this amount of time will reduce the moisture content to about 20 to 40 percent. When field-dried to this moisture content, only about 250 to 1,000 pounds of water must be evaporated to produce a ton of dry hay.

Hay to be pelleted is normally harvested from the field with a forage harvester. These harvesters may be either tractor-powered or self-propelled. Depending upon whether the material is to be dehydrated or partially field-cured, either a direct-cut or pickup attachment may be used. The direct-cut attachment has a cutterbar, similar to a mower, which cuts the standing forage. The forage is then conveyed to the cutting cylinder which cuts it into a predetermined length and blows it into the hauling unit.

For forage which has been partially field-cured, a pickup attachment is used to pick the forage up from a windrow and convey it to the cutting cylinder. From this point on, the operation is the same as when the material is direct-cut.

Some of the self-propelled forage harvesters have a large self-unloading bin as an integral part of the machine. These bins normally hold 5 to 7 tons and eliminate the need for either a separate trailer or a truck to follow the forage harvester around in the field. The discharge of the bin is high enough to unload into a truck for transport to the next operation.

After the hay has been mechanically dried to the desired moisture content, it is ground through a hammermill. Just before the ground material goes into the pelleting chamber, steam and water are mixed to produce a pelletable mixture. The mixture is then forced through the die by rollers. As the extruded material leaves the die, knives cut it to the desired length. A wide variety of die sizes and shapes are available. The $\frac{3}{8}$- and $\frac{1}{4}$-inch diameter sizes appear to be the most popular for pelleting forages.

Pellets made from high quality, dehydrated material are normally used as feed supplements in mixed feeds, especially poultry feeds. Those made from partially field-cured or field-cured hay are fed to animals merely as a more convenient form of hay. Hay in the pellet form can be easily hauled, handled, stored, and fed with conventional grain handling and storage facilities. Thus, it is a form of hay in which the handling can be completely automated.

Chopped hay is another form of hay which can be harvested and handled with a minimum crew and a minimum of labor input. In most of these operations, the hay is dried in the field, picked up with a field forage harvester, chopped, and blown into self-unloading wagons. At the storage site, the hay is conveyed into storage and distributed. The facility may be designed to allow drying to be completed in storage. This allows harvesting to be done at slightly higher moisture content and reduces dustiness and leaf loss. Storages for chopped hay are usually designed for self-feeding.

Hay silage increased in popularity during the 1960's. It was found that hay could be field-wilted to 40 to 60 percent moisture and stored with a minimum of loss. The resulting silage, termed haylage, is well accepted by animals. Since harvesting at this moisture content results in low field losses, haylage appears to strike the best balance between field and storage loss when the total range from direct-cut silage to field-cured hay is considered.

The combination of higher capacity field forage harvesters, self-unloading wagons, powerful blowers for rapid silo filling, and silo unloaders have made it possible to completely mechanize silage harvesting, storing, and feeding. When the forage is to be fed on the farm which produced it, silage offers a good potential. Since forage in this form must be consumed within a short time after it is removed from the silo, it cannot be considered a potential cash crop as is hay.

Hay is harvested from more than 20 percent of all cultivated land in the United States and yet is considered a secondary crop on most farms. Since less than 20 percent of the crop is sold off the farm, hay cannot be considered a strong cash crop, yet the change to mechanized harvesting and handling has taken place almost as rapidly as with the major cash crops.

With the apparent trend toward specialization, the demand for machines to harvest and handle forage faster and more efficiently will increase. We can expect these demands to be met in the future even more readily than they have in the past.

ONE MAN FEEDS 5,000 CATTLE OR 60,000 BROILERS

WE LIVE IN AN ERA marked by technological change. The livestock and poultry industry is no exception. Ever-increasing demand for better performance and greater efficiency is intensified because individual producers have so little effect on the prices they receive for their products. Their recourse is to reduce production costs per unit of output.

Thus, producers adopt better breeds and strains of livestock; feed better balanced, high-energy rations; mechanize their feeding rations and feeding methods, and expand the size of their operations. Many also become more specialized.

One goal sought by large-scale feeders is to reduce the amount of labor required in feeding operations. Feeding systems for broilers, for example, now require the services of only one man to care for 60,000 to 75,000 birds. A man can feed upwards of 5,000 head of cattle in a modern feedlot, or one man can handle 50 to 60 milk cows in a loose housing, mechanized feeding system. In a real sense, mechanization of feeding has been substituted for labor.

Although large-scale enterprises exist in all types of livestock and poultry production, at present the meat-poultry industry is the major part of agriculture which approaches complete coordination (through economic integration or contract) of various stages of production from breeding flocks through processing of finished birds. Considerable close coordination is also found in the egg industry.

Traditionally, the Corn Belt has been the center of cattle feeding in the United States. In recent years, intensified cattle feeding has developed in the western and southwestern regions of the United States. In these finishing feedlots, feeder cattle receive a high-energy ration until ready for slaughter.

Capacities of feedlots range from less than 1,000 head of cattle to 100,000 head or more. The larger feedlots are maintained near full capacity year around. When one lot of cattle is finished, it is marketed and replaced by another lot. In 1968, although only 1 percent of the cattle feedlots had capacity for over 1,000 head of cattle, this group fed about 47 percent of the fed cattle marketed.

In the hog industry, large-scale specialized enterprises are also developing, but not as rapidly as in poultry and fed cattle, nor with the same degree of coordination. Probably less than 10 percent of market hogs come from such firms.

Specialization and integration of feeding enterprises have tended to bring a more regular flow of uniform, high-quality poultry and livestock to market. The goal continues to be that of producing products which consumers want from the standpoint of quality and quantity needed.

The commercial broiler industry has led in application of efficient pro-

✦

AUTHOR EDWARD C. MILLER is a Research Management Specialist in the Cooperative State Research Service.

COAUTHOR EARL F. HODGES is an Agricultural Economist in the Economic Research Service.

duction methods such as high density housing, control of housing environment, bulk feed delivery and mechanical feeding, use of fat and antibiotics in feed, and least cost feed formulation. Many of these progressive practices have been applied to production of turkeys, hogs, and beef cattle, or are being applied.

Broiler meat production consists of many phases, such as production of breeding stocks, hatching of eggs, manufacturing of feed, growing of broiler chicks to market age, and processing. In the early days of the broiler industry, independent operations existed at each stage of production. Now, most of these stages are under control of a single management. This close coordination permits alignment of output of one stage to the needs of others. About 95 percent of the broilers are produced under some type of integration or contractual agreement.

The broiler industry has utilized a discovery by the Connecticut Agricultural Experiment Station in 1947 that "high energy" diets promoted rapid growth and more efficient conversion of feed into meat. Today, broilers can achieve live weights of over 3 pounds at 8 to 9 weeks of age with only slightly more than 2 pounds of feed for each pound of gain in live weight.

Broilers are grown to live weights that meet specialized needs of the market. "Take home" chicken outlets and producers of frozen dinners require processed broilers within a specified weight range to obtain uniformity of pieces for better portion control.

Broilers produced in 1968 averaged 3.6 pounds per bird. But in the future they will probably average lower in weight as a much higher proportion of production goes into "carry out" outlets.

To obtain maximum production of meat from livestock or poultry, it is important to use the best breeds or strains available to producers. Breeders have recognized that some animals

Confinement housing of turkey hens, showing trap nest used to obtain eggs for incubation, Frederick County, Md.

will perform consistently better than others, and have promoted their use in breeding stocks.

In 1935, the U.S. Department of Agriculture initiated the National Poultry Improvement Plan to improve production and marketing qualities of chickens and turkeys through performance testing. These performance tests are held in appropriate regions of production. Poultry breeders can enter stocks in these tests and compare their performance with that of others. Available to all producers is information obtained on live weight at the end of the test period, efficiency of feed utilization, mortality, and economic carcass characteristics.

Systematic crossbreeding of different breeds and strains of poultry is used to incorporate desirable production characteristics into the offspring, and to utilize hybrid vigor to improve performance.

Hog and cattle breeders have also used performance testing to improve production and carcass quality of their products. Today, more than 90 percent of all hogs marketed are crossbred. The consumer's desire for tender pork with a high proportion of lean resulted in changes in carcass quality. Substantial progress also has been made in improving breeds of beef cattle to obtain a more uniform carcass with less waste.

Since feed is such an important part of the cost of finishing livestock and poultry, producers continually seek rations which will meet nutri-

Each week baby chicks by the millions hatch from automatic incubators for use by the Delmarva Poultry Industry of Delaware, Maryland, and Virginia.

tional requirements, but which will also make use of lowest cost ingredients.

There is no one best feed formula for rapid and efficient growth. Nutritionists must use computers for formulating least-cost, high-efficiency rations with the same nutritional value to take advantage of ingredient price changes.

Information on composition and availability of nutrients contained in feed is developed through research. This information, cost of feedstuffs, and nutrient needs of the animal for whom the feed is formulated are programmed into computers to formulate a ration that is lowest in cost, and that meets nutrient needs.

Beyond nutrients in diets to meet nutritive criteria, additives such as hormones and antibiotics are used to improve growth and feed utilization. Most broiler rations contain from 4 to 10 grams of antibiotics per ton of feed to improve efficiency of feed utilization and rate of gain in live weight.

Fermentation byproducts, fish solubles, and dried whey are sources of unidentified growth factors that improve gains in broilers. One or more sources of unidentified growth factors are usually added to broiler rations.

A single antibiotic, or combination of antibiotics, is added to hog rations from weaning to market age. The greatest response to an antibiotic is during the early growth period.

Low levels of antibiotics are also added to beef cattle rations to increase gain and improve feed efficiency. Use of the hormone diethylstilbestrol, or other growth stimulants, is common in most beef finishing rations. Although rate of gain of beef cattle is normally improved by about 10 percent from adding diethylstilbestrol to the diet, the response may be variable.

Drugs in animal feeds must be used in accordance with the requirements of the Federal Food, Drug, and Cosmetic Act. Current practices in the use of antibiotics in animal feeds have been examined and approved by the Food and Drug Administration.

Urea is a nitrogen-containing com-pound used to replace part of the protein in diets of cattle and sheep. Cattle and sheep have a rumen that is part of their compartmental stomach. The micro-organisms that develop in the rumen use the nitrogen from urea or other nonprotein nitrogen-containing compounds to synthesize microbial protein for their own body structure. This microbial protein is digested and used by the animal.

Urea, or other nonprotein nitrogen, cannot be fed to hogs or poultry because these animals lack the ability to convert urea to protein.

Most feed urea contains 45 percent nitrogen, and a pound of urea—through microbial synthesis—should yield 2.8 pounds of protein. It is advantageous to use urea because its cost is normally lower than the cost of an equivalent amount of oilseed meal that has been the customary source of dietary protein. For the 1968 feeding year, it was estimated that more than 500,000 tons of urea were fed.

More use is being made of steam processing and flaking of feed grains such as sorghum grains (milo) to improve nutrient utilization by fattening beef cattle.

Confinement facilities for livestock and poultry vary considerably from open feedlot pens for cattle in regions of the West with a dry, mild climate, to complete environmental control facilities in regions that experience extremely hot or cold temperatures. Increasingly, confinement facilities with insulation and controlled ventilation are being used for pigs and poultry.

Optimum health is essential to obtain maximum efficiency in feed utilization. Good sanitation and disease control programs are vital to successful production of large numbers of animals in close confinement.

Diseases that cause serious economic problems for broiler producers are leukosis, infectious bronchitis, and mycoplasma infections. In 1968, about 1.5 percent of all broilers inspected were condemned because of leukosis. Recent research has increased the effectiveness of selecting breeding stock for resistance to leukosis. Most broiler feeds contain coccidiostats, drugs used to arrest protozoan parasites that cause coccidiosis in poultry.

Diseases such as cholera, erysipelas, and enteritis are frequently observed in feeder pigs. Cholera is a highly contagious disease. The States and the U.S. Department of Agriculture are cooperating in a program to eradicate it from the United States.

Feeder cattle are subjected to stresses during shipment to the feedlot. These stresses appear to lower the resistance of animals to such respiratory diseases as shipping fever and bovine rhinotracheitis.

Preconditioning feeder cattle by the producer is one way to reduce losses in transit and after arrival at the feedlot. Preconditioning is a combination of nutritional and managerial practices plus a vaccination program to maintain the feeder cattle in good nutritional state, and to develop an immunity before the animal is exposed to respiratory diseases. Feedlots for growing cattle prior to the finishing operation are also becoming more important.

Upon arrival at the feedlot, animals are usually vaccinated for certain diseases, sprayed to control external parasites, and fed rations containing an antibiotic. The cattle are rapidly conditioned to low roughage, high concentrate (grain) rations. A too rapid change to high grain rations, however, may bring about digestive disturbances.

The length of time that cattle will be fed the finishing ration varies from 90 to 150 days depending upon the weight and quality of the animal when placed in the feedlot, and desired slaughter weight.

The most pressing problem associated with large confinement production enterprises that remains to be solved is manure disposal and odor control. Odors associated with animal production become serious problems as urban centers expand into rural areas. Producers have been subjected to lawsuits for creating a public nuisance. In addition, the low cost and ease of application of chemical fertilizers for crop production decreased the economic value of manure for improving soil fertility.

New technology to handle and dispose of manure in a way that does not pollute air or water needs to be developed. Until economically feasible methods are found for converting manure into useful products, waste disposal will continue to be a sizable cost of production.

YOUNGER, BIGGER, RICHER—THE FARM MARKET OF TODAY

THE FARMER'S MARKET is changing fast. It's bigger, richer, younger, more demanding, and farther away.

Biggest factor in market change is the increasing size of our population— up more than a third from the late 1940's to over 200 million people, and growing by more than 1 percent per year.

This population is getting younger, too. The proportion of youngsters under 18 has increased from 30 to 35 percent (the proportion of older people has also increased modestly due to better health care).

People live farther from the farm today. They're concentrating on the East and West Coasts. The most spectacular increase in population has been on the Pacific Coast, where population increased about two-thirds since 1950. The Eastern Seaboard has also grown substantially faster than the rest of the country, particularly the Middle Atlantic area and Florida. It means a longer haul for most farm products.

The strong trend toward urbanization has also continued to take people farther from the farm. Almost two-thirds of the total population lived in metropolitan areas in 1968. The growth has been concentrated almost entirely in the suburban rings, with only a very small increase in the central cities. In contrast, the farm population declined by 56 percent between 1950 and 1968, to only 5 percent of the total.

The sharp fall in farm population has gone hand-in-hand with the rapid improvement in farm technology and productivity. Each U.S. farmworker supplied food and fiber for 43 others in 1968, compared with only 15 others in 1948.

The second major factor behind the changing farm market is the rise of the affluent consumer. Our disposable personal income tripled between 1948 and 1968. Per capita disposable income increased from about $1,300 to $3,000 a year in the same period.

In the late 1940's, about 50 percent of the families had incomes of less than $3,000. In 1968, only 10 percent of our families were below the $3,000 level. At the other extreme, only 3 percent of U.S. families had incomes over $10,000 in the earlier period, compared with 40 percent in 1968.

Even with some price inflation, the average consumer had plenty of extra money to increase the quantity and quality of his purchases. During the 20-year period, per capita disposable income increased 130 percent, while the consumer price index rose 35 percent and the food price index rose 30 percent.

Food distribution and welfare programs bolstered the effects of higher incomes on the market for farm products. In fiscal year 1967 an estimated 20 percent of the U.S. civilian population participated in at least one of the

✦

AUTHOR WILLIAM A. FAUGHT is Chief, Fibers and Grains Branch, Marketing Economics Division, Economic Research Service. COAUTHOR EDWARD H. GLADE, JR., is an Agricultural Economist in the Marketing Economics Division.

programs such as School Lunch, Food Stamp, and Commodity Distribution.

Transfer of workers to off-farm jobs has cut the proportion of consumers who produce their own food, and has expanded the commercial market.

On the other hand, the relative increase in white-collar jobs and year-round air conditioning of offices and homes has changed the farm market by cutting caloric intake and revising clothing needs.

The increasing number of job-holding women has expanded the market for such built-in-maid service items as convenience foods and permanent press clothing.

Housewives reflect these changes in the volume and mix of products purchased.

The total volume of food and fiber consumed has been increasing faster than population—a boost in per capita consumption. The per capita food consumption index, which incorporates values of different foods at constant market prices, has continued its long-time upward trend, increasing 5 percent between 1950 and 1968. In contrast, the pounds of food and the calories consumed both dropped.

This indicates an increasing demand for concentrated high-price foods such as meats and ready-to-eat foods, and a trend away from bulky low-priced items like macaroni and bread.

Beef and poultry consumption have jumped dramatically in recent years. Beef consumption rose about 50 percent per person in the last 20 years. Poultry consumption doubled as demand soared and technological breakthroughs brought lower prices.

Pork consumption dropped off, on a per capita basis, reflecting a considerable decline in demand as well as short supplies and higher prices for parts of the period.

Consumption of eggs and dairy products also declined in spite of relatively stable to sharply lower prices.

Total consumption of crops has increased, but not as much as population.

Beef and poultry consumption has risen, while processed fruits have come into increasing favor. Above, an automatic carton filler for frozen strawberries. Left, a young consumer bites into chicken. Below, steaks.

Demand for vegetable oils has risen as the demand for animal fats declined.

Processed fruits and vegetables have been substituted for the fresh forms, largely because of more favorable prices and advances in technology which have helped improve the convenience and quality of the processed product. However, the relatively higher prices for all forms of fruits and vegetables have been accompanied by a decline in total per capita consumption of these products.

Cereal and bakery product per capita consumption has fallen, possibly reflecting a change in consumer taste as well as substantially higher prices for these products resulting from higher processing costs. Home use of sugar and other natural sweeteners has tended upward slightly, but processors have been substituting noncaloric sweeteners in many uses. However, recent restrictions on the use of cyclamates may slow or reverse this trend.

In fibers, higher population and incomes boosted total consumption sharply. However, natural fibers have not been able to stave off competition from synthetics, and consumption of natural fibers has tended slightly downward. Per capita consumption has fallen sharply.

Total domestic mill consumption of cotton averaged about 4.5 billion pounds annually in both the 1948–52 and 1964–68 periods, but per capita consumption fell from an average of 29.4 pounds to 22.3. Cotton's share of the fiber market fell from an average of about 70 percent to about 50 percent and continues downward.

In the case of wool, per capita consumption dropped from 3.7 to 1.8 pounds and average total consumption fell from 555 million to 351 million pounds. Wool's share of the total market fell from about 9 to 4 percent.

The major factor in the deteriorating market for natural fibers probably has been the demand by consumers for durable press fabrics which do not require ironing after laundering. Also contributing to the downtrend have been other quality requirements in some products, particularly in some industrial uses, and noncompetitive prices for a portion of the period.

Total agricultural exports have moved up irregularly since 1948, rising from an annual average of $3.5 billion in the 1948–52 period to $6.4 billion in 1964–68. A record high was reached in 1966, when exports totaled $6.9 billion. The relative importance of exports to agriculture also has risen. The harvested acres used for producing exported products rose from about 13 percent in 1948–52 to 21 percent in 1964–68.

Food grains led the list of farm exports, with about one-fourth the total in 1968. Oilseeds and oilseed products were second, accounting for about 19 percent. Feed grains ranked third with about 16 percent and animal products fourth, with a little over 10 percent. Cotton, formerly one of the leading export items, fell by about half from the earlier period and accounted for less than 8 percent in 1968.

Japan has become by far our most important foreign customer. In 1968 shipments to Japan and Western European countries accounted for 45 percent of our total agricultural exports and over 60 percent of our commercial sales. Exports to Western Europe peaked in 1966, declining since that time; but exports to Japan have continued to rise.

Shipments to less developed countries also have continued to rise and now make up about 40 percent of our total foreign shipments. However, two-thirds of these shipments are financed through various Government programs.

Farmers have responded to the changing demand at home and abroad. Farm marketings increased from an annual average of $30.4 billion in the 1948–52 period to $41.4 billion in 1964–68. Prices received by farmers averaged lower in the latter period so that the rise in total marketings has been due to an increase in quantity sold.

The increased domestic demand—

This terminal at Toledo, Ohio, ships about 25 million bushels of grain to all parts of the world in the course of a year. It is owned by four regional farmer cooperatives. Both lake- and ocean-going steamers use its facilities.

including the effects of population and income growth and shift from other meats—accounts for most of the very sharp jump in marketings of cattle, calves, and poultry. Cash receipts from sale of hogs, sheep, and lamb declined. Marketings of dairy products rose in spite of some dropoff in domestic per capita consumption and relatively stable prices. Aside from poultry, developments in foreign markets had relatively little effect on these products.

Marketings of field crops were more influenced by foreign developments, with particularly marked increases in exports of oilseeds, grains, and feeds. Cotton, facing a tightening domestic market, has also been confronted with declining demand abroad. Fruits and vegetables have benefited from stronger foreign demand, together with the effect of population growth. These have countered the lower per capita demand so that total quantities sold and prices have trended upward.

A number of industrial segments closely related to agriculture also have been affected. Some of these effects have been causes of changes in agriculture and some have been results.

Suppliers of farm inputs have helped bridge the gap in technological development. The wide array of new fertilizers, herbicides, insecticides, and equipment which they have helped develop and make available have increased yields and reduced per-unit costs.

Many suppliers have integrated operations forward into the production marketing processes. For instance, a number of feed manufacturers are deeply involved in poultry production, feedlot operations, and—more recently—pork production. Some equipment dealers are offering to provide land leveling or clearing and drainage or other services. Many suppliers continue to provide financing to meet the steady expansion in the capital

65

requirements associated with adjustments within agriculture.

Many processors or users of agricultural products have integrated backward in the marketing system—some even to the farm level. Some flour and textile mills, largely in an effort to obtain desired qualities, have increased contract buying or direct purchases from growers, bypassing established merchandising firms in terminal or central markets. Citrus and other food processors are taking on additional marketing and production functions, including pickup of products at the farm and, in some instances, even harvesting, spraying, or other production functions.

Merchandising firms also have changed. New types of contracts with more rigid quality specifications and greater varieties of delivery alternatives are being offered. Laboratories with specialized equipment for quality evaluation have been added. Marketing firms providing physical services also have adjusted their operating practices, frequently automating elevator and warehousing facilities in efforts to combat rising costs and remain competitive.

Recently, transportation agencies have provided a steady stream of innovations, including giant hopper cars, rent-a-trains, ocean-going barges, and containerized shipments.

Government continues to exert a strong influence on marketing of many farm products, although the impact varies from time to time and product to product.

As in previous decades, Government programs which provide for production controls and price supports have the major effect. But perhaps the chief impact of Government action peculiar to the last two decades has been its support of foreign shipments. As indicated earlier, our shipments to developing countries have steadily increased and the main portion of these shipments has been with the assistance of Government programs.

Establishment and expansion of various Government-sponsored welfare programs also has had an impact. The broad range of programs such as those providing market information, assisting in quality determination, and establishing marketing orders continue to be major influences in marketing operations.

Changes in demands by final consumers or industry users at home and abroad have expanded the total market for farm products, changed the product mix, increased the importance of foreign outlets, widened marketing spreads, and required many adjustments by farmers and marketing firms.

For the future, we expect continued expansion of the domestic market for food in view of current trends in population and income; however, the rapid substitution of manmade fibers indicates a further decline in the domestic market for natural fibers. Abroad, farm production is increasing, particularly in developing areas. These areas should be able to meet a greater proportion of their own requirements and increase modestly their supplies exported. In all areas, competition from industrial goods is likely to continue and even increase.

Expect farm markets to keep on changing.

SYNTHETICS POSE A CHALLENGE TO FARM PRODUCTS

SOME SYNTHETIC FOODS and nonfoods are successfully penetrating traditional farm product markets. Noncaloric sweeteners, nonleather shoes, synthetic fabrics, and imitation flavor are common examples in today's market. Next year and the years thereafter we will see many more of them.

Modern scientific knowledge, expanding incomes, and our changing living patterns initiate development, encourage production, and allow marketing of innovative synthetic products.

Manufacturers continually develop new products and new ways of manufacturing old products. Some changes are small additions to our present system—like adding a minor amount of a chemical to a food to enhance its flavor or stretch its storage life. Others are big changes in the sense that a completely new process, package, or product ensues.

As our living patterns change we demand different quality products and this means we need a wider variety to choose from. Agricultural producers and manufacturers, both using modern technologies, attempt to satisfy these new demands. Each competes for a share of the expanding market. A case in point is the growth of synthetics as substitutes for farm products in food and nonfood markets.

Traditionally, agriculture supplies most of our basic food needs. This will be the case for a number of years in the future. Manufacturers have had many tries but little success in developing and marketing a complete synthetic food. A notable exception is the noncaloric sweetener saccharin.

Another success story is in the field of ingredients. Manufacturers have developed synthetics that are a small part in processed foods. Synthetic flavorings, colorings, vitamins, amino acids, and minerals now are commonly accepted by all. They are additions rather than replacements and are used to enhance appearance, taste, texture, or nutritional qualities of agricultural foods. Thus, even though we forecast that we will always depend on agriculture as the primary source of basic foods, synthetics will become more important as additive ingredients.

✦

AUTHOR RAY S. CORKERN is an economist in the Marketing Economics Division, Economic Research Service, stationed in New Orleans.
COAUTHOR WILLIAM S. HOOFNAGLE is Deputy Director of the Marketing Economics Division.

Some future changes can be expected in food markets. Whole foods made from a combination of agricultural and synthetic ingredients are appearing on the market. Imitation milk and meatlike products that are derived from vegetable oils and protein are now available to consumers. Similar fabricated foods designed for specific consumer groups can be expected in the future.

In tomorrow's world homemakers may choose from a greater variety of complete meals that are supplemented or fortified with synthetics. Some will be precooked. Most will be nutritionally balanced and packaged for rapid home serving.

The movement of food preparation from the kitchen to the factory will simplify food purchasing and meal planning. Shopping time can be reduced and each family member can have his favorite meal without imposing additional kitchen work on the homemaker.

Although the form of future foods will be changed, marketing methods currently used to move foods from farms to consumers will not be appreciably altered.

Agriculture's major nonfood markets include textiles, leather, soap and detergents, feed, paint, and adhesives. Each market has been successfully penetrated by synthetics, in fact synthetics are more successful in the nonfood markets. Manufacturers use those raw materials that reduce their cost or add desirable characteristics or esthetic appeal to their products. The source of the raw materials is of little concern to them. Competition between agricultural and synthetic raw materials in nonfood markets will continue and even become more intense.

Cotton and wool fibers now must share the textile market with a number of synthetic fibers. Notable among them are nylon, polyesters, and acrylics. Many apparel and household fabrics now are made from these synthetics alone or in blends with agricultural fibers.

Since consumers like these fabrics,

Cotton seeks to retain its markets with ever-better products.
Above, style show at National Arboretum features materials using
new USDA-developed processes. Below, USDA is working on
way to treat durable press cotton so it will dry on a line wrinkle
free. Chemist R. M. Reinhardt compares treated and
untreated fabric at laboratory in New Orleans, La.
Right, 1969 Maid of Cotton displays a cotton creation.

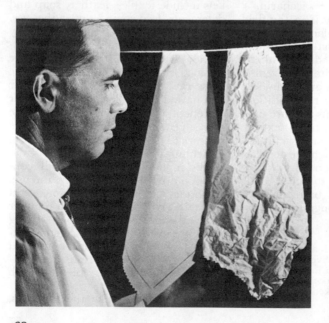

their sales increase. But cotton and wool processors fight to retain their markets by improving their natural fibers. Examples are permanent press, wash-and-wear, soil resistance, and other new developments that permit cotton and wool fabrics to compete more favorably with synthetic fabrics.

Synthetic leathers (poromerics), vinyls, and synthetic fabrics now compete with leather in manufacture of shoes, baggage, belts, and upholstery. Processors of natural hide leather meet competition by developing softer, more flexible, and easy care leathers. Soon, consumers may be able to purchase leather shoes that can be easily dyed daily to match other wardrobe items.

Soap and detergents have traditionally used great quantities of animal and vegetable fats and oils. Now, great quantities of synthetics are used. These synthetics come from chemical raw materials obtained from the petroleum, coal, and wood pulping industries. Currently, most household and industrial soap and detergent products include some synthetics.

Farmers and commercial feedlot operators are using urea, a synthetic chemical compound. This chemical ingredient replaces some high protein oilseed meals in livestock feeds.

Changes in the feeding practices of beef cattle, sheep, and dairy cattle come from a pressure to lower production costs.

The expanding market for paint favors increased use of synthetics rather than vegetable oils. Paint users, both household and industrial, are demanding one coat, low odor paints that are easy to apply and dry quickly. Paint manufacturers have found they can obtain these features at a lower cost by using synthetic resins and driers instead of the traditional tung and linseed oils.

Casein, soybean meal, cereal starches, and animal byproducts now are commonplace in the adhesive industry. One advantage of using agricultural material in adhesives is their lower cost. Although use of farm-originated materials is expanding, they

A leather fashion designed to meet consumer demands for high style and casual wear. New leathers have greater serviceability in terms of resistance to water, perspiration, dry cleaning, and even washing in soap and water. USDA research, through the development of glutaraldehyde tannage, has contributed to these improvements.

are not keeping pace with the overall growth of the adhesive market. Synthetic resins yield adhesives with tailor-made physical and technical characteristics not available in agricultural materials.

Many other agricultural nonfood markets are being penetrated by synthetics. These include inks, plastics, cosmetics, and waxes.

As nonfarm products substitute for farm items, there will be changes. Some farmers' production, sales, and incomes will be reduced. Their equipment and land may become idle, at least for a while. In the past, however, farmers have successfully adjusted to market changes, shifting their production to the next most profitable crop or livestock enterprise.

It is even possible for whole farm communities to sustain losses as synthetics displace agricultural raw materials. Economic activities associated with production of the displaced agricultural product are reduced or no longer needed. Community labor is no longer required to harvest, transport, store, and process the displaced agricultural product. Wholesale and retail sales of farm production items like fertilizer, insecticides, and fuel may decline if farmers cannot adjust to declining markets.

Reduction in the use of farmlands and other economic activities associated with agricultural production could lower the taxes which rural areas depend on for revenues. In this situation they could reduce their community services or develop new revenue sources by encouraging economic activities not based on agricultural production.

Agricultural processors also feel the effects of synthetics as they replace farm products. Some plants become idle. Other facilities may be used at less than capacity. Some processors may have to relocate their plants or re-equip them to produce synthetic materials.

In summation, the food and nonfood markets for synthetic products are different from each other. The use of synthetics in foods will be limited in future years. Foods produced naturally are still cheaper than those synthetically produced. Besides, consumers recognize that the nutritional qualities of agricultural foods are still a bargain.

The future of synthetics in nonfood markets presents a different picture. Synthetics have been gradually gaining an increasing share of the total nonfood market. But efforts toward improving the quality and reducing the cost of agricultural products in conjunction with the development of new products and processes will tend to moderate the rate of market penetration by synthetics.

Farmers, rural communities, processors, and marketers are adjusting to new market situations that affect the use of agricultural products. Farmers are changing their production patterns, improving the quality of their products, and increasing their efficiency. Rural communities are seeking and developing new economic activities that are not dependent on agricultural raw materials. Processors and marketers are developing new products and improving old ones. With these types of adjustments, agriculture can meet the challenge of synthetics.

HOW THEY SAVED THE SOUP: THE TECHNOLOGY OF MARKETING

A GAME OF CHESS can be confusing unless you know how the various pieces move, and what they can do. The same is true about the serious game of marketing food. As users of food, we are intimately affected by marketing. But most of us are not fully aware of the moves of the marketing pieces or how we are involved.

Marketers profit when they buy foods from farmers, and change them in some way to provide satisfaction to us—users of the food. But, just as chess is easily learned and yet difficult to master, so indeed are the fundamentals of food marketing easily seen but often obscure. Its changing nature makes the industry complex, but also adds to its interest.

To illustrate changing technology in marketing and its impact upon our lives, let's explore three basic elements in the food marketing system—*containers, computers,* and *convenience* foods. These three C's of change play a major role in food marketing today.

Containers tie in closely with transportation changes, and the two together are extremely important in this country where much of our food is raised in areas distant from where it is consumed.

Computers are devices that allow us to think faster. With them we can count, remember, and recall faster and more effectively. Our food marketing system becomes more efficient with their use.

Convenience foods are a way of shifting preparation or processing time or labor from kitchens to factories. Where workers can specialize, there are distinct labor savings. First, let's discuss food containers with special reference to their use in transportation.

MODERN PEGASUS

In chess, a knight moves over the tops of other pieces. The similar movement of a jet cargo plane suggests that we think of one as a winged white knight. This modern day Pegasus could even be considered as a winged container.

How containers become mobile and are used to satisfy apparently simple consumer desires is best illustrated in a fictional—but potentially realistic—situation. Consider the can of mushroom soup at your local supermarket and how it got there.

At 8:07 one Tuesday morning the sales manager of a Pennsylvania mushroom growing firm receives a telephone call. It is from the purchasing agent of a California soup company whose firm has an emergency: "Can you ship us 22,500 pounds of fresh mushrooms tonight so they will arrive at our West Coast plant by noon tomorrow?"

Mentally, the sales manager pictures the air trip across country. He foresees two truck hauls—one from the mushroom farm to the airport and

✦

AUTHOR KERMIT BIRD is an agricultural economist, Marketing Economics Division, Economic Research Service.

COAUTHOR CHARLES O'DELL is also an agricultural economist in the same Division.

the other from the western airport to the mushroom processor. Two trucks and one plane will have to be loaded and unloaded. That's a lot of miles, a lot of handlings, many containers, and a lot of mushrooms—especially since the mushrooms have not yet been picked. He replies, "I'll call you back."

For a busy 45 minutes he checks current shipping schedules, prospective orders from nearby processors, and inventories. At the same time his office associate calls the cargo plane terminal and arranges for shipment. They check to see that their own truck and driver are available that night. Then they reserve a truck and a driver at the California end of the route. They also arrange for additional pickers, who will be assigned work stations as soon as the order is confirmed.

The sales manager returns the call, "We can have 22,500 pounds of fresh mushrooms arrive at your dock by noon tomorrow." The sales manager stresses that the price per pound of this particular air-shipped load will be considerably higher than if the same mushrooms were shipped by truck. The buyer assures him that air shipment is necessary because of the time element involved.

After the two men discuss grade and size, and types of containers, they agree upon the price.

This is an unusual order. Generally, the mushroom growing firm ships its West Coast orders by refrigerated trucks. So, the time pressure begins. At seven that morning the regular picking crew had begun filling their 10-pound plastic picking baskets. Now at nine o'clock extra pickers start work. By two that afternoon, the miner-lamped girls have harvested enough mushrooms to fill the special order.

A driver, skillfully weaving his tow tractor through the dark corridors, has been continuously hauling rubbertired wagon loads of filled baskets to the refrigerated workroom. There white-uniformed girls sort, trim, grade, and pack the earthy-scented fungi into light-weight containers.

71

These specially designed baskets move along a conveyor belt where a series of automated machines check-weigh, label, lid, pack them into their master cartons, and palletize them. A pallet is a rigid wooden frame on which packages of merchandise are packed together. This makes a unit load that can be handled by a fork truck.

While some women are still picking part of the mushroom order, other workers have started packing some for shipment. Mushrooms ready to go are placed in a room where vacuum equipment cools them to retain their freshness. By nightfall, the mushroom workers have the whole load chilled and ready for shipment.

A fork truck places the pallet loads into the prechilled refrigerated trailer. The driver, after getting his last minute instructions from the sales manager, heads his 40-foot trailer for the airport. His load will fill two-thirds of the plane's cargo hold.

The cargo plane stands by with attendant loading crew and specialized loading equipment. It, too, like the trailer, has been chilled to keep the mushrooms in near perfect condition. Warehousemen stack the filled cartons into dome-roofed shipping containers that resemble eskimo huts and are called "igloos" by the crew.

In a matter of minutes the crew has loaded the plane with its 12-igloo load, and by 11 p.m. it is winging westward. A five-hour trip puts the mushrooms at the San Francisco airport in the middle of the night. There the night crew quickly unloads the pallets from the plane and repacks it with a mixed load of artichokes, cut flowers, and lettuce destined for Newark.

Meanwhile, our perishable mushrooms have been loaded onto another refrigerated truck that had been arranged for the previous day. When readied, the driver starts his dawn run to the soup processing plant. Well before the Wednesday noon deadline the 11¼ tons of 24-hour-old mushrooms have arrived at the plant, and

soup company warehousemen store them in refrigerated rooms. They are in prime condition and ready to be processed into cream of mushroom soup.

Several months later, a Tucson woman buys a can of mushroom soup—one from that particular day's soup pack. To her it is an everyday occurrence, the hot item for tomorrow's lunch. The only container she comes in contact with is the 10½-ounce soup can. But the many larger containers used in getting mushrooms from the Pennsylvania farm to the California processor assure her family of their bowl of mushroom soup. Because the fresh mushrooms were so quickly and carefully handled, the can of soup she now buys, months later, has the food quality she expects.

The West Coast food processor needed mushrooms to keep his 1,000 dozen cans per hour soup line operating. The purchasing agent for the company was not able to procure this large a quantity from mushroom growers nearby. Because of the speedy service, this hypothetical soup factory was able to maintain its production schedule—so important in modern day food processing operations.

Had it not been for the high speed transportation network, that day's 283,000 10½-ounce cans of mushroom soup might not have been packed.

So, even though in this case air freighting was considerably more expensive than comparable truck shipping would have been, the manager of the soup plant was justified in paying the extra transportation cost for the mushrooms.

Not only did he keep his soup line operating, but in doing so he was able to prevent lost mushroom soup sales that might have occurred if some grocery stores were to run out of stock. It is vital to a food processor to keep his brands stocked on store shelves. It is important to homemakers, as well.

Although the example we have discussed is partly fictional, it illustrates how various containers expand the usefulness of transportation. Food packages not only make flying of food possible, but they are also necessary in many other marketing chores such as storing, advertising, and handling. Let's review some of the containers used in our mushroom story.

The mushrooms were picked into one type of basket. After being sorted and graded, they were packed in 10-pound plastic containers that keep bruising at a minimum.

These baskets were placed in master cartons that also protect the delicate contents. The pallet on which the cartons were loaded is a form of container as well.

Each truck handling the pallets, probably five or six in all, we call a wheeled box. Finally, the plane itself is a flying container. Then there's the 10½-ounce can. Two dozen of these cans were packed in a cardboard carton. These cartons were grouped on pallets for ease in storage and shipping.

The wheeled basket used by the woman in the Tucson store was a container, as was the brown bag used to pack her groceries. Her kids' tummies were the final containers these mushrooms had been aiming toward.

Special containers and the shorter travel time involved in air freight cut down on spoilage losses. Shipping damage may be less. If air freight rates become more competitive, and availability of service increases, additional foods may be shipped by air. All will need special containers.

So much for plane containers. How about containers used by our railroad system?

Like the consumer who finds economy in buying a large jar of jelly, a giant bag of potato chips, or jumbo boxes of dog food, so also trainmen like to use large food containers. Their new sizes include the 100 ton "big john" and 125 ton whopper-hopper railcars, Super C, and rent-a-train.

Yet another development somewhat new to food handling, although old hat to potato and grain carrying, is the unit train. All cars carry the same

merchandise. Picture a trainload of purple plums from Idaho to the East Coast. Or one train, 50 hopper cars, of Montana wheat, carrying 5,000 tons to market.

Having their runs well planned in advance, these series of rolling containers reach their destinations with a minimum of stops.

Speaking of potatoes, an all steel car has been designed for the bulk shipment of potatoes. It is refrigerated with temperatures automatically controlled at either 40°F or 60°F, depending on whether the potatoes are to be table stock or "chippers." The car, still in experimental stage, holds 167,000 pounds. This is in contrast to the usual refrigerated car that holds 36,000 to 40,000 pounds.

A new concept, now being increasingly used for food, is the piggy back train. The idea is to use a highway truck trailer as a container, and ship it on a rail car. The advantages of country pickup, loading, unloading, and city delivery are obvious. Whole trains may be composed of these special flat cars. At present, these cars operating on American railroads carry 1¼ million truck trailers each year. Of course, not all of them carry food.

The newly-developed covered-hopper is also a container—so large that it covers a whole flat car. An advantage is that it may be taken off the car for loading, storage, or even for moving by other transportation means.

This hopper unit can carry over 100 tons of items like sugar, grain, or molasses. With loading through top hatches that can be battened down when the container car is full, the design minimizes contamination and loss as well as handling costs. At point of delivery, trap doors at the bottom of the hopper allow the contents to flow from the container-hopper into storage bins or tanks. Its future use is still uncertain since equipment to handle it is expensive.

Giant rail cars complement and bring about other rail innovations. Grain arriving at elevators in the new, larger railcars requires more time to

Left, fresh strawberries grown through plastic sheeting are picked in field, then rushed by truck to airport. Above, strawberries pass through an airline's Los Angeles terminal on way to east coast by jet. Below, cargo handler nets pallet load of strawberries for air shipment.

Fresh produce is either netted on pallets like cargo in foreground, or placed in "igloos" like one inside hatch of plane. Some growers prefer to lease their own igloos for direct loading at farm.

unload. So engineers invented large hydraulic lifts that tilt over a fully loaded railcar sideways and empty it in seconds. Another car is raised at a 60° angle, and its 100 tons of grain flow out one end of the car into a storage bin.

Handling innovations preserve the benefits of the large cargo carrying units. Hence, changes in food containers almost always lead to other changes in the food marketing system.

Most changes in containers and their handling methods take place behind the scenes. Thus, when a mother buys a cake in her local bakery she is mostly concerned with the quality, convenience, and price of the pastry she takes home to her family.

Package changes take place, nevertheless, for this is the way our American industrial system operates. Most container changes, no matter where they occur, lower marketing cost, provide some service that previously was impossible, or improve the product. So the cost, variety, and convenience of the housewife's cake purchase depend somewhat upon the size or the shape of the containers that may have hauled the wheat in each stage of its movements.

The satisfaction she gets from the cake also depends on whether the egg handlers used specially designed containers, or whether or not the sugar in the cake's icing was hauled in a hopper car. She is involved in the container changes although she may not know how.

COMPUTERS

Meanwhile, back to our chess game. The shiny white rook of modern food marketing, the computer, does not march forward one pace at a time as a mere pawn. In the last decade it has been striding forward in seven league boots. As one reflects on the computer's outer space accomplishments, we wonder whether it may do as much for our "inner-spaces"— our digestive system.

Computers promise a million-fold increase in man's capacity to handle information. Although just beginning widespread use in food handling, their potential in this field appears rewarding.

Perhaps more than any other single innovation, computers have the power to change our food marketing system beyond present comprehension. They have capacity to bring new orderliness to food distribution—previously inefficient because of its complexity and widespread geographical nature. Here are some current uses of computers.

Farmers are beginning to use computers for various farm tasks:

They figure market averages that farmers hear on market newscasts.

Farmers benefit by their weather predictions.

They specify the blend of feeds used by broiler producers and cattle feedlot operators. Leased wire access to them helps these livestock managers find which feed ingredients to use— the ones that give them the lowest cost mix at the specified nutritional and caloric levels.

A seed grower checks viability and genetic inheritance traits. In other laboratories, computers combine with electronic mechanisms to provide precise instrumentations.

Processors and handlers find many uses for computers.

Millers use them to help tear wheat apart into its various protein, starch, gluten, and other components. Then, millers use computer formulas to assist putting the flour together again in the desired proportions.

A fruit cold storage warehouse computerizes management methods.

A meat packer uses computer services to determine various proportions of a carcass to be divided into the many cuts.

The soft drink industry finds wide use for computers in sales statistics, payrolls, billings, marketing statistics, sales analysis, and market research.

Computers process salary checks of food company employees.

A vegetable processor uses his computer to calculate acres needed to contract.

A citrus cooperative uses one to check inventory, sales distribution, and production statements.

A piggyback train load of refrigerated trailers moves into the Chicago area.

Food promoters, product developers, and sales agencies find them useful in getting news of their foods to the public.

A milk plant distributor computerized his delivery men's sales. Processing of billing gives milkmen more time to attend to customer needs.

Computers help a grocery manager decide how to manipulate stock on his shelves with the products most likely to be bought. This system, called COSMOS, is a means of planning the most effective merchandising for each product. The grocery manager thus is able to maximize revenues per unit of costly shelf space.

Computers help a food processor plan market strategies in his next market promotion.

A promoter uses his computer to analyze results of new foods in test markets.

In making a new food, recipes may be programmed mathematically by a computer. This new food development method is now being used to conceptualize analogs or "meat-substitute" type foods from soybeans.

A housewife of the future may use computer services in planning her week's meals—taking into account her husband's paycheck, the children's food likes, and the family's nutritional needs. In this way, both the meal and the food budget could be really balanced—in many ways.

Sometimes in a game of chess two pieces team up to increase their effectiveness. In marketing we also see interesting combinations of computers at work:

• At an airport cargo terminal, computers direct the breaking out of "hula huts," "igloos," or other palletized cargoes of food. The computer senses individual shipments and then directs them over computer-controlled conveyors to waiting trucks These trucks make preassigned deliveries—based upon computer-selected schedules—which minimize delivery time and costs.

• Shipments of perishable foods concern marketers if there are sudden shifts in consumer buying patterns or delays in arrival of shipments. In these cases the marketing men need to know the precise whereabouts of their supplies that are in transit. Keeping tabs on a particular railcar, as it winds its way across a maze of trackage, would be virtually impossible were it not for the computer's ability to store and retrieve the necessary information at a moment's notice.

Color sensing devices, located trackside along the rail system, note the passing of each uniquely color-coded railcar. They then relay the pertinent information to the computer which, on command, provides necessary information to the marketer so he can do his planning.

IMPACT OF CONVENIENCE

If, in our game of food marketing, knights stand for airplanes, and rooks signify computers, what then might a queen symbolize? In chess, she sweeps clear across the board and can overcome in combat any other piece. So in food marketing the change having the greatest impact is the increased emphasis on convenience.

In foods, convenience is anything that saves time or labor on the user's part. It could be a new container, like a strip pull can or a multiwall pouch. Or it may be the newly-developed instant sweetpotatoes that don't have to be cooked. It may even be a deboned pork loin or a cooked rump roast.

An everyday example of a convenience food that has been around for decades is bakery bread. Bread has changed its coat of convenience over the years. First it was unwrapped, then wrapped, then sliced, then made in sandwich size, and so on. We take other convenience pastries for granted; ready-made doughnuts, cakes, pies, cream puffs, and tarts as well as rolls, muffins, buns, and biscuits. Even cracker and bread crumbs now are purchased ready made. Many bakery items may now be purchased ready to bake.

Other common examples of old

standby convenience foods that save the user's time and labor include: dried soups and stews, casseroles, free flowing brown sugar, a variety of snacks, dips, and instant hot cereals.

Meat convenience items are so handy that we forget that the "good old preconvenience days" were also work-filled days for the food preparers of that age. Imagine, if you will, a modern man curing bacon or ham for his family's use. Can you picture his modern wife stuffing sausage or stirring scrapple? How many make ketchup, apple butter, or even root beer at home these days?

Formerly, most food preparation people worked in the kitchen of the place where the food was served. Now, relatively more people work in the "kitchens" of food processing plants.

This is what convenience foods are all about: some of the food preparation work is done at central places where the work may be done more efficiently—and generally at lower costs. Advantages of this changeover from home kitchen to processing plant are not always obvious, but they are there nevertheless. How are the various groups of people affected?

The housewife has less work to do in her kitchen. She now can prepare her meals faster and they involve less skill on her part. This leaves her a choice of working, if she chooses, or engaging in recreational activities, or even doing other housework.

Because she now does little or no preserving (canning, drying, curing, pickling, or freezing) of the family food, this also gives her more free time for other activities.

Members of her family now eat a greater variety of foods than they would if all were prepared or processed by mother. Because they eat more processed foods than formerly, their eating patterns change.

The farmer now sells more of his produce to processors. In many cases the processor arranges with him on what to grow, when to plant it, how to take care of it, when and how to harvest it, and where to deliver it. The processor may even supply the farmer with some of the capital, equipment, labor, seed, feed, or livestock.

Thus, the modern farmer is tied much more directly to the processor who is more quality-, quantity-, and economy-minded, as well as uniformity-minded.

The processor, in turn, is tied more closely to the wants and desires of the consumer. He performs more of the preparation chores formerly performed by food workers in the kitchen—housewife or chef, as the case may be.

Now a team of food researchers design the food and its container. Economists test it in the market and make estimates of its future volume. Food engineers buy or build equipment to produce it. Finally, after many other steps, specialized workers prepare the food by preserving, cooking, seasoning, coloring, and otherwise making it table-ready.

The processor finds that in order to get the quality, supply, and uniformity he wants, he needs some control of food production. Thus, he may contract some raw product ingredients (as broilers, peas, or potatoes), or he may grow his own product (for example, large scale mushroom processors have their own mushroom farms).

Institutions use convenience food in increasing quantities to save labor. Although many convenience foods are designed with the housewife in mind, some convenience items attain their market success in the away-from-home eating market.

Restaurants, institutions, plant and school cafeterias, hospitals, and dormitories use dehydrated potatoes, portion-controlled meats, vegetable flakes, frozen vegetables, and dairy products that are specifically manufactured to save labor in away-from-home kitchens. This has happened because in recent years keeping kitchen help—whether it be in a hotel or fast food unit—is a primary problem.

Labor governs, in some degree, which foods are served in these establishments. Workers do this not

A 65-foot-long automatic continuous freezer is factory assembled before shipment to a food processing plant.

by taking management's role, but by being expensive and/or unavailable. Management of food service units shun foods that require a great amount of preparation labor. A transition from kitchen labor to convenience items may be illustrated.

A plant cafeteria, with a food preparation staff of 10, prepares 2,500 entrees a day for employees of the factory. If, for some reason or other, one cafeteria worker quits, what happens?

In the usual course of events another person would be hired to replace him. But kitchen help is not easy to find, because of low wages, long hours, and the hard work. The

Quick frozen cut beans are discharged from freezer at plant, ready for bulk storage.

manager seeks another alternative. The cafeteria cannot serve 10 percent fewer meals to adjust to the 10 percent decreased size of the work force, so it adjusts another way—by buying more prepared foods. Simple!

The particular convenience foods the manager selects depend on the degree of preparation of the foods he is now using, the ones available to him as substitutes, the particular job of the man who left, and many other factors.

If the man who quit was a vegetable peeler, it would be natural to substitute prepared potato products and frozen vegetables. Fortunately for this imaginary cafeteria, there are many processed potatoes and frozen vegetables available.

Hundreds of partially or fully-prepared products of this type are available to institutions. Some items are canned, some frozen, and others dehydrated.

A frozen turkey roll may replace a whole turkey that formerly had to be thawed, stuffed, and baked. The kitchen could make use of cut up chicken pieces rather than whole broilers. A deboned, fully cooked ham may be used instead of a standard ham. Prefried bacon substitutes for regular bacon. Already breaded veal cutlets may be purchased. Many institutional kitchens have discontinued all meat cutting.

Rolls can be purchased from a bakery rather than baked at the plant. Instant iced tea mix becomes a regular menu item. The cafeteria can use dehydrated or frozen prepared scrambled eggs. Ready made soups, stews, hash, and countless other mixes are available to institutional outlets.

Generally, substitutes raise the cost of food purchased. But in substituting labor-saving items in each meal's menu, the manager of the cafeteria finds he now can do without the tenth man who has been replaced by prepared foods. The kitchen manager maintains about the same level of service to the same number of customers, by having some service work done outside his own kitchen.

This is a remarkable achievement, and is possible because of the wide range of convenience foods available. Institutional managers do it out of necessity. Housewives also do it, because they would rather do other things than work in a kitchen—if given a choice. Now they are being given this choice.

Like the positions and pieces in our heroic-size chess game, the convenience queen, container knights, and computer rooks constantly bring changes into our lives. The pace may slow, then quicken, but in food marketing one innovation follows another. The game of food marketing becomes more interesting as we learn more about it.

LONG, LONG BATTLE AGAINST BIG ODDS: THE DIARY OF A NEW LOW-CAL FOOD

IN OUR FOOD SYSTEM a striking achievement is taking place. This is the increasing number of new foods being placed on the market. Arising from our expanding technology and drive for progress, these innovative items appear at our grocer's as if by magic.

If we look closer, however, we find that workers in the food industry use a lot of imagination and years of diligent efforts to get these new foods developed and on the supermarket shelves. How does all this take place?

To see what happens and how long it takes, let's follow the developing and marketing of one new food. Our example is the market genesis of a new low-calorie bread—the realization of a fat man's dream. Does this sound simple? Well, it's not, and you will soon find out why.

Let's pretend that our new bread is to be created by two imaginary scientists, Mr. Hamish and Dr. Timrek. These two make believe heroes of our story are food researchers in a U.S. Department of Agriculture laboratory. Here's a likely time sequence of their actions that could appear in a diary drawn from our two researchers' notes.

1964 June—Our food researchers, Hamish and Timrek, specialists in flour and grain research, meet to discuss final work on a current project. They have just finished work on a new wheat flour test. It quickly tells the amount and quality of protein in cereal grain flours. Now they must consider some new problem areas to work on.

One of them suggests seeking a quick method for measuring wheat gluten strength. This would be a close twin to the work just completed. The other believes they can develop a truly low-calorie bread with good flavor.

The low-calorie bread idea challenges their imaginations. They believe it could be of greater benefit to the bread eaters of the country than any other projects suggested.

Is the concept possible? These two, Hamish and Timrek, believe it can be done.

After discussing the idea with their supervisors, and with research associates, they agree—tentatively at least—on the low-calorie bread proposal. They search the library and find little work has been done on this specific problem.

Hamish and Timrek feel the proposed new bread, when developed, will be bought by many American adults who like to eat bread, but don't want the calories supplied by present types. To discuss their idea at the market level they meet with several research acquaintances, their counterparts in

✦

AUTHOR KERMIT BIRD is an agricultural economist, Marketing Economics Division, Economic Research Service.

the baking industry, who give it a general approval.

July—Hamish and Timrek write a project proposal of the work planned. Their objectives outline what they will do. The justification makes a strong statement that we have become a weight-conscious people and still are looking for cereal foods that will satisfy our appetites for bread, yet keep us slim.

The new bread will combine high nutrition and low calories with palatability at moderate cost.

September—Researchers Hamish and Timrek, now officially assigned to the low-calorie bread project, start work—a job that may take as long as two years.

Each man is well aware of the other's capabilities.

Hamish will deal with the broad aspects of the project; Dr. Timrek will get deeply immersed in small segments at a time. Together they make a well-balanced, scientific study team.

Their long range objective is to create a flavorful and nutritious bread, with no more than 777 calories per pound, that can sell at regular bread prices.

This is a tall order. They know today's breads have from 1,100 calories a pound in rye to French with its 1,315 calories per pound. Most low-calorie diet breads already on the market not only are considerably above the desired 777 calorie level sought, but are not as well accepted as they should be in our diet conscious world.

November—In outlining the procedure they will follow in making the new bread they decide upon a high protein and low carbohydrate mixture that will be accepted because of its palatability.

To attain this they include enough of several wheat flours to provide the desired high protein level. Their blend of hard spring and winter wheats gives just the right gluten content that they want.

Oat and rye flours in small quan-

81

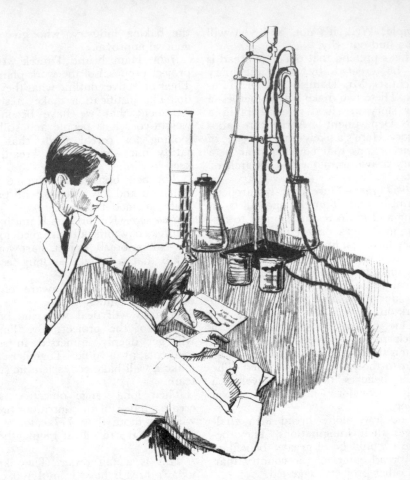

tities add nourishment and texture. Barley flour ups the minerals, but its main characteristic wanted in this mixture is its low fat content. The finely ground whole cereal grain flours (with the bran left in) help keep caloric values at low levels, and their high protein will help the moisture-retention capability of the finished loaf.

Because of the low calorie restriction, this new bread will, of necessity, be lower in fats than other breads—it will be less than 2 percent fat. Since most natural fats have about 4,100 calories per pound, all the added fat ingredients will be of a kind recently developed for low-fat diets in hospitals. These new fat compounds have only about half the digestible calorie values of natural fats.

Working with fats helps some in the calorie reduction, but most of the work has to be done with the flours.

1965 February—When the researchers finally combine the new high protein flours with the low-calorie fats, they carefully check their nutritional levels. Vitamin and mineral analyses of test loaves show all nutrients are well above the prescribed levels and thus they do not need to fortify the bread with enrichment vitamins.

Fat content is very low, and the calories are within their anticipations for the first approximation—down to almost 800 calories per pound. Their main research effort now centers on getting a dough with high water retention ability. They do some shifting of their flours to obtain high protein flours that allow the bread to hold maximum water.

82

May—Our two technology research-ers now have four low-calorie bread recipes, all of which meet the nutri-tional requirements. Calories are down to their goal of 777 per pound. Their present need is to select one from among the four which offers the best taste and texture appeal.

They submit their four samples to an "expert taste panel." They will use this and other Department panels several times in the months ahead and in doing so become well acquainted with a panel's usefulness along with its limitations.

The bread ranked "best" by the five expert bread tasters goes back to the laboratory for further work. In its selection the panel has pointed out the weaknesses as well as strong points of the bread sample. They discard the other three recipes.

The team has been involved with this bread work for a year. They should be half way through, but feel that they are just getting warmed up.

August—They send samples of the new bread to an "untrained consumer panel" of about 100 persons. These people rate the bread "acceptable," relative to a standard diet-type bread used as a basis of comparison. The researchers, though, are not satisfied with the panel results, for their long range goal is to achieve a superior palatability.

So, the panel results spur them to begin work on microwave ovens. They found that these ovens did not contrib-ute much to flavor. Their work with baking temperatures, type of baking pans, optimum size and shape of the loaves also did little to help. They test variations in the bread caused by addition of soy flour and milk powders. Their main aim now is to raise the panel's acceptance rating without adding to the 777 calories per pound that their recipe specifies.

In the winter months, they transfer part of the process investigation to a pilot plant where larger scale baking runs and performance ratings are possible.

1966 January—A problem in baking arises. In the pilot plant system the bread does not rise the way they planned. More work needs to be done

SENSORY EVALUATION TEST LAB

with the leaving agent, and they must redesign the new type "brew."

They discover the source of the difficulty. Low-fat shortening does not have the same handling qualities as liquid lard normally used in the pilot plant equipment. Solution: substitute 25 percent regular vegetable shortening.

How much did this raise the calorie count? They find it is now slightly higher than the desired level, so back to the laboratory.

More work shows they can bring the calorie count back down to the prescribed level by reducing the total fat proportion of the ingredients to less than 2 percent. They do so by adding somewhat more rye flour, besides a small amount of dry skim milk powder. Those changes add to the flour's protein content, and this allows adding slightly more water. Their bread's moisture content is now at the maximum allowable level—38 percent.

April—Hamish and Timrek are in hourly touch with the pilot plant crew. Are things going smoothly? No Pilot plant problems appeared solved, but when their high moisture formula went into continuous mixing—simulating the way it would be in a commercial bakery—the whole system bogged down.

Fortunately, our two men have had many years experience, not only with laboratory equipment, but also with scaled-down commercial breadmaking machines. Dr. Timrek, in fact, was assistant chief chemist at a commercial bakery before coming into Government work. He is familiar with the pilot plant jungle of gages, valves, wires, and pipes.

Working with the crew of specialized pilot plant technicians, Timrek finds

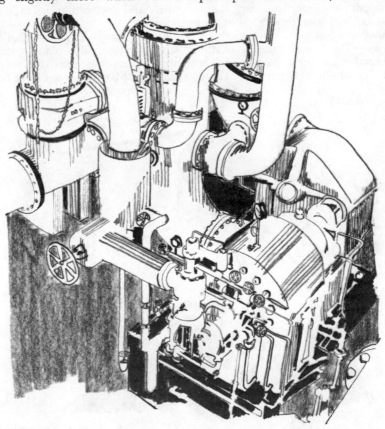

there is an interaction between the cellulose gum and protein. The mixture sticks to the insides of the plastic pipes feeding the mixers. Changing several items of tubing to stainless steel solves the problem.

June—Although 23 months now have passed since work started on the project, it is not finished. Yet our two researchers are as enthusiastic as ever. When their supervisor calls them in to discuss terminating the investigation, they ask for and receive a year's extension to complete the job. They had to convince him that the new bread had a better than 50-50 chance for successful development.

October—The first test batch of continuous mix dough has been baked into 48 loaves of bread. The pilot plant facilities actually worked! The researchers start shelf-life tests of the bread. Result: pilot plant bread has satisfactory storage capabilities.

The two researchers write preliminary results of their study, and submit the manuscript to a baking journal for publication.

1967 January—The team invites several baking industry people in for a day of bread sampling and evaluation. Their comments: "Concept sound. Bread palatability okay. Baking procedure complicated. Material cost satisfactory, but would be better if lower." Back to the laboratory once more.

The baking journal, to which they had submitted their manuscript, accepts it for publication.

March—Dr. Timrek reviews his tests of several lower cost materials and selects the ones most suitable. He has simplified the molding procedure. A coworker suggests that the ingredients be volume-measured, rather than weighed. He tries this but finds it not feasible because of variations in the density of the ingredients. He adopts some changes that promise lower costs to a bakery.

April—Samples again go to both the expert and untrained taste panels for reevaluations. Results: adding lower cost ingredients has not lowered

the bread's acceptance scores! In fact, the bread's present rating surpasses ratings of almost all diet breads and is equal to those of many regular breads.

The two researchers breathe a sigh of relief. Panels seem to be a bother, but they act as judges in the courtroom of food development. Without their assessments our researchers would be almost helpless in knowing what their bread really tastes like. They sometimes feel the panels are too harsh, but know from experience that such panels represent the buying public, who will really be final judges of the new bread.

July—Now, after they have finished three years of work on the bread project, their Division Director extends the project another year. He agrees the researchers have a potential success. Their good track records of research success helped him present their case to his Deputy Administrator. The men take sample loaves of the bread home to try out on their families. Verdict: "Good!"

August—The industry representatives again meet at the flour and bread laboratory to appraise both the baking system and the bread. These businessmen reserve final judgment, but recommend a test of the bread in a retail store to simulate actual market conditions. They offer to help carry out the test.

September—A research team consisting of market economists from USDA and industry develops a market-test plan. These researchers will place sample loaves of the new bread on display in several carefully selected grocery stores. Loaves of the new bread are to be sold from the regular bread counter along with other brands.

First, however, they must attend to many details label design, package type, package, and preliminary color arrangements for the wrapper. Yellow is chosen as the dominant color. The bread now gets a name—"777."

The pilot plant's baking crew gets ready to bake 600 loaves a day—the amount needed to be offered for sale

each day of the November test. The plan calls first for a 1-week trial study in Walla Walla, Wash., to assure that the test plans are workable. The 13-week study, to be conducted in January, February, and March, will be held in two other test cities—location still to be decided.

From only two researchers, the new bread project is now the worry of five leaders and 14 specialists working full time.

October—The team of leaders agrees upon the label, package, and design. A packaging company volunteers to donate the wrappers, all printed and ready to go.

November—The 1-week test in two stores in Walla Walla has gone well. Cooperation with both the store managers and store personnel was excellent. In fact, the whole week was successful except that one shipment from the pilot plant went to Bend, Oreg., instead of Walla Walla.

Results are used to refine plans for the 3-month study that will take place in Morgantown, W. Va., and Wichita, Kans.

1968 February—The market-testing team conducts similar tests in three chains in each of the two market areas. Retailers sell 23,500 loaves of "777" bread over the 13-week period from 15 stores. The pilot plant crew bake these loaves on a day-to-day basis and ships them by air to the two cities.

April—The tests show "777" bread sold successfully in the 15 stores. Phone interviews with a sample group of housewives who had tried the new bread prove that the original concept —a medium-priced, nutritious, good tasting bread of low-calorie content— was wanted by a large percentage of households.

Seventy-nine percent of the home makers interviewed said they had repurchased "777" bread during the course of the study and said they would continue to make regular purchases if it were regularly available. All consumers, irrespective of income levels and ethnic groups, liked the new bread.

On the basis of the store tests, the market research team suggests that "777" be put on the market as soon as feasible.

May—Heartened with results of the store test survey, the two food innovators, Hamish and Timrek, meet with food equipment suppliers, bread packaging firms, and industry representatives to design a better package. Storage tests indicate the need for a package that is airtight and moisture proof to retain the bread's freshness. The package they specify is one that will not affect flavor.

June—Patents on the new bread composition and breadmaking process, applied for several years earlier, now have been granted to the Secretary of Agriculture. (U.S. firms may obtain permission to use them without paying royalties.)

The market researchers are preparing a rough draft of their research bulletin in manuscript form ready for review.

Department officials close out the 4-year-old project.

To date, no commercial bakery has shown interest in manufacturing the "777" bread. For one reason or another all the companies that cooperated in the earlier phases of the work lost interest in the novel bread baking process. This stalemate will continue for another 8 months, during which time Hamish and Timrek become involved in other work.

July—Dr. Timrek is the author of an article for a trade publication. It describes "777's" high protein, finely ground flour, the low-calorie shortening, and the new brew process.

Mr. Hamish presents a report at the annual meeting of the Institute of Baking. It gives a complete description of the baking process they developed for the "777" bread, and the article includes a production cost analysis.

Copies or excerpts of his talk appear in journals and newsletters.

During the months following, these two research papers are the subject of much study and discussion on the part of decision-makers in the baking industry.

1969 January—The Director of Research and Development of a small bakery in the Midwest visits the laboratory. He reviews the bread baking system, and interviews the two researchers. He takes samples of the flour, leavening agents, and the "777" bread, along with packaging information, back to his own company laboratory. There, his technicians bake loaves and make technical tests.

April—The Midwest bakery initiates a market test of the new bread, since its own panel tests have yielded favorable responses. There is little question about the palatability and keeping qualities of the bread. The big question, "Is there a potentially large market for the low-calorie bread?", is what they seek to answer. For a bakery item, such as this, they need a large volume to keep costs and retail prices low. Low prices to the consumer help bring about the desired large sales volumes.

October—The bakery starts limited production for preliminary market testing. Six weeks of trial store tests in two small cities provide needed basic information on probable future sales volume, competitive position, and complementary role with other foods— especially diet foods. The sales force assigned to the project map out a sales promotion program to be used in larger cities.

Market promoters, hired by the bakery, help design the brand, label, color, and type of package. As a promotional gimmick they recommend using a rigid container. This box is red, brick red in fact, and leads to a suggestion that the bread be named "Brich." "Brich" bread is to be protected by an air-proof, moisture-resistant, waxed liner.

December—Meanwhile, at the company bake shop the production workers try various combinations of ingredients, but return to the ones originally specified by Hamish and Timrek.

The bakery increases production and supplies other cities. The promotional scheme that appears most effective in introducing the bread is having girls dressed as bricklayers give free miniature loaves to every person entering the test stores. The little "Brich" loaves, wrapped in red paper to resemble bricks, are especially popular with mothers of small children. A local dairy company gets into the act by giving out pats of butter at the test stores.

Again, success! "Brich" outsells all but the most highly advertised diet breads in the stores where displayed. In some areas it surpasses brands of regular white bread.

1970 February—The Midwest bakery increases its output and offers "Brich" in every outlet it serves. It drops production of its old diet bread. The director of research tells his technicians to start work on "Brich" formula doughnuts.

Several national baking companies conduct audits in the test cities to check the effect that "Brich" bread has on sales of their own bread and other brands. They continually test the Brich loaves in their own laboratories.

March—The decision-making required by commercial baking firms takes place during this long waiting period. Word is passed along about trials and results in the Midwest. News of these events keeps Timrek and Hamish watchfully hoping for the time when they can feel the new bread is "on the line" at every grocery store.

April—The final wave of development of the bread begins. A large baking company, marketing nationally, decides to perform its own market test. It requests permission of the Secretary of Agriculture to use the patent. The company plans to have some of the new bread on the national market by July. Exactly 6 years have gone by since the new bread project was initiated.

Hamish and Timrek consider this step the final one in the birth of the new food. It is also a milestone in their professional careers.

The two men regard the occasion worthy of a celebration—they ask their wives to dine out. The wives toast them for their success.

Our story of imaginary bread hits some high points but not many of the nail-biting details in development of a new product. Nor does it tell all the disappointing blind alleys encountered. It does not even mention the statistical analyses of test results. It does little to describe the separate actions in market promotion, product changes, or package design by the commercial bakeries in their attempts to get the products on the market.

All of these efforts involved months of planning and outlay of several million dollars. Who says new foods appear by magic?

The new product we have described, a make believe one, turned out to be a success in our story. But many other "dreamed-of" new foods, with just as much costly technical effort, just as much application of experience and knowhow, and equal applications of promotion, fail. In food development work, there are more failures than successes. Many new food ideas are dropped at each stage of development.

No one knows, without trial, which new foods will survive and "arrive," for much depends on the desires (and whims) of the customers—in this case the homemakers. These women in turn, are affected by the impressions they receive from their harshest critics—their own family members.

Turning a new food concept into a market success is hard work, as Hamish and Timrek can attest. It takes time. For each new food placed on the market there is a long span between the idea and arrival of the food in our shopping carts. It is also costly—as their supervisor and the market development people know.

New foods not only require a great deal of money to bring them into being; they also need the concentrated effort of a team of researchers. The workers need not be Government employees, as in our story. Indeed, most new foods come from private industry's food processing firms.

All new foods, no matter where developed, have this in common: they go through a long, complex, expensive process.

WHERE QUALITY IS COMMONPLACE

FARM PRODUCTS TODAY must be high quality if they are to compete successfully in domestic and foreign markets. They must have the various characteristics and properties that buyers want. Oranges are expected to be orange in color, free of blemishes and decay, juicy, and sweet. Lemons should be yellow, juicy, and sour. Beef should be red, tender, and free from off odors.

Shoppers in today's supermarket or the buyer for an institution have such a wide choice of fresh, canned, frozen, and dehydrated products that they can pick and choose and buy only the products that suit them best.

A buyer for a processing plant is even more demanding about quality. The product he buys must have a minimum of waste and must possess the quality characteristics that will yield a uniformly high-quality processed product.

Quality is made up of many characteristics of products. It is a measure or expression of goodness. Some of the characteristics that make up quality are shape, size, color, maturity, ripeness, firmness, texture, juiciness, composition, taste, and presence or absence of defects and spoilage.

Quality may be good or bad, depending on the nature of these

Above, baking quality of wheat is determined by lab tests. Below, grain inspector uses sense of smell to judge quality of grain sample. Instruments are being sought that will be more accurate than human judgment to do this job.

characteristics and upon the use to be made of the product. For instance, a fully ripe peach would be good quality for eating but poor quality for shipping. Mealy potatoes are high quality for serving baked or mashed, but moist, waxy potatoes are better for salads. Flour made from hard red and hard white wheats which contain 11.5 percent or more protein are good quality for making bread, but soft wheats with a protein content of 10 percent or less are better for pastry.

The quality characteristics are used for describing grades and standards. Standard grades are essential for modern marketing because buyers for chain stores, supermarkets, and institutions frequently make purchases by telephone from sellers who may be thousands of miles away, without being able to examine the products. The grades must mean the same to both buyer and seller. Official United States Grades have been established for many products.

Quality and composition of agricultural products are constantly changing as the product develops to maturity and during preparation for market, storage, transportation, and display in the store. Methods and instruments are needed to detect and measure these changes and to prevent deterioration in quality.

Measurement of quality at one time depended largely on the judgment of experienced graders who relied upon their senses of vision, feel, taste, and smell. It was subject to human variation and differed from one grader to another and from one day to the next.

Now instruments and chemical and physical methods are available for measuring many quality characteristics. They eliminate the errors due to human variation and are more accurate and rapid. The day is fast approaching when most of the grading will be done by instruments and much of it will be automated.

✦

AUTHOR HAROLD T. COOK is director of the Market Quality Research Division, Agricultural Research Service.

Ripeness of apples, peaches, and pears used to be measured by pressure with the thumb. In 1925 the Magness-Taylor pressure tester was introduced which measures the firmness of the fruits in number of pounds required to force the tip of a plunger into the flesh. Red Delicious apples are ready to pick when the pressure test is 20 to 16 pounds, firm at 17.5 to 14 pounds, firm ripe at 15 to 11 pounds, ripe and prime for eating at 12 to 8 pounds, and overripe at less than 8 pounds.

A fault of the Magness-Taylor pressure tester is that it punctures the fruit. A modified pressure tester called a "mechanical thumb" has been developed which only indents the flesh about one-eighth of an inch. This makes it possible to measure firmness without causing any serious damage to the fruit.

The color of tomatoes is important to processors, especially the manufacturers of tomato juice. Inspection for color formerly depended on the judgment of inspectors. An instrument is used now at canneries that quickly measures the hue, intensity, and relative lightness or darkness of the extracted juice, and it automatically calculates a color index that agrees closely with the judgment of experienced inspectors.

Tomatoes that are to be shipped to distant markets are picked while still green and allowed to ripen in transit or at the retail store. Some turn red in 1 or 2 days and some are not ripe even after 6 days. This makes it necessary to sort the tomatoes several times before they are displayed for sale. Each sorting costs money and adds bruises that lower the quality.

An instrument called a Multiple Wavelength Difference Meter has been designed and built by the U.S. Department of Agriculture that can measure the internal development of tomatoes and tell how long it will take for them to turn red.

The experimental instrument can be used to detect internal defects such as hollow heart and black heart in pota-

toes, brown core in apples, and internal defects in other fruits and vegetables.

Moisture in agricultural products was formerly measured by drying the product in an oven. Now it is determined electrically by moisture meters of various types which measure electric conductivity of the product.

Sugar content of some products is easily measured in the field or packing shed by using a pocket size hand refractometer. Only a drop of juice is needed for the test. The instrument shows the percentage of soluble solids which is closely correlated with the percentage of sugar. It is used for testing of citrus fruits, grapes, plums, cantaloups, tomatoes, and watermelons.

Sugar in grapes also is measured with a Balling or Brix hydrometer.

Palatability in grapes and citrus depends on the relative amounts of acid

Left, Multiple Wavelength Difference Meter tells how ripe a tomato is without cutting it. Below, colorimeter developed by USDA measures quality of tomatoes for juice more accurately than can be done by eye.

Chemical tests insure good quality of orange concentrate that is processed under USDA's continuous inspection program.

and sugar in the juice. This is called the sugar-acid ratio and is calculated by dividing the percentage of sugar by the percentage of acid. The acidity is measured with a pH meter.

To prevent shipment of immature poor quality citrus fruit, Florida law requires that the fruit meet minimum juice content, sugar-acid ratio, and color standards before it is marketed.

Cotton quality depends upon its length, strength, fineness, maturity, trash content, and color. Instruments are being developed that will measure these characteristics objectively. Some of the instruments used for cotton are the Fibrograph which measures the length and uniformity of length of the fibers, the Micronaire which measures the average fineness and maturity, the Presley-Strength Tester that measures strength, and the Colorimeter that measures color.

Many of the changes in quality and composition are chemical in nature. The rate of change is affected by temperature, moisture, composition of the storage atmosphere, and injuries.

Quality of garden peas and sweet corn deteriorates very rapidly after harvest because the sugar changes to starch. The speed of this change is much faster at normal air temperature than under proper refrigeration. For example, corn loses about 60 percent of its sugar in 1 day at 86° F. but only about 20 percent in 4 days at 32° F.

To maintain high quality in these products, peas are packed in crushed ice when shipped to the fresh market. Sweet corn is hydrocooled in ice water and packed in crushed ice. When these vegetables are to be canned or frozen they are taken directly from the field to the processing plant, and canned or frozen as rapidly as possible.

Quality of potatoes is changed by the reverse process. When potatoes are stored at low temperatures some of the starch is changed to sugar, and the potatoes develop an undesirable sweet taste. Potatoes that are sweet are not satisfactory for processing. Potato chips and french fries made from them are dark brown colored and dehydrated potatoes are brown.

Potatoes stored at 40° F. are satisfactory for most purposes but those for processing should be kept at 50° to 60°. It is necessary to use chemical treatments to prevent sprouting if they are stored more than 2 or 3 months. The sugar in some varieties stored at low temperatures will change back to starch if the potatoes are held at 60° to 70° for 2 to 4 weeks.

When meat is first cut the color is purplish-red. After it is cut oxygen from the air changes the meat pigment from myoglobin to oxymyoglobin which gives the meat the bright red color that shoppers expect. Longer exposure to air causes the pigment to change to metmyoglobin and the meat color becomes brownish-red or grayish-red. Bacteria on the meat speed the discoloration and cause the meat to spoil if kept too long at temperatures above freezing.

Preparing the retail cuts under sanitary conditions, wrapping them in plastic films that admit oxygen but retard loss of moisture, and adequate refrigeration in the display case prevent discoloration and spoilage during a normal marketing period.

Even the dehydrated, frozen, and canned products deteriorate in quality if they are stored too long or kept under unfavorable conditions.

Dried fruits and vegetables are affected by loss of color, browning, off flavors, moldiness, and insects. Development of these defects can be retarded by storing dried fruits at about 55 percent relative humidity and temperatures just above freezing. Since the sugar content is rather high, the freezing point of these products is 22° to 26° F.

Dried vegetables are usually packaged in an atmosphere of nitrogen to retard deterioration. Refrigeration is desirable for long storage.

Frozen foods undergo changes in color, appearance, and flavor during storage, transportation, and marketing. Peach slices turn dark brown, strawberries become discolored, and the color bleeds from raspberries into the syrup. In vegetables, snap beans darken and later turn olive-drab and finally brown. Peas turn grayish-green and then yellowish. Cauliflower becomes gray. Both fruits and vegetables lose vitamin C.

These changes are affected by temperature. They are slow at 0° F. or lower but increase rapidly as the temperature rises. The rate of deterioration doubles several times between 0° and 25°. To maintain quality best, frozen foods should be kept at 0° or lower at all times during storage and transportation.

Canned foods are usually considered very stable but they deteriorate in quality if kept too long, especially if exposed to high temperatures. Changes occur in color, flavor, texture, and nutritive value. Storage life of canned foods is about 1½ to 6 years at 40° F. depending on the kind of product, but only 1 to 3 years at 70° and 3 to 18 months at 100°. In general, canned vegetables have a longer storage life than canned fruits.

Overall quality of the large variety of agricultural products in the market today is far superior to what it was yesterday. We can expect it to be better tomorrow. Better products will be produced and prepared for market; better storage, transportation, and packaging will protect it from deterioration from the farm to the consumer; and automated instruments will measure and control the quality.

THE MARKETING SYSTEM FOR FOOD, FABULOUS AND DYNAMIC

IN EARLY YEARS, farmers took their products directly to towns and often dealt directly with consumers. Local custom governed market days, and the prices were subject to individual bargaining at many different places. Street stalls and peddler carts were early forms of specialized retailing. Most of the food sold was of local origin. Specialized wholesaling and warehousing were rare.

With the growth of cities, the food supply system changed. The big cities came to depend on shipments from distant areas. Commercial farming spread west and south. The increasing urbanization and its reliance on food supplies from long distances created the need for country assembly points to collect and sort farm products into wholesale lots for transportation to consuming centers.

Terminal wholesale centers were established to receive from country assembly points and to redistribute to the retail food trade. Specialists in transporting, wholesaling, brokerage, and warehousing multiplied. Processing moved from farm and home into the factory. Commercial meat-packing, butter- and cheese-making, canning and baking became commonplace. Larger manufacturers established sales branches.

Terminal wholesale centers were more than a place to receive, store, display, and distribute a line of products. It was the pricemaking center, the place where supply and demand forces over a wide area converged. Many services were needed and pressures developed for public market information, grades, inspections, honest weights, and so on.

On the retail front, grocery stores, meat markets, bakeries, and other food specialty shops arose in great numbers as enterprising families scraped together the means of leasing stores and stocking shelves. Many businesses adopted systematic markons; haggling tended to disappear.

These were historical developments in the organization of food marketing up to the 1930's. But then things really began to happen. Retail chain organization, which arose in the twenties, spread. Self-service shopping, with a low markup policy, began.

After World War II, changes came rapidly. In a significant step, an independent retailer in Wisconsin demonstrated in 1947 the feasibility of extending the self-service principle to fresh meats. This heralded a revolution in merchandising perishables in refrigerated display cases.

As this retailing system expanded, procurement methods changed. Farm products increasingly bypassed established country assembly points and urban terminal market wholesaling districts. Eggs, dressed poultry, fruit and vegetables began moving in great volume, for long distances, from country points directly to retailers.

✦

AUTHOR ALLEN B. PAUL is Chief, Competition and Pricing Branch, Marketing Economics Division, Economic Research Service. COAUTHOR WILLIAM T. MANLEY is Director of the Marketing Economics Division.

Moreover, grain and livestock increasingly bypassed the great terminals as shifts occurred in location of processing. The great price-making centers where farm commodities had collected declined. Thus, the marketing system came full circle, from direct to indirect dealings then back again.

But the new direct marketing system is much different. There are fewer, larger farms, and fewer, larger retail stores. Many processing plants have moved closer to sources of supply. There are many more products. There are modern highways. The system is fluid. Products move great distances, in any direction, at a low unit cost. There is a system of efficient warehouses which are materials-handling masterpieces. One could enumerate many other features.

Fundamentally, the major developments are reflections of general economic growth. Growth means increase in per capita incomes and, therefore, more spending power. It implies a demand for more variety of output. In the food field, this means more seasonally produced items the year around, more manufactured products, more stages of preparation, and more types of away from home eating service.

Growth also means urbanization, mobility, and congestion, which in turn cause a demand for centralized shopping. By expanding the market, growth provides increasing opportunity for specialization, large size businesses, and applications of new and improved methods, all of which lead to lower costs. Looked on another way, growth occurs because capital is channelled into the most profitable ventures.

There was no one physical invention that unlocked the possibilities of cost reduction in retailing food. Rather, the modern self service supermarket, large scale buying, and efficient supplier organizations simply applied methods that were around for years. One would be hard-pressed to find much in food retailing that was not known before. But what was new was

Frozen foods section of supermarket in Queens, N.Y.

the opportunity at a certain stage of economic development for adapting known methods to a very ancient business.

The grocery chain organization became feasible when the individual store, small as it was, had enough volume to allow some labor to become more efficient running the store if others could apply their skills to reduce the cost of purchasing, warehousing, advertising, and financing, for many stores together. The small sales per store belonging to large chain organizations is evident as late as 1939.

Enlargement of the individual store since 1939 was a response to a different set of forces. The principle of one-stop shopping calls for a line of merchandise broad enough to attract a steady following of customers.

The modern supermarket is merely the application of the long-known department store principle to the food area but with distinctive features of self service, cash and carry, and community location.

The number of items stocked by the average supermarket has more than doubled during the past two decades. Nowadays, there is little difference in the average size of stores belonging to the smallest and the largest chain organizations.

When a grocer chooses to broaden his merchandise line he thereby provides a service. Its value is measured by the inconvenience customers would incur by going elsewhere to complete their shopping lists. Because different customers have different wants, the problem of satisfying all the needs of

Average Sales Per Grocery Store in the United States by Size of Chain (in 1963 Dollars)

Grocery stores per firm	1939	1948	1963
4–10	$258,000	$398,000	$910,000
11–25	272,000	512,000	1,090,000
26–100	186,000	382,000	1,265,000
101 and over	184,000	492,000	1,150,000

Based on "U.S. Census of Business."

An oldtime meat market.

every customer seems boundless. A retailer would feel warranted in stocking an item if he thinks the cost of doing so would be covered by the added sales volume it would cause.

Thus, opportunities for small stores have shrunk. But they have not been eliminated. There are pockets of demand that the supermarket cannot fill. There is a continuing search for new locations and new types of retail services which the growing market would support.

Economic growth not only hurt the small grocery store but also the independent store, large or small. As more possibilities occurred for reducing buying, warehousing, store delivery, advertising, and other costs through enlargement of size, the sovereignty of the individual store had to yield.

Cost advantages are realized where stores become part of a larger system. But the private chain is not the only system. Independent stores joined cooperative buying groups in order to survive. Similarly, the traditional full-line grocery wholesaler sought alliances with stores as business affiliates.

A basic difference among these systems is the location of ownership. Any successful system uses inducements and compulsions. The success of each form of organization depends on how well it adjusts to changing conditions. A private chain might delegate more authority to store managers. A voluntary or cooperative chain might tighten operating standards of member stores. Thus, each type of system bends in the other's direction.

Retail chains have the advantage of "captive" stores who buy from the company warehouse. This insures volume needed for efficient materials handling.

Part of the problem in reducing costs of supplying stores is to build more volume per store. A store needs a minimum of $500,000 sales to enjoy most advantages of truckload deliveries. Most stores belonging to private chains are above this size, but fewer than half the cooperative and wholesaler-affiliated stores are. Still, average sales per store in the latter groups have been on the increase, which is necessary so as to have an improved competitive position with the large chain organizations.

Part of the bottleneck to improving the efficiency of retailing lies with the nature of today's cities. The most efficient size store is the newer unit— usually located in the suburbs. Smaller, higher cost units tend to be located in older, close-in neighborhoods. Hence, the problem of further increasing the physical efficiency of the overall system is the problem of improving the city itself.

Economies in warehousing, delivery, and store operation feed one another. For example, while affiliated wholesalers always have supplied dry groceries, it is only in recent years that they have supplied more dairy products, meat, produce, and nonfood items. Additional services become possible only with growth of the group. But growth of the group usually requires growth of individual stores.

Definite cost advantages accrue to stores that price and advertise as a group in a metropolitan area. There would be little difference between the cost of a newspaper ad for one store and for twenty stores, but there obviously would be a large difference in the cost per store.

The problem of setting retail prices has become more critical and costly with the development of low markup, high volume methods. In the competitive struggle for customers, the sales special has become a standard method of selling. It is but a part of the larger problem of setting prices which requires skill. Any individual firm will find it hard to meet all competitors' prices at all times, yet it will set some distinctive prices to attract customers. But it also will rely on nonprice techniques to get trade.

Mass merchandising depends on procuring assured supplies of products of uniform quality, condition, and appearance. It also depends on stable price to induce sustained promotional effort.

Faced with procurement difficulties, mass retailing has developed remedies. For lack of reliable information, the retailers have placed buyers, grading stations, and packing sheds at appropriate country points to get the produce they want. They have generated supplies of some things by offering to buy to their own specifications.

These practices now are common for carcass meat, shell eggs, and fresh fruits and vegetables. For some manufactured products, like canned and frozen fruits and vegetables, retailers have entered into contracts with the processors to make them to specification for their own private labels.

Finally, larger retailers make some things themselves, like bakery products, where each firm can impart some degree of distinctiveness to its offerings. They also frequently manufacture other things in volume, like roasted coffee and table-ready meats, but difficulties in buying these items usually are not the reason. For the greater part, retailers have left most food manufacturing to others.

Beside the food retailing industry, the restaurant industry has begun to exert its influence on the system of supply. As one example, the modern franchise chain that features a limited menu and quick service may find it advantageous to buy its chicken, ground beef, or other featured item to its own rigid specifications.

These are new developments of a very old business. Commercially-prepared meals trace back to country inns and bazaars. With the rise of cities, numerous specialized restaurants appeared. With industrialization, the cafeteria, and now the coin-operated vending machine, have replaced the lunch box. These modern techniques are applied wherever large numbers of people congregate during the day— offices, factories, schools—and where incomes can sustain them. Being large volume, low markup businesses, they spread rapidly once they become economically feasible.

In short, the task of buying supplies which faces retail food stores and restaurants has become more complex as a result of the increasing array of possible products and services, the costs of searching the market, the problems of maintaining balanced inventories, and so on.

Most foods nowadays pass through some factory stage. Some—like fresh fruits and vegetables—merely have washing, cooling, grading, and packaging. Hence, steps are often carried out in simple plants at country points either by retailers, cooperatives that are owned by growers, or by independent shippers. But most farm products are substantially altered in factory processing and such factories tend to be large and elaborate. They are mostly owned by separate firms, ranging from big national food manufacturing companies down to small independents that own a single plant.

With the growth in demand for factory processing services, the food manufacturers have responded by developing new products and by elaborating product lines. Thus, for example, ice cream is no longer the only frozen dessert, and ice cream itself is now offered in an increasing array of flavors, kinds, sizes, and types of packages. The same goes for milk, cheese, bread, vegetables, and many other foods that formerly were simple and well standardized.

The second tendency is for manufacturing to become more specialized and for the size of operation to enlarge, with further opportunities to apply technology. Because most farm products are bulky or perishable, the historical reduction in ton-mile cost of transportation has allowed the plant to reach out for its supplies over a wider area.

Together, these tendencies have resulted in larger and fewer plants in the food manufacturing industry. Between 1947 and 1967, the average size of food manufacturing plants had almost tripled and the number of plants decreased by one-third. However, experience for individual sectors

in the food manufacturing industry was diverse.

Altogether, there were about 30,000 food manufacturing plants in the United States in 1967. About 9,000 of these units belonged to companies that had two or more plants. These accounted for two-thirds of food industry manufacturing.

As firms grow larger and fewer, they tend to exert more buying power. It means that each firm is able to make more specific demands on suppliers for quality, conditions, delivery schedules, and perhaps, price. This is in addition to the tendency of the large retailers to make their own buying power felt, as described above.

Percent Change in Number of Establishments and Average Output Per Establishment, U.S., 1947 to 1967

	Number of establishments	Output per establishment
	Percent	Percent
Food manufacturing	−33	+175
Retail food stores [1]	−42	+194
Eating places [1]	+22	+83

[1] 1948 to 1967.

From the larger viewpoint, the methods of organizing the food economy look quite different than they once did. The terminal market used to be the nerve center. Grain terminals, stockyards, wholesale poultry and eggs districts, fruit and vegetable auctions—each brought together competitive forces over a wide area. Prices were openly established and news of their changes was spread widely by press and radio. The behavior of these wholesale price centers was understood in terms of cyclical, annual, and seasonal influences. Producers largely decided what to produce for tomorrow's market by their interpretation of today's prices.

The rise in more direct dealings caused a decline in the terminal markets and a change in their roles. While the volume of products traded in these

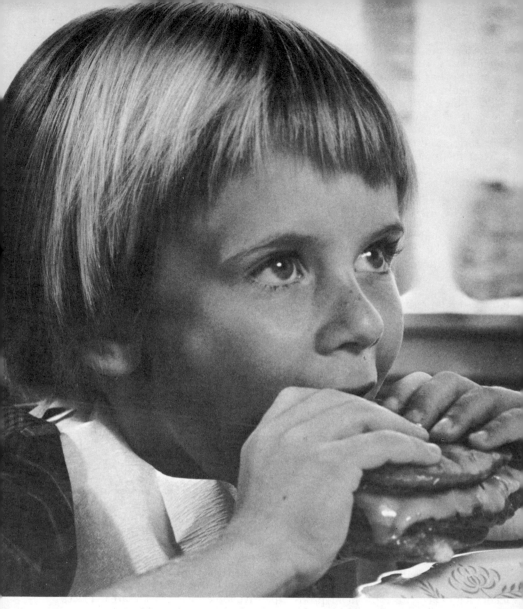

Varieties of away-from-home eating services are increasing.

markets has drastically declined, they are still used as basing points for pricing such products as butter, eggs, and cattle. For example, a retail chain organization in Philadelphia may buy fresh eggs from the Midwest based on a price established by the New York Mercantile Exchange.

This system of pricing is sometimes questioned. Partly it is because of the thinness of trading at wholesale mar-

kets on which the side dealings are arranged, which suggests the possibilities of abuse. But partly, the uneasiness is based on the difficulty of trying to make prices in a market that is so widely dispersed.

But it is no longer economically feasible for all commodities to be physically present when buying and selling occurs. It would be wasteful. Nor is it necessary. As long as one

can describe a commodity to the reasonable satisfaction of others and assure delivery, payment, and redress of grievances, a satisfactory exchange can occur. As a matter of fact, the commodity need not even be in existence at the exact time that the trading occurs.

In the modern economy, there are emerging possibilities for many kinds of pricing that heretofore were nonexistent. In large measure, problems of market organization become problems of making such pricing more efficient. The new vistas for the functioning of commodity markets include not only formula pricing but also a wide range of possibilities for contract growing, future trading, and the application of electronic computers to searching the market and even for trade negotiations.

The problem of achieving satisfac-

Manufactured products are on the upsurge in the food field. Above, continuous pressure cookers for sterilizing cans of food.
Left, in-line juice extractors, for orange juice concentrate, at Lakeland, Fla.

tory market organization is indeed difficult. It depends on solving several problems. As the economy continues to expand, new production possibilities will arise—due to new products, more specialization, and new technology. More stages in the production of a given commodity can be separated out and brought into a separate market decision. Thus, there constantly will emerge new ways of doing business. These pose not only opportunities but also hazards.

Each way of doing business might meet the needs of some different participant as he reviews his comparative advantage, resources, and the uncertainties that will face him. In short, a range of potential trades open up that are far different from the simple spot, cash-and-carry deals of the traditional wholesale markets. The problems of market organization are indeed great, but then, the economy is attempting to do far more than it ever did before.

Achievements of the food marketing system may be judged on four levels. First is maintenance of quality standards and provision of significant choices. Here, results have been generally good. The main questions concern excessive tie-ins of advertising and promotional gimmicks with the food supply, and to some extent the excessive difficulty of comparing real unit prices of different size packages.

Second is the economic efficiency of physically getting farm products to the ultimate consumers. Costs can be lowered by eliminating needless transport, processing, and storage activities. And they can be lowered by reducing the costs of performing remaining services. On these counts, results of the system have been good.

Third is efficient transmission of consumer wants back through marketing channels to guide production. In this respect, the modern system is much improved over what it was. Large scale merchandising exerts effective pressures in this direction. Years ago the system absorbed whatever the farmer decided to produce. Today

there may be no profitable markets for some products.

Fourth is minimizing the costs of change. Increasingly, established farmers and middlemen are being bypassed to their disadvantage. They cannot easily shift into other occupations or businesses. This is a severe problem, but it is a general problem of a rapidly changing society. With increased understanding, more people are coming to regard the plight of the individual as society's plight. Society is constantly searching for ways to soften the blow to individuals who are hurt by economic growth and change.

A MARKETING ORDER MAY BE THE ANSWER

A SEVERE FREEZE wiped out the south Texas citrus industry in 1951, and growers faced a market rebuilding job.

Favorable growing conditions for California raisins resulted in consecutive years of near-record production in the 1960's, seriously threatening market stability.

A 1967 State court decision invalidated Georgia's milk control program, requiring a new approach to stabilizing fluid milk prices.

A California water pollution control board outlawed dumping a salt brine solution used to store black ripe olives, and the olive industry had to replace an age-old process.

Each of these situations was unique and different. Yet the answer in each case was found in a Federal marketing order.

Citrus producers adopted a dual approach of regulating the quality of oranges and grapefruit going to the fresh market, and promoting the use of their products by advertising.

Raisin producers developed a program to regulate the amount and quality of raisins for domestic markets, with the balance going into an export reserve and producers sharing pro rata in the gross proceeds.

Milk producers adopted a Federal marketing order which set minimum producer prices and provided audit, weighing, testing, and market information services.

Olive producers turned to a marketing order research program to develop new storage preservatives, with side benefits in the form of improved flavor and reduced shrinkage.

These examples illustrate the versatility of the Federal marketing agreement and order program—described by Dr. Edwin G. Nourse, former Chairman of the Council of Economic Advisers, as "a truly unique marketing institution, neither quite free nor fully controlled but heavily 'conditioned' by both private and public mechanisms and policies."

Other unique and distinguishing features of the program are:

• The opportunity provided for industry groups—those closest to the problem situations—to participate in developing programs to solve their marketing problems.

• The participation of industry in program administration.

• The formalized procedures and internal checks and balances between public and private interests.

• The essentially self-financing nature of the program.

Authority for marketing agreements and orders first became a part of Federal law in the "depression" legislation of the early 1930's. After several years of experimentation and legal challenge, the authorities were rewritten and incorporated in the Agricultural Marketing Agreement Act of 1937. Basic authorities have remained substantially unchanged.

✦

AUTHOR JOHN C. BLUM is Deputy Administrator, Consumer and Marketing Service. His responsibility includes marketing agreements and orders.

Marketing orders and marketing agreements differ in significant respects. A marketing order may contain only certain specified types of provisions. However, once approved by a required number—usually two-thirds—of producers of the regulated commodity, the order is binding on all handlers of the commodity in the area of regulation.

A marketing agreement may contain more diversified provisions, but is enforceable only with respect to those producers or handlers who voluntarily enter into the agreement with the Secretary of Agriculture.

A marketing order is not a fixed entity which can be described and understood in unchanging terms. The Agricultural Marketing Agreement Act provides a variety of authorities— a kit of tools—among which choices must be made to select the combination best suited to a given marketing situation.

For milk, the Act authorizes the fixing of uniform minimum prices to producers according to use (drinking milk, ice cream, butter, cheese, etc.), and related weighing, testing, auditing, and market information provisions.

For commodities other than milk, marketing orders cannot directly fix prices, but they can prescribe marketing conditions designed to achieve given price objectives. These include limiting the quality or quantity of products marketed, regulating rate of flow to market, establishing producer or handler marketing allotments, pooling returns to producers or handlers, market research and development, and sale at filed prices.

For fruits, vegetables, and tree nuts, orders may specify size, capacity, weight, dimension, or pack of container. For certain designated commodities, they may provide for paid advertising. For other designated commodities, the Act requires that when grade, size, quality, or maturity regulations are imposed domestically, the same or comparable requirements must be applied to imports of those commodities.

Thus, the available kit of marketing tools varies among commodities. And amendments to the Act over the years have extended or modified the application of authorities to particular commodities as the marketing conditions changed.

In developing an order, the working together of agricultural producers and their government (represented by the Secretary of Agriculture) begins at the earliest stage. The Secretary looks to producers—usually through their cooperatives or in some other organized way—to identify and analyze their

gram to meet the essential marketing needs of their industry—which they know best. The Secretary of Agriculture sees to it that the resulting order meets the statute's standards and serves the public interest as contemplated by the statute.

The 1969 Florida tomato program provides an interesting case study. The order administrative committee recommended progressive tightening of grade and size regulations as the season progressed, to maintain producer returns in the face of increasing supplies. Under the law, the same regulations

Fruit and vegetable marketing orders benefit consumers by providing a steady market supply of high quality products, as in Fort Worth, Tex., supermarket, left. Milk marketing orders assure consumers, like tot, right, an adequate supply of pure and wholesome milk.

marketing problems and to select those tools provided by the statute which are best suited to the problems at hand.

Since the tools and the legislative authorities are not the same for all commodities, producers generally seek and obtain assistance from the Secretary in analyzing their problems and in developing appropriate marketing order proposals.

This process of working together leads to an accommodation of private and public interest which is an essential ingredient of successful order operations. Producers mold the pro-

would have to be applied to imported tomatoes.

This gave rise to complaints from various sources. Mexican producers, the Mexican Government, and U.S. importers of Mexican tomatoes feared that shipments from Mexico would be unduly restricted. (Actually, 1969 imports from Mexico reached a record high.) Chain stores were concerned with the impact on established merchandising programs. And consumers feared high prices.

The regulations issued by the Secretary of Agriculture did not com-

104

letely satisfy any of these groups, but represented a reasonable balance of the interests of producers and others, within the statute's limits.

Each marketing order proposal must complete a rigorous schedule of formalized procedures—including public hearing—before it becomes an established order. Every provision of an order must be supported by a public record, and an order cannot become effective until approved by at least two-thirds of producers (by number or volume) voting in referendum.

The Secretary must terminate an order when conditions make this action necessary.

So carefully have marketing order procedures been designed, and so painstaking has been the work of both industry and government representatives in developing and administering orders, that the veto power has seldom been exercised by either producers or the Secretary. But it does exist, and it has been a restraining influence and a motivating force for responsible administration.

Marketing order procedures also provide opportunity for other inter-

Fruit and vegetable marketing orders contain grade and size provisions under which the highest quality products are sorted and packed for the fresh market, like navel oranges, left, being sized automatically. Marketing orders may specify standard containers or pack, as with grapes, right.

order whenever he determines it no longer fulfills the declared policy of the Act, or whenever a majority of the affected producers no longer desire its continuance.

Marketing order procedures provide a system of internal checks and balances which assure protection of both private and public interests. If private interests are not served, producers can withhold necessary approval or can require the Secretary to terminate an order. If public interests are not served, the Secretary either will not issue an order in the first place, or will termi-

ested persons—processors, distributors, and consumers—to make known their views and to have their interests considered. All data presented in hearing testimony and in post-hearing briefs become a part of the official record to be evaluated in the decision-making process.

Under many marketing orders, producer and handler representatives participate in order administration. In the fruit, vegetable, and tree nut programs, the Secretary appoints an administrative committee for each order, selected from persons nominated by major segments of the industry. This brings administration down to the "grass roots" level, without impairing the Secretary's final authority and responsibility.

Principal costs of administering marketing agreement and order programs are financed by assessments against those regulated. Thus, each program is largely self-supporting within the commodity sector regulated. Government expenditures are limited to the relatively small amounts required for general surveillance of the program by the U.S. Department of Agriculture.

Marketing orders are not equally adaptable to all commodities and all marketing problems. They have been the most effective in situations where the production and/or marketing area and the marketing problem were limited and definable, and where producers had common economic interests and were organized (usually through cooperatives).

Milk producers and growers of fruits, vegetables, and tree nuts have been the principal users of marketing orders. Orders for these commodities have continued to expand since the 1930's. Other commodity groups have shown occasional interest, but generally have not progressed to the point of adopting programs.

In early 1970, there were 68 milk marketing orders, setting minimum prices to producers for milk having an annual farm value of nearly $3.6 billion, or three-fourths of all milk eligible for fluid consumption in the United States. There were 46 marketing agreement and order programs for fruits, vegetables, and tree nuts, regulating commodities with a farm value of $1.9 billion.

Outside these commodity areas, there was only one marketing order in effect in early 1970. This was an order regulating the quality of shade-grown (type 62) tobacco marketed in Georgia and Florida.

During the decade of the 1960's, the trend in the milk order program was toward mergers, with fewer and larger orders regulating an increasing proportion of the Nation's fluid milk supply. In the fruit, vegetable, and tree nut programs, the trend was toward more diversified use of marketing order authorities, with increasing attention to volume controls as well as to market research, promotion, and advertising provisions.

The Agriculture Department in its search for new ways to deal with agricultural surpluses and depressed commodity prices in the early 1960's actively encouraged the consideration of marketing orders in new commodity areas.

A national order to limit the marketing of turkeys was developed to the point of a national referendum in 1962, but failed to receive the producer approval required to go into effect. Similar efforts for potatoes and ryegrass seed were terminated in the face of producer opposition before going to referendum.

Severe problems in marketing flue-cured tobacco in the 1967 and 1968 seasons led producer groups to develop a marketing order proposal to regulate the flow of tobacco to market from the several Belts in the production area. However, marketing conditions improved and the Secretary of Agriculture determined that issuance of the order was not required for the 1968 season. It was still being held in abeyance in 1970.

Egg producers did extensive work on a volume control order proposal following the extremely low prices of 1967, and special authorizing legislation was introduced (but not passed) in the 90th Congress.

Interest in farm bargaining power during the late 1960's led additional commodity groups to consider the use of marketing order authorities to strengthen their marketing position. However, nothing concrete had materialized by early 1970.

To sum up, three decades of experience with marketing agreement and order programs led to the conclusion that they are a valuable tool for dealing with a wide range of marketing problems—where the regulatory goals are limited and well defined, producers are organized to deal with their problems, and there is substantial community of interest and support for the regulatory proposal. Marketing orders are unlikely to succeed in the absence of these conditions, or without full understanding by affected producer groups.

Concerning the future of marketing orders, the crystal ball is not clear. They offer no panacea to cure all marketing ills. On the other hand, as the traditional farm programs of the past 30 years continue to wane, marketing agreements and orders are likely to receive increasing attention among agricultural commodity groups.

The versatile, adaptable, self-financing, do-it-yourself, democratic nature of the marketing agreement and order program suggests a continued active role in farm policy for this "truly unique marketing institution."

MARKETING COSTS ARE DOUBLE THE FARM VALUE OF FOOD PRODUCTS

IT'S TWICE AS COSTLY to market farm products as to produce the food in the first place, surprising though this may seem.

When they left the farm, food raw materials produced by U.S. farmers in 1969 were worth $32 billion. By the time they reached the consumer, their cost had soared to $96 billion. The big increase in cost between the farmer and consumer represented the value added to farm products by the marketing system.

Over the years, the cost of marketing farm products has increased compared with returns to farmers. Thus, marketing costs have represented a larger and larger part of consumer expenditures for food. Since 1949, the proportion of food expenditures attributed to marketing costs rose from 60 percent to about 66 percent.

With an expanding urban economy, more marketing services are required relative to farm production. As the city population grows and as farm production becomes more specialized geographically, both farmers and consumers become more dependent on the marketing system. The products that farmers grow and sell must be stored, transported, and delivered in the form and at the time and to the places that consumers desire.

Farmers recognize that the marketing system performs essential functions in moving products to consumers. They want those functions performed as efficiently as possible and at the lowest attainable cost. However, marketing expenses increase nearly every year. As a result, farmers as well as consumers, no doubt, wonder at times if something is wrong with the system and if costs are too high. Even more important to farmers is the influence of increases in marketing costs on the level and stability of farm prices.

Marketing expenses rise because more services are provided or because of higher costs of performing the same services.

First, let us consider the impact of added services. New or added marketing services—built-in maid services particularly—often are cited as the principal factor tending to increase costs. Consumers, with more money to spend and greater pressures on their time, have transferred many chores of food preparation from their kitchens to factories.

✦

AUTHOR DENIS F. DUNHAM is an agricultural economist in the Marketing Economics Division, Economic Research Service.

In 1969, consumers bought nearly as many frozen, canned, and dehydrated potato products as they did fresh potatoes. Sales of frozen prepared dinners reached almost a half billion dollars—nearly double that of 4 years earlier.

We know that products with built-in services, such as frozen dinners, prepared mixes, freshly squeezed fruit juices, ready-to-serve bakery products, and many other "convenience" foods have, to some extent, added to marketing costs. In addition, it would seem that added services associated with food retailing, such as larger parking lot facilities, larger and more appealing stores, music and air conditioning, check cashing, etc., have boosted costs.

The amount probably has not been as much as generally assumed, however. Outlays for parking lots and many other services offered by supermarkets today have been offset by economies of scale or large volume, self service, and more efficient handling of products in stores.

Then too, processing does not necessarily increase costs. Added processing and packaging of many products are at least partially offset by reductions in waste and spoilage and by savings in transportation and storage.

Increases in marketing expenses because of added services do not affect farmers if consumers buy as much as formerly, at a price which covers the extra outlay. And in general, consumers seem willing to pay the added charge.

Actually, added processing has expanded the market for many farm products over the years because the new services have increased consumer demand. Demand for farm products works backward from the consumer through the marketing system to the farmer. Thus, when added marketing services increase consumer demand, there may be a rise in sales at the farm level.

Increases in the cost of performing the same services have affected the marketing bill more than the expense of added services. Marketing agencies, like other businesses, are confronted with soaring costs of doing business virtually every year.

Between 1959 and 1969, the total outlay for marketing farm foods to consumers went from $42 billion to $64 billion. We find that a third of this hike is accounted for by rising costs, or inflation, while added marketing services caused only a sixth of the increase. The rest of the rise reflects the greatly increased volume of food that was marketed to feed the growing population.

Farmers are more likely to be affected if marketing costs go up because of the rising expense of doing business rather than as a result of added marketing services. If cost increases are passed on to the consumer in the form of higher prices, consumers may buy less. With a decline in purchases, farmers usually have to take lower prices, particularly in the short run, to move the same volume of a product.

Another measure of marketing costs is the difference between the retail price of a product and its farm value. We call this the farm-retail price spread or marketing margin. The U.S. Department of Agriculture regularly calculates the marketing spread for a "market basket" of farm foods. In the basket are average amounts of different kinds of foods purchased annually per household in 1960–61. Foods in the market basket are held constant for long periods of time so that changes in the margin are due mainly to changes in the cost of doing business. The spread or margin includes payments received by all agencies performing services in moving food products from farmer to consumers.

The 1960's witnessed a significant increase in the marketing margin and retail food costs, particularly during the general price inflation in the latter half of the decade. Between 1959 and 1969, retail cost of the market basket rose from $985 to $1,173 or 19 percent. The marketing margin rose from $608 to $696, or over 14 percent.

Increases in the margin reflect a

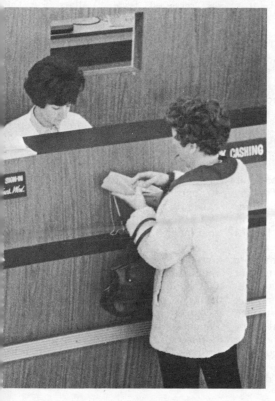

Check cashing and
other consumer services
at food stores.

FOR
CUSTOMER
SERVICE
CALL
OPERATOR

Making butter.

rise in expenditures by food marketing firms. Wages of their workers edged upward at an average rate of about 4 percent per year in that period. Other costs of doing business also rose. Prices of containers and packaging materials increased 15 percent over the 10-year period. Services which include such items as rent, property insurance and maintenance, and telephone service increased the most, 41 percent.

Marketing margins have not gone up as much as wages and other costs because of increases in efficiency. A main reason for these increases has been the greater productivity of labor, the largest cost element in marketing.

Labor charges per hour in food marketing averaged 59 percent higher in 1969 than in 1959. However, improvement in output per man-hour held the rise in labor costs per unit of product marketed to 33 percent. By improving output per worker, the food marketing system has kept pace with productivity in the total non-agricultural economy. But neither one has matched the gains in agricultural output per man-hour.

Farm prices of food products during the early 1960's did not keep pace with increases in marketing margins. Farmers received fewer dollars for the market basket of farm foods in 1965 than in 1959, and their share of the consumer's food dollar was at a record low for the post World War II period.

In general, farm prices are more variable than nonfarm prices. During periods of inflation, farm product prices often move farther than other prices. Such a situation developed late in the 1960's. The farm value of the market basket jumped sharply, partly as a result of reduced supplies of some foods, but mostly due to stronger consumer demand spurred by rising personal incomes.

The marketing margin for the market basket declined in only one year between 1959 and 1969. Changes in marketing costs are, for the most part, independent of supply and demand factors affecting farm prices. When the farmer's price for his product drops because of a large supply, most costs of marketing are not affected.

Some of the larger expenses of marketing—as for transportation, rent, utilities, and taxes—change slowly. The relative stability of margins in

110

absolute amount is a matter of great importance, particularly if consumer demand slackens and retail prices decline. When this occurs, the stability of the marketing margin tends to accentuate the relative decline in farm prices and reduce the farmer's share of the food dollar.

Marketing margins and the farmer's share of the consumer's food dollar differ greatly from product to product. For example, in 1969 the farmer's share averaged 67 cents for eggs, 50 cents for milk, 49 cents for frying chickens, 22 cents for fresh oranges, and 14 cents for bread. But this is not because the marketing agencies handling eggs are more efficient or make less profit than an orange juice processor or those firms handling wheat, flour, and bread. The principal reason for the variation is in the tasks performed by farmers and marketing agencies and the differences in resources required to perform them.

Animal products, like eggs, milk, and chickens, tend to have a higher farmer's share than most crop products, such as oranges and bread, because animal products require more resources to produce than crops.

In general, the more highly processed the product, the smaller the farmer's share. Eggs reach the kitchen in the same form in which they left the farm. By contrast, wheat has to be ground, and flour baked, and the bread sliced and wrapped, between the farm and consumer.

Classifying of most foods as processed or unprocessed is a matter of degree. All of the animal products, except eggs, go through some change of form after they leave the farm, as do practically all the crop foods with the exception of fresh fruits and vegetables. Even though the fruits and vegetables do not change form, the marketing margin makes up two-thirds of the retail price. This is mainly due to the distances shipped and the perishability of these products, which affect the relative cost of transportation and storage.

Marketing margins for all major food groups in the market basket have been going up. The increase in the margin between the retail cost and the farm value of fresh fruits and vegetables between 1959 and 1969 was 38 percent—the largest percentage rise for any food group. The cost to consumers went up by a similar percentage, which may account in large part for the decline in consumption of these foods.

The margin for meat products rose 12 percent, or about the same as the increase in the market basket margin. A relatively small rise of only 10 percent occurred in the margin for poultry and eggs.

The reason marketing margins for poultry and eggs have gone up much less than for fresh fruits and vegetables is difficult to explain. The main reason seems to be cost-saving innovations.

Several machines have been developed in recent years for grading and packing eggs that have reduced costs per unit of output. Considerable use is made of assembly line methods and automatic equipment in poultry processing plants. Meanwhile, marketers of fresh fruits and vegetables have had only limited success in improving the efficiency of their marketing system.

Increases in marketing margins usually result in higher prices to consumers. Since the margin is the dominant component of retail price, a rise affects the retail price more than an equal percentage hike in the farm price. The fact that margins account for more than half the retail price of most foods and have risen steadily means that our ability to hold down food prices depends largely on the efficiency of the marketing system.

While increases in marketing margins may have an adverse effect on farmers, particularly on prices received in the shortrun, they are not the primary cause of either unstable or low farm prices over the longrun. In some ways, marketing contributes both to the level and stability of farm prices.

Because of the vast network of

Top, operator rides traveling platform above cages in high-rise egg "factory." He inspects birds and loads chickens in and out. Wheels roll on feed pipes. Below, mass candling of eggs.

transportation and distribution facilities, the market for most farm product is nationwide. This tends to reduc local and regional price difference resulting from surpluses or deficits Price variability resulting from sea sonal changes in farm production an marketing is reduced by storage refrigeration, and processing facilitie that help provide a more even flow o products to consumers.

It is reasonable to expect that a the marketing system performs mor and more services relative to agricul ture and as costs rise, a larger shar of the consumer's food dollar will g to marketing. Whatever the future de velopments in marketing costs an margins, an efficient marketing system is in the best interests of farmers a well as consumers.

20,000-MILE TRAIN
FULL OF CORN, OR
FACTS AND FOOD

IMAGINE A TRAIN more than 20,000 miles long, with over 2 million boxcars full of corn. The train would reach from New York to San Francisco about five times.

That's the size of the 1969 corn crop as predicted by the Crop Reporting Board in its December estimate. This is corn used primarily to feed cattle, pigs, chickens, and turkeys. In work figures, it comes to 4,577,864,000 bushels.

Estimates like this are measures of change, within season, month to month, or year to year, but who needs measures of change? What needs to be measured? How will change be measured? The corn crop makes a good example.

Practically all of us are affected and have an interest—whether we realize it or not—in the Agriculture Department's estimate of the corn crop. Let's see why.

During 1968 we in the United States produced and consumed 20.7 billion pounds of beef, or about 110 pounds for each man, woman, and child. More than two-thirds of the 35 million cattle needed to provide this much beef were raised on a diet with a substantial amount of corn. Besides beef we produced and consumed 12.9 billion pounds of pork from more than 85 million pigs, most of which were raised on diets heavy with corn. We also consume 7.5 billion pounds of chickens each year, Sundays included, to say nothing of the turkeys that eat out of the corn pile."

Meat production is not the only use made of corn—corn oil goes into salad and cooking oils and margarine—everyday commodities in nearly every housewife's kitchen. Then there are breakfast cereals as well as corn starches that are basic ingredients in many food products ranging from baby food to desserts. Add alcohol and plastics among numerous other products to which some portion of the annual corn "pile" is important.

See why you have an interest in the corn crop?

Decisions by hundreds of thousands of farmers and firms doing business with farmers are affected by the corn crop estimate. Our highly developed production and marketing system depends on accurate estimates to insure stable supplies and prices of agricultural commodities. Too, if you're a housewife you expect to find "corn fed" beefsteaks, pork chops, and plump chickens any time you go to market.

Besides the corn estimate, the Statistical Reporting Service—in its role as the Agriculture Department's primary fact-gathering agency—issues some 650 reports each year. They include current estimates on acreage, yield, and production of crops; livestock numbers and products; supplies of grain in storage; prices received by farmers; and farm labor reports.

Other articles in this book deal with the dramatic changes in agriculture. These changes have resulted in equally dramatic changes in the need for agricultural statistics and the methods of collecting them.

The first Monthly Crop Report describing the condition of a number of crops was issued by the newly established U.S. Department of Agriculture in July 1863. Since then the number and kinds of statistical reports related to agriculture have developed like an ever-widening stream.

✦

AUTHOR GLENN D. SIMPSON is Chairman of the Crop Reporting Board and Deputy Administrator, Statistical Reporting Service.

Today probably no major segment of the American economy is as well served by statistical intelligence as agriculture. And the end is not yet in sight. The backlog of requests by data users for still more detailed information about agriculture exceeds by far the added financial resources that Congress and the State legislatures may reasonably be expected to provide for statistical purposes.

Farms are becoming larger and more specialized, and significantly the largest and most specialized are increasing in number. Just one-third of our largest farms now account for over 85 percent of agricultural sales, and this share will increase.

Operators and managers of the larger farms are becoming increasingly aware of the value and influence of statistics in decision making. One can also observe an increasing capability as well as desire on the part of some commodity organizations or groups to provide a share of their own sta-

tistical intelligence. They are developing expertise in statistical and economic analysis that makes them les vulnerable to the out-and-out marke speculator.

Changing farm technology has als altered the need for statistical da on agriculture. Increasingly, farme have acquired safeguards against cro failures that frequently crippled the forefathers.

Supplemental water supplies an irrigating procedures, new varietie fertilizer, pesticides, herbicides, an crop insurance have combined to mak many farmers considerably less de pendent on day-to-day weather an environmental conditions. Once crop is planted, there is now fa greater assurance that a crop of pre dictable magnitude will be harvested

Still another factor bears close ex amination so far as farmers are cor cerned. There is evidence that futur reports should include less frequer but more accurate statistical measure

Measuring crop frontage on the highway, in 1947.

114

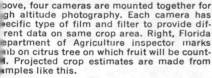

Above, four cameras are mounted together for high altitude photography. Each camera has specific type of film and filter to provide different data on same crop area. Right, Florida Department of Agriculture inspector marks limb on citrus tree on which fruit will be counted. Projected crop estimates are made from samples like this.

commercial agriculture. Also, demands for new data nearly always include measures of commodity quality and market timing, currently not available. These facts may be more important than many of the time honored statistical series now produced.

If the foregoing indications of change are valid, conditions exist to reevaluate the Federal crop reporting program for agriculture.

Again using the corn crop as an example, the annual Federal report program is now made up of estimates of acreage farmers intend to plant in March, acreage planted as of July 1, and the acreage harvested in December. Each month from July through November a new monthly forecast of production is prepared. In December the final estimate of acreage and production is published.

A suggested future statistical program for corn could include the estimate of acreage planted in late July. Next would be an early season production forecast the first of September after the crop has grown to the stage where the potential output can be predicted with a high degree of certainty.

The crop is "made" by about October 1 and the next production estimate would be appropriate as of this date. The wrap-up at the end of the season would provide a full accounting including the new statistics that measure the important aspects of crop quality.

These less frequent estimates would be based on highly refined sampling procedures and have a predictable degree of accuracy at a very high level, say one percent or less for the United States.

Many farm operators now have the capability to keep track of crop progress between the less frequent dates suggested above. Any future

115

advances in the science of weather forecasting could be expected to increase this capability. Farmers would improve their decisionmaking ability by the increased accuracy of reports when they are issued.

This example, using a modification of statistics for corn, can be applied as well to a wide array of commodities including fruits and vegetables. Statistics on livestock must be improved as regards accuracy, additional needed detail, and improved timeliness.

In the past, data were obtained from a cross-section of farmers chiefly by mass distribution of questionnaires to a broad spectrum of farm operators by rural mail carriers, or by direct mailing of questionnaires to large numbers of names and addresses without knowing whether they were big or small producers or how they specialized. These methods are just about obsolete, if greater accuracy in statistical measurement is going to be achieved.

What are the recently developed sampling procedures currently in use and eligible for future use? One of them is the area sample, a set of small blocks of land (segments containing about one square mile) selected at random across the United States.

In June and December each year paid enumerators visit these segments to account for the activities of interest taking place on a given date, whether in crops, livestock, poultry, or farm labor.

This sample data can be projected into estimates for the States, regions, and the United States with any desired level of statistical accuracy. The size of the sample (number of area segments) controls the level of statistical accuracy, assuming good workmanship by the hired enumerators.

The area sample is an expensive

data collection procedure, and that limits its use. To overcome this deficiency, USDA's Statistical Reporting Service is extending its efforts to compile lists of farm operators that are as nearly complete as possible. The objective is to draw up lists that contain names, addresses, and principal agricultural activities of practically all the farms in the United States.

These lists will permit a statistical breakthrough. It will be possible to select from a list a random sample of farm operators of known size and commodity specialization to which questionnaires can be mailed. The area sample will be jointly employed to measure the changes or incompleteness in the list sample.

Complete coverage of these samples for major surveys by mail, telephone

Infrared photos are taken from aircraft at USDA research station in Weslaco, Tex., with data from ground obtained simultaneously by use of a lift. "Ground truth" data correlate actual crop condition with aerial photos.

id personal visit will provide the
vels of statistical accuracy being
·manded by data users.
The complex agricultural produc-
on and marketing systems required
feed and clothe our growing popu-
tion cannot operate without more
·curate and timely measures of
ιange.
Much progress has been made to
duce the need to take the time of the
rm operator in answering survey
ιestionnaires. The objective measure-
ent procedure is currently being
idely used to measure yields per
·re for such crops as corn, cotton,
ybeans, wheat, oranges, filberts,
ιd others.
In the major producing areas for
ese commodities, fields where very
·ecise measurements and counts can
· made are randomly selected. These
llies are converted into forecasts and
timates of yield per acre or per tree
ith a high level of statistical accuracy.
Once the fields are selected, the
rm operator's permission is sought
enter them to select and identify for
ture visits precise locations where the
·unts are made. The work is done by
ained enumerators. When the crop
mature the sample plots are har-
·sted and the product measured for
eld, moisture, and other useful crop
ιality factors like protein and oil
·ntent.
Following harvest, sample fields are
eaned to get measures of crop losses
hich could eventually lead to im-
·oved harvesting practices.
Probably before another decade has
ιssed the use of high-level or earth
tellite photography will have taken
· place in providing additional
easures of American agriculture.
This technique may provide new
ιses for sample selection and meas-
·es of crop progress. It should permit
·curate counting of some major
·pects of the livestock population,
ch as the number of cattle being
ttened to produce the steady flow of
ιoice beef to consumers.
Remote sensing and accurate iden-
ication of plants from satellite

photographs should permit selection of
high and low yielding fields of growing
crops, providing a refinement in selection of sample fields for actual objective
tallies on the ground. Development
and progress of crop diseases or insect
infestation should be measurable, as
well as the condition of growing crops
due to excess or shortage of moisture.
These new capabilities based on
advances in space age science figure to
help greatly in improving agricultural
estimates. They could reduce the
burden on farmers in gathering data,
and permit more accurate, less frequent, yet more useful measures of
change that will benefit both producers and consumers of food, feed,
and fiber.

COMMODITY POLICIES AND PROGRAMS

SINCE THE DEPRESSION of the 1930's,
nearly every industrialized nation has
sought to protect farmers from low
prices. The United States is no exception. Over the past four decades, this
country has created and maintained
an extremely complex agricultural
price-support system. Commodity programs have demonstrated remarkable
ability to survive despite widespread
criticism, and a marked reduction in
the political influence of agriculture
in Congress.
Falling farm prices, high indebted-
ness, and a wave of foreclosures set
the stage for direct government intervention in pricing farm products in
the period between the two world
wars. By the mid-1920's, a majority
of those in Congress were convinced
that government intervention was
essential to improve farm prices, but
it was not until 1929 that Congress

and the President could agree on a program.

This first attempt to support prices indirectly, by making loans to cooperatives and quasi-government corporations so that they might buy farm products and hold them off the market, ended in failure. Within two years, the resources provided by Congress were exhausted.

The amount of money made available simply was not sufficient to cope with a major world-wide depression. It became apparent in the early 1930's that any further attempt to hold up prices would be prohibitively expensive or ineffective unless some means were employed to limit production.

This experience was not lost on those who drafted the Agricultural Adjustment Act of 1933. In this act, Congress gave the U.S. Department of Agriculture the authority, not only to support prices through a loan and storage program, but also to curtail the acreages planted to certain crops.

While the original Agricultural Adjustment Act was later declared unconstitutional, the principle of supply control was carried over into subsequent legislation including the Agricultural Adjustment Act of 1938. This act, although much amended, has provided the legal authority for price-support and supply-control programs for such commodities as wheat, cotton, rice, tobacco, and peanuts over most of the past three decades.

The decision to support or not to support the price of a particular commodity is inescapably influenced by political as well as economic considerations. Votes cannot be ignored in deciding which commodities to support and what means should be used to make supports effective.

Partly for political and partly for economic reasons, the United States has created a highly selective support system.

✦

AUTHOR KENNETH L. ROBINSON is Professor of Agricultural Economics at Cornell University, Ithaca, N.Y.

Commodities which account fo about half the total cash receipts farmers have been supported directl although at widely varying level while the remainder have not.

Major commodities supported hav been grains, cotton, tobacco, peanut soybeans, wool, sugar, and dai products. Other livestock produc including beef, pork, poultry, an eggs, as well as fruits and vegetable have received little if any direct sup port. Nor has any attempt been mad to control production of the latte group of commodities. However, price of the "non-supported" commoditi have been influenced indirectly b support programs on grains and, i some cases, by government purchas programs or marketing orders.

The farm products supported in tially, sometimes referred to as "bas commodities" (wheat, corn, cotto rice, tobacco, and peanuts), wei among those most adversely affecte by the loss of markets in the 1930' These commodities also are the on which account for a high proportio of the total cash receipts of farmers i areas most strongly represented in th House and Senate committees whic traditionally have dealt with agr cultural matters.

Supports have been maintaine almost continuously over the past 3 years on wheat, cotton, rice, tobacc and peanuts, in part because a larg proportion of growers have accepte the principle of limiting the acreag which could be planted to these crop In contrast, the majority of farmei selling livestock products have bee strongly opposed to controls on pro duction.

No attempt has been made in recen years to maintain support prices fo perishable commodities other tha dairy products. The reluctance of bot Congress and the Secretary of Agri culture to become involved in attempt ing to support the prices of commodi ties which are difficult or costly t store can be traced in part to the brie experience with support programs ol eggs and potatoes in the 1940's.

Above, harvesting rice in Rapides Parish, La.
Right, cutting sugarcane in Puerto Rico.

Support prices were sufficiently attractive at that time to encourage producers to increase output. The Government was forced to store eggs, and some of these eventually spoiled. At times, the Government also found it necessary to destroy part of the potato crop. The high cost and adverse publicity that accompanied these programs led Congress to abandon supports on eggs and potatoes just prior to the Korean War.

While the prices of most of the items that go into the home refrigerator (other than milk and dairy products) have not been supported directly by the Federal Government during the last two decades, the prices of such commodities as beef, pork, eggs, turkeys, apples, and citrus fruit probably have been influenced to a very modest degree at times by Government purchase programs. These purchases have occurred mostly in years when supplies have been excessive and prices relatively low.

In some cases, subsidies also have been paid to assist marketing firms in diverting part of the surplus to secondary markets, especially overseas. Funds used for this purpose are often called "Section 32" funds. The designation refers to the relevant section of an act passed in 1935 which commits Congress to set aside each year an amount of money equal to 30 percent of all customs receipts for use by the Secretary of Agriculture in removing surplus commodities.

The amount of money which the Secretary of Agriculture has available to make direct purchases or to assist exports of perishable commodities is not sufficient to influence prices very significantly. If all the funds were used, no more than about 2 percent of the total value of all perishable commodities could be purchased in any one year.

The Secretary also is prohibited by law from spending more than 25 percent of the money on any one commodity. Furthermore, he cannot initiate a purchase program unless there are outlets available which will not compete with normal commercial sales. Commodities purchased with Section 32 funds are most often donated to schools and other public institutions or to families receiving public assistance.

Since the Korean War, four major changes have been made in commodity programs: First, price-support loan rates (which strongly influence market prices in years of large production) have been reduced in order to make U.S. farm products more competitive with substitutes and to avoid the need for export subsidies; second, surplus disposal programs have been liberalized; third, land retirement programs have been introduced in order to reduce the total area planted to crops; and finally, payment programs have been added—especially for the feed grains, wheat, and cotton—in order to compensate farmers for lower market prices and to induce farmers to participate in the land-retirement programs.

At the beginning of World War II,

119

support prices were raised to provide incentives for farmers to increase production. Relatively high support prices were maintained all during the 1940's and early 1950's for grains, cotton, and dairy products. During the war and for a brief period immediately thereafter, prices remained above support levels. But in the early 1950's, surpluses began to accumulate at support prices. This was due in part to rapid changes in agricultural technology. At the same time, export markets began to sag as production in Europe recovered.

This forced the Secretary of Agriculture to reimpose acreage allotments on wheat, corn, and cotton. However, increases in crop yields continued to offset a substantial part of the effects of reduced acreages. In addition, some of the land taken out of allotment crops was planted to noncontrolled crops like soybeans, barley, and grain sorghum, which led to surpluses of these commodities.

The problem might have been solved by further cuts in acreage (to compensate for higher yields), but the Secretary of Agriculture was denied this authority by Congress which imposed a lower limit on national allotments for wheat and cotton. Eventually, however, Congress did accede to the request of Secretary Benson for authority to reduce support prices on the major surplus commodities.

Efforts were made in the mid-1950's to halt the buildup of surpluses, not only by imposing acreage allotments, but also by encouraging exports through various forms of government assistance, including export subsidies. Beginning in 1954, the sale of surplus commodities for foreign currencies as well as donations for relief were authorized under Public Law 480, later known as the "Food for Peace Act." But even with this additional assistance, exports failed to rise by enough to eliminate surpluses.

It became apparent in the 1950's that the United States was faced with the problem of excess capacity for agriculture as a whole, not simpl[y] too much wheat and cotton.

To cope with this problem, Congre[ss] authorized a series of voluntary lan[d] retirement schemes, beginning fir[st] with the Soil Bank program in 195[6]. Under this and succeeding program[s] including the Feed Grain and Cro[p] land Adjustment programs of th[e] 1960's, farmers have been paid [to] keep idle between 40 and 60 millio[n] acres of land that otherwise mig[ht] have been planted to crops.

The United States is unique amon[g] major agricultural exporting natio[ns] in having made a determined effo[rt] to reduce the area planted to grai[n] and cotton during the decade of th[e] 1960's.

The use of direct government pa[y]ments to augment the incomes [of] farmers, especially those producin[g] wheat, cotton, and feed grains, ro[se] dramatically in the 1960's. Towar[d] the end of the decade, these paymen[ts] amounted to nearly $3 billion annuall[y] and contributed approximately 7 pe[r] cent to the cash receipts of farmers.

The decision to rely more on pa[y]ments from the Treasury to maintai[n] the incomes of farmers rather tha[n] high price-support loan rates w[as] based on two considerations: Firs[t,] by pursuing a more moderate pri[ce] policy, the government hoped to mak[e] U.S. farm products more competitiv[e] on world markets; and second, b[y] offering cash payments, it hoped t[o] induce substantial numbers of farme[rs] to participate in the voluntary whea[t,] cotton, and feed grain programs th[at] had been adopted in the mid-1960'[s.]

These programs were introduce[d] after attempts to enact compulsor[y] supply-adjustment programs had bee[n] rejected either by Congress or b[y] growers. Price-support payments un[der] the wheat, cotton, and feed grai[n] programs have been made only t[o] those farmers who agree to keep [a] certain proportion of land idle.

Acceptance of price-support pa[y]ments has made it possible to main[tain] much lower market prices f[or] grains and cotton in recent years. As

120

result of the shift to payment programs, export subsidies have been reduced or eliminated. Market prices of grains and cotton in the United States during the late 1960's were very competitive with those of other major exporting countries. One of the objectives of reducing the loan rate for cotton has been to help regain markets lost to synthetic fibers. Farmers have been compensated for cuts in loan rates by direct government payments.

The historical record of the past third of a century indicates clearly that it is possible to use agricultural commodity programs as a means of transferring income from the nonfarm sector of society to agriculture. But it has not been possible to guarantee farmers full price parity, at least as defined in legislation adopted in the early 1930's. The parity standard is based on the relationship between the prices received and those paid by farmers in the period just preceding World War I.

Despite widespread government intervention in production and pricing farm products in the 1960's, farm prices during the decade averaged slightly below 80 percent of parity. Even with adjustments for price-support payments the ratio averaged in the low eighties.

Agricultural commodity programs have helped to stabilize as well as to raise the average level of farm prices over much of the past two decades. At times consumers have been forced to pay more for food because of our support policies, but at other times they have benefited from lower prices due to the presence of large reserves. Society as a whole has gained from support programs insofar as they have helped to create an environment favorable to innovation and investment in agriculture. Some of the additional money pumped into agriculture through commodity programs has been used to finance improvements which ultimately have led to larger farm output and lower market prices. Some of these benefits have been passed on to agribusiness firms who produce and distribute fertilizer, agricultural chemicals, and farm machinery.

A number of food deficit countries, likewise, have shared, at least indirectly, in the benefits of our support programs. It is doubtful if Congress would have been so generous in providing food aid if large surpluses of agricultural commodities had not first been accumulated. These, of course, were largely a byproduct of the price-support loan and storage program maintained during the 1950's.

Gains from commodity support programs have been very unequally distributed among farmers and regions. Most of the direct benefits have gone to those producing grains, cotton, tobacco, peanuts, and dairy products. Regionally, the direct or "first-round" benefits have been concentrated in the Great Plains, the South and the Corn Belt. These clearly are the areas that would be most vulnerable if support programs were to be eliminated. In the late 1960's between 10 and 15 percent of gross farm income in such states as Texas, Oklahoma, Kansas, Arkansas, and Mississippi came from government checks.

The top third of all farmers have obtained a large fraction of the benefits of support programs. This has occurred, not because programs were deliberately "rigged" to assist large farmers, but simply because these are the farms which account for over 80 percent of the value of all farm products sold. Gains from price-support and payment programs have been distributed among farmers roughly in proportion to sales.

Small farmers, especially those producing cotton and tobacco, have shared slightly more than proportionately in government price-support and payment programs during the past ten years. But the additional amount of money made available to low-income farmers has been limited primarily because they have so little to sell.

Over a period of years, the gains from the farm programs have had a tendency to become capitalized into the value of farms with allotments or bases. Farms with tobacco or cotton allotments, for example, have generally sold for much more than similar farms without allotments.

The original owners of farms with allotments have been the primary beneficiaries of commodity programs insofar as possible future gains have become capitalized into the price of farmland. New owners have been forced to pay for the privilege of continuing to receive higher prices or government payments.

The capitalization of farm program benefits makes it difficult to reduce the degree of support. Those purchasing farms with allotments or bases have been reluctant to accept changes which would result in low prices or reduced land values.

Producers of nonsupported commodities such as beef, pork, fruits, and vegetables often claim that they have been adversely affected by the programs that have been adopted to maintain the prices of grains, oilseed crops, and cotton. But it is not clear precisely what the net effects have been on producers of perishable commodities. To the degree that cropland has been kept idle rather than diverted to nonsupported crops, they probably have gained indirectly from support programs.

In the absence of such programs, some additional land undoubtedly would have been shifted to the production of beef, but it is unlikely that very much of the land kept idle under the wheat, cotton, and feed grain programs would have been used to produce fruits or vegetables.

Prices of livestock products probably have been enhanced somewhat as a result of support programs on grains. Whether or not this has been sufficient to compensate for higher feed costs which have been a byproduct of such programs is more difficult to determine.

In the absence of support programs on grains and oilseed crops, there is no doubt that more of these crops would have been available to feed livestock in the 1960's. This, in turn, would have led to increased production and lower prices for meat animals, milk, eggs, and poultry.

Agricultural commodity programs have had only a modest influence on the rate at which farmers have left agriculture. Apparently benefits from support programs have not been sufficient to keep many small farmers in business.

Without commodity programs, the squeeze on incomes in the 1950's and 1960's undoubtedly would have been more severe and this might have forced additional farm operators to leave. However, studies which have been made of migration from agriculture show clearly that the pull of nonfarm jobs is a much more critical variable affecting off-farm movement than the push of low incomes.

An increasing proportion of the income of small-scale farmers comes from off-farm jobs and many of them produce nonsupported commodities, which means that changes in commodity programs have only a marginal effect on their net incomes. The farms most vulnerable to changes in commodity programs are the large scale producers of such crops as wheat, cotton, and corn.

Some additional consolidation of farms might have occurred in the absence of commodity programs, but it is unlikely that this would have materially reduced the total number of farm families.

Agricultural commodity policies adopted during the 1950's and 1960's had both a positive and negative effect on total output and efficiency. Support programs during this period undoubtedly encouraged farmers to apply more fertilizer and to adopt other practices which resulted in higher yields per acre. But the effect of higher prices on both total output and efficiency was offset in part by the allotment and land retirement programs.

In some areas, such programs delayed land use adjustments. As an example, in the absence of acreage allotments, the area planted to cotton undoubtedly would have declined more rapidly in the Southeastern States and increased in the irrigated areas of the West. On the fringes of the Great Plains and parts of the South, commodity programs also provided incentives for farmers to keep land in supported crops that otherwise might have been shifted to grass or forestry.

Whatever the effects on individual commodities, it is clear that agricultural commodity programs have not seriously interfered with overall gains in productivity in agriculture over the past two decades. Between 1950 and 1968, for example, output per man-hour in agriculture rose more than twice as fast as in manufacturing. The acreage harvested over this 18-year period declined about 13 percent while total output increased nearly 40 percent.

It is perhaps appropriate at this time, after reviewing more than 30 years of government efforts to improve farm prices and incomes, to attempt to draw some conclusions from this experience.

First, one must recognize that there are very practical limits to the amount by which farm prices and incomes can be raised through government action. These constraints are imposed by Congress which has shown great reluctance to appropriate unlimited sums for support activities and by farmers who have refused to accept tight controls on production or sales.

Second, voluntary land retirement programs can be used to achieve a tolerable balance between supply and demand, provided support prices are only moderately above those that could be expected to prevail in the absence of government intervention. Such programs cost more than compulsory supply controls, but are much more acceptable to farmers.

Third, unless commodity programs are divorced from historical patterns of production or current output, they can do little to help the low-income farmers. Such programs can be used successfully to increase the incomes of commercial farmers, at least in the short run, but they are an inappropriate means of altering the distribution of income among farmers.

Fourth, unless some method can be found to prevent potential gains from being capitalized into the value of farms, subsequent owners will gain relatively little from commodity support programs. Most of the benefits will accrue to the original owners of farms with bases or allotments.

Finally, it is apparent that programs once adopted tend to persist. Congress has demonstrated over a period of more than 30 years that it is easier to retain support programs than to drop them. Changes that occur are usually forced by external events, such as the buildup of excessive stocks, loss of markets, a series of short crops, or pressure to cut government costs.

Whether or not Congress will decide to continue commodity support programs similar to those which were in effect during the late 1960's will depend very much on future demand and supply prospects for agriculture.

If world food shortages develop, one can expect considerable relaxation of controls on production and less support for agriculture. But if, as seems more likely, the United States will be confronted with the problem of excess productive capacity, some kind of supply adjustment program probably will be retained. The alternative is to reduce support prices or payments rather substantially. However, this approach has little appeal, particularly among influential members of the Senate and House agricultural committees.

The future of commodity programs also will depend on the political climate. The number of active supporters of farm programs in Congress obviously is shrinking. For this reason, it would be quite unrealistic to expect that the producers of wheat, cotton, and feed grains will be treated as favorably in the future as they have been in the past.

FOOD FOR ALL
IN NEED GETS
TOP PRIORITY

THE DECADE OF THE SEVENTIES must see the end of hunger and malnutrition in America. The people of this Nation have irrevocably committed themselves to reaching this goal.

Over a year ago, President Nixon in his landmark message to Congress on May 6, 1969, said: "That hunger and malnutrition should persist in a land such as ours is embarrassing and intolerable." He spelled out the most comprehensive, ambitious plan to put an end to hunger among the American people ever put forward by any administration.

"It is a program that will build on operations already in progress to combat malnutrition. We are not starting from scratch," said Secretary of Agriculture Clifford M. Hardin. "We are working to streamline and expand existing food help programs so they will better meet the need for improved nutrition."

An important first step was the setting up of the Food and Nutrition Service which brought all of the U.S. Department of Agriculture's family and child nutrition programs under one roof and gave them new priority and focus. For these programs to be truly effective in providing food for the hungry they must work as a coordinated package reaching people in need wherever they are in the community—at home, at school, at day care centers and summer recreation programs, at senior citizen centers.

This national drive to end hunger gained fresh momentum at the White House Conference on Food, Nutrition, and Health, which convened in December 1969 to forge a new national policy on food and nutrition.

The 3,400 or so people who attended that conference—including food executives, migrant workers, Indians, business leaders, representatives of the poor, school lunch officials, welfare recipients, dietitians, lawyers, doctors, scientists—again brought to public attention the urgent immediate food needs of the poor. The thoughtful, sometimes brilliant recommendations that came out of that conference may well affect the eating habits of all of us in the seventies.

In the first year of this decade we gained a foothold on overcoming some of the basic obstacles in the way of meeting food needs of the poor.

Progress in extending family food help across the Nation has been matched by equally dramatic progress in the child nutrition field. At the beginning of the last school year a goal was set to reach 6.6 million poor school children with food service. That meant doubling the number of needy children served the year before, and reaching virtually every school-age child in need of better nutrition.

Congress appropriated funds to get the job done through the 24-year-old National School Lunch Program, which provides food and cash assistance and high nutrition standards to help over two-thirds of the Nation's schools serve their children good low-cost lunches. Over the years, Congress has amended the National School Lunch Act to provide higher reimbursements and needed equipment to low-income area schools.

This has made the school lunch program a workable delivery system for bringing food help to needy school children. It proved its value during the last school year as Federal, State, and local school lunch officials pooled their skills and ingenuity to bring food service to schools which had

✦

AUTHOR EDWARD J. HEKMAN is Administrator of the Food and Nutrition Service.

previously been unreachable because they were in isolated rural areas or in crowded ghetto areas of large cities. Many were schools that had been built with no kitchens or cafeterias.

Children attending these schools sometimes went all day—restless or listless—with nothing to eat, then perhaps a candy bar or soft drink on the way home would soothe the hunger pangs.

That picture is changing rapidly. With the help of the National School Lunch Program, local school officials are making use of modern technological advances, new management techniques to open central kitchens which serve not just one but several schools with hot and cold nutritious meals.

Philadelphia, Baltimore, Indianapolis, Boston, Pittsburgh, Chicago, and Cleveland are just a few of the cities making dramatic advances in feeding needy children this way.

Before Indianapolis opened its central kitchen almost a year ago, none of the city's schools had been taking part in USDA's National School Lunch Program. The new central kitchen, which was built in a former soft drink bottling plant, soon brought hot and cold pack lunches to children in 27 surrounding schools and there were plans for further growth of its service.

How this kitchen came about illustrates the kind of Federal, State, and local cooperation needed to get food to people in need. The owner of the bottling plant sold his facility to the Indianapolis city government for only 15 percent of its assessed value. USDA, with funds and authority under the school lunch program, put up 75 percent of the necessary costs to buy equipment needed to prepare the lunches. USDA also provides a substantial cash reimbursement and donated foods which help meet the program's food costs.

State and local governments finance most of the remaining costs of the Indianapolis lunch program, including labor. The city schools are finding that using a modern central kitchen system helps hold labor costs down. At the same time the central kitchen can bring new jobs into an area.

A worker in the bright, modern Indianapolis kitchen said, "I'm so glad I got a chance to work here. My friend told me the kitchen was coming and I asked for a job right away."

Lunch service can also mean parttime work in the receiving schools for non-professional aides who are often employed to help serve and supervise the children during lunchtime. Or, in some areas, parent volunteers help out at lunchtime.

Increasingly, schools are also providing breakfast for their students who arrive at school hungry, either because they come from homes too poor to provide breakfast, or travel a long distance to school.

The School Breakfast Program, although small in relation to the National School Lunch Program, has more than doubled the number of children it serves for the past couple of years.

Federal contributions of food and cash help provide nutritious breakfasts of fruit or juice, milk, bread or cereal, and eggs or meat, served as often as possible. Most of the breakfasts served are free or at reduced cost to needy children.

In addition, USDA can help communities serve nutritious meals to groups of children in out-of-school programs—such as day care centers, summer recreation programs, and settlement houses.

The two-year-old Special Child Food Service Program offers needed flexibility in reaching under-nourished children, by providing Federal donations of food and cash to help provide up to three meals a day and between meal snacks, along with financial aid to buy equipment.

So far, the heaviest use of this aid had tended to be in summer recreation programs, which make use of existing school cafeterias to provide food for needy youngsters who get no school lunch during vacations.

125

More and more non-profit day care centers are joining the program as they grow in number and develop their capability for food service. This young and growing food service program provides room to innovate, to bring new kinds of food service to youngsters not helped before.

A teen-age boys club in Gary, Ind., began getting to some of the toughest kids on the street with supper served every evening after school.

Last summer, a Maine farmer invited the local recreation department to bring a group of needy youngsters to the farm for their summer program, complete with cookouts and picnics, produced with the help of the Special Food Service Program.

Altogether the Federal, State, and local expenses for the Child Nutrition programs come to something over $2 billion. The lion's share of the food, more than $1 billion worth, is bought by local school systems from local suppliers. That means a going market for food distributors and food producers all over the Nation.

While food service for children is being improved and expanded we must continue putting a tremendous amount of push behind food programs designed to bring better nutrition to the whole family including the aged, the sick, mothers, and infants.

These are critical areas of concern, and we have continued working to improve and modify the kind of help available under USDA's Food Stamp and Commodity Distribution Programs to better meet nutrition needs of the poor.

President Nixon underscored the need for change when he said, "Let's face it, for years, food programs were designed as much to get rid of surplus commodities as to feed hungry people. Now for the first time, we propose that every American family shall have the resources in food stamps, commodities and other assistance to obtain a minimum nutritious diet with free food stamps for those with very low income."

We believe that food stamps are the preferable form of family food help and plan a gradual phasing out of the direct distribution of commodities to

Children enjoy school lunch in Fulton County, Ga.

With food obtained through food stamps, mother feeds 2-year-old on Maryland's Eastern Shore. She credits program with helping daughter become strong enough to pull herself up in her crib.

families except in emergencies or other specialized situations.

Stamps offer the family a free choice to buy foods that suit their cultural patterns, individual food tastes, and special nutrition needs. Food stamp shoppers can spend their coupons at regular retail stores just like other consumers.

Food stamps put low-income families on a cash and carry basis with their local grocers—no more back bills and credit that soon runs out.

Stamps mean good business for local stores and an economic shot in the arm to an area where people are poor and business is slow. The stamp plan makes use of this Nation's great commercial food distribution system which a Government food distribution system can't begin to duplicate.

We look upon the stamp plan as a step toward a system of family assistance which will provide low-income families with a basic floor under their income and which will not rob them of the incentive to work, nor force families to break apart. These have been tragic flaws in the kind of welfare assistance available in recent years.

To work toward a comprehensive approach to the income problems of the poor, benefits available under the Food Stamp Program must be complementary to any family assistance system. By giving poor families an opportunity to take part in both programs at once we can provide them with added income and a chance to allocate a fixed portion of this income to food.

In each program, the assistance is reduced on a gradual basis as income rises, so that the incentive to work is preserved. Then as income reaches a level above the poverty line, both cash and food stamp assistance are phased out.

For the immediate future the first priority must be put on meeting the nutritional needs of the poor and hungry, using every available delivery system—including direct distribution of commodities along with the Food Stamp and Child Nutrition Programs.

This year the Food Stamp Program has greatly enlarged its capacity to help meet the food needs of low-income families. For fiscal year 1970 Congress appropriated $610 million for the Food Stamp Program about halfway into the fiscal year (which ran from July 1, 1969, to the end of last June).

Since most of the increase was committed to expanding the program to new areas and improving benefits to families during the latter half of the year, the Food Stamp Program was actually spending at the rate of $1 billion annually by last June 30, or over three times the annual rate of spending the previous year.

With these additional funds, the Food Stamp Program was expanded to new counties and cities, many of which had never had a food program before. The major step was taken of providing every family participating in the program with enough stamps to pay for a minimum adequate diet, USDA's economy level diet.

Coupon allotments are set at a uniform level nationally. For a family of four this amounts to $106 in food stamps, compared to the previous minimum of $58 for that same family. The amount the family has to pay for the stamps has also been reduced in line with requirements of the Food Stamp Act that the family's payment must be about what they normally spend for food.

These improvements in program benefits, plus an accelerated outreach effort in local food stamp areas to tell low-income families about the changes in the program, have greatly increased the number of people participating.

Every means is being used to encourage the counties and cities responsible for interviewing applicants and issuing food stamps, to make improvements in their part of the operations to help serve families better.

Many permit families to buy stamps twice a month or even four times a month to avoid one monthly payment that is hard to scrape together. And many have opened up neighborhood food stamp application offices, close to the people they serve.

Other local governments have begun mailing food stamp coupons to eligible families, to save them a trip to the bank or an issuing office. Los Angeles County inaugurated a system of bringing the "food stamp" bank to the recipient families' neighborhood, via armored truck.

Many areas have volunteer groups who serve as "proxies" for invalids and shut-ins who can't get out to buy their stamps or shop for groceries.

Areas operating the Commodity Distribution Program as an interim step to food stamps are also adopting new measures to make the nutritious foods available under the program accessible to more families in a dignified, convenient manner.

Many localities have not had the facilities or staff to handle all foods available under the commodity pro-

gram, in the quantities recommended by USDA. So USDA has initiated a financial assistance plan to help share some of the local food storage and administrative costs with those counties and cities least able to carry the load alone.

The aid is apportioned among the States on an equitable basis, to be used in areas that present workable plans for improving food help to their low-income families.

In some areas this may mean opening more distribution centers in convenient locations with more flexible hours, as Nassau County, N.Y., did without Federal help about a year ago. Within 3 months their store front operations, open every weekday and some on weekends, were serving twice as many low-income families as the program did before. And former welfare recipients got paying jobs in the donated food stores.

A section of New York City opened a self-service style "donated food store," in which recipients can choose for themselves the foods they want to take home, within their monthly allotment.

Other parts of the country serving the rural poor have begun mobile distribution by truck or bus to take food help into remote corners of America where it's needed.

These are only samples of the ingenuity and effort it will take to wipe out hunger in this vast and complex Nation.

Besides the regular family food help programs, the Food and Nutrition Service has a program of supplemental food help for expectant mothers and young children, to help counter the risk of hunger and malnutrition in this very vulnerable group.

In most of the 300 or more areas operating the program, selected nutritious and fortified foods are distributed to mothers and their children on the advice of local health officials. But the logistical problems of this method have hampered the widespread use of the program.

So early this year a series of pilot

projects were launched to test a food certificate method of getting selected nutritious foods to expectant mothers and their infants through private markets. The first project opened in a section of the South Side of Chicago.

Low-income expectant mothers and mothers with infants can get, through neighborhood welfare centers, free books of coupons, which can be spent for selected foods such as milk, fortified baby cereal, and prepared baby formula at neighborhood drug stores or food stores.

This supplementary help is available to mothers already getting food stamps or other public assistance, as well as to others needing better nutrition. Hopefully, the test of the food certificate plan will lead to an effective way to guard against poverty-caused malnutrition among young children.

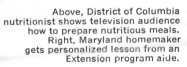

Above, District of Columbia nutritionist shows television audience how to prepare nutritious meals. Right, Maryland homemaker gets personalized lesson from an Extension program aide.

One thing we do know about overcoming malnutrition is that it usually isn't enough to merely deliver food assistance. There is widespread need for training and education, not just for the poor but for all income levels. But lack of knowledge works a special hardship on the poor family because they have no leeway in their food budgets for mistakes or bad buys.

Many of these people, in fact, do a remarkably good job of using their limited resources to feed their families. But others are at a great disadvantage because they don't know even the basics of good nutrition. They may be young and inexperienced. They may have moved away from their home territory to unfamiliar surroundings, where even the language is strange.

Recognizing this problem, Congress about 2 years ago began appropriating a special fund for an educational program that talks the language of the poor. Conducted by the Extension Service, the expanded nutrition program hired some 5,500 nonprofessional program aides from hard to reach low-income areas in every State.

These aides—who make personal visits to families in their own area, conduct neighborhood meetings, even go shopping with some homemakers— have reported remarkable success stories of improving family diets and, in fact, their way of life. This program, which has increasing support from Congress, is being surveyed and closely monitored to learn where and how it is most effective in helping the poor get the maximum nutrition for their dollars.

Certainly the experiences of these program aides, working close to home, show the importance of concerted local action to bring about real improvement in the nutritional status of the poor. In fact, the Nation's drive to end hunger and malnutrition cannot be successful without strong leadership and concerned action by States and local communities.

The private sector has an important stake in this campaign, too. Churches, civic groups, businessmen, food industry leaders, farmers, civil right groups, labor organizations, and others are putting their knowledge and efforts behind this humanitarian drive to bring good nutrition to every child and family in America.

DEVELOPING FARM POLICY: THERE IS MORE TO IT THAN YOU MIGHT THINK

THE DEVELOPMENT of farm programs hinges on the question of what is the "best" agricultural policy, a complex subject involving political and social pressure, urban as well as rural people. An effective up-to-date agricultural policy requires decision makers to undertake a continual reassessment of national needs and opportunities, studying which groups in society share the benefits and which the costs of their programs.

The goals of agricultural policy are fairly straightforward: to produce enough food and fiber for domestic needs and for exchange or aid abroad; to furnish an adequate level of income for farm people and provide for its equitable distribution among producers and workers; and to achieve these production, trade, and income objectives for a minimum budgetary cost while allowing a maximum of individual freedom of choice.

Because of conflicting situations of many kinds it is sometimes difficult to attain these well-accepted goals. For example, complete freedom of action by farmers may not result in conditions leading to a wise land and water use policy in the eyes of the rest of society.

The benefits and costs of economic growth and development, including agriculture, are distributed unevenly throughout the Nation. There are differences in regional shares as well as among the people in a region partly because technology and the changes it causes in product and resource markets is an uneven process.

The risks and uncertainty for producers and workers in a rapidly developing agriculture contribute to pressures aimed at both aiding markets to function more effectively, and devising programs which help people who have trouble making necessary economic and social adjustments to market actions.

Our overall agricultural policy includes programs directed to commodities, land and water use, credit, youth, homemaking, forests, electricity, education, and pesticides. While there are many more aspects, these are enough to see the program breadth that makes it difficult to decide which combination of programs best serves the national interest.

General criticisms about agricultural policy are that it's too narrow in scope, too costly, does not produce enough farm income nor distribute it "equitably," and disrupts "normal" marketing channels.

Successful critics and designers of agricultural policy must possess several qualities. They must be able to answer questions about the economic and social consequences of their programs to rural and urban people. They should be able to explain the effect of their plans on our markets, and whether (or how much) government "intervention" is necessary to achieve the basic policy goals. They need also to recognize that some policies can hold people and resources in undesirable situations, while other more flexible policies let them move freely into and out of agriculture.

✦

AUTHOR L. T. WALLACE is an economist with the Agricultural Extension Service, University of California, Berkeley. He is a former senior staff economist on the Council of Economic Advisors.

Initially, some of the strongest pressures underlying the development of agricultural policies were counteractions to unemployment, economic depression, and losses in international trade. The removal of price uncertainty and the goal of income stability were tied to concepts like the family farm, parity, and conservation.

Government farm program payments were essentially tied to land and commodities. Rapid technological transformation of farming increased production and income differences between large and small farms. Payments dependent on production, or production potential, did not erase these differences.

How much should the Government step into the "free" market process to change income distribution effects? How much should it help to create countervailing powers among the producers, processors, and consumer groups?

Slowly policy makers began to understand that commodity prices supported above free market levels did not necessarily result in higher net farm incomes because the higher prices were quickly absorbed into increased costs of farming, nor did price supports themselves guarantee an equitable distribution of farm income.

After concentrating on commodity programs to achieve income and price stability goals for over 20 years, some policy pressures were shifted to land as possibly being the critical factor. It was thought that if only enough land could be withdrawn from production purposes, supplies might be limited enough to draw reasonable prices on farm markets. In addition, surplus crops in storage during the 1950's might be reduced.

Further, the farm income distribution picture might be brightened if foreign food aid programs were introduced, domestic food distribution programs broadened and liberalized, and development and planning loans and grants for rural communities emphasized.

The major farm organizations, the

131

commodity groups, and others began to reassess their positions. New farm organizations were created.

Throughout the 1950's it became increasingly apparent that it was virtually impossible for commodity programs to handle effectively both the commercial farm and social welfare problem aspects in agriculture. There was a continuing policy difficulty of linking program activities to program goals.

For example, the land retirement program payments of the 1950's and 1960's have, in effect, been personal income supplements more than they have been production controls. This was partly as a result of increasing technology and its rapid adoption, partly because the programs did not remove sufficient acreage, and partly because much of the acreage removed was not very productive.

Although voluntary program participation was the "freedom" goal, mandatory acreage diversions (an attempt to control production) were required for price support payments. Additional payments were made to farmers who wished to withdraw acreage above the mandatory minimum from production. However, by the end of the 1960's, land retirement programs had not solved either the economic or the social effects of excessive farm production. It should be said, however, that without these land programs the severity of market forces could have been more pronounced on all farmers.

What are some pressure points within agriculture that help guide its policy course? One focus is a desire for local control stemming from the belief that decisions made on the "home ground" are better than those made elsewhere. This feeling has led to a proliferation of pressure points from county committees, State committees, regional committees, commodity groups, farm business groups, and farm organizations each having its own set of "local" pressures.

The achievements expected from agricultural policy have varied over the last 30 years. For example, in the 1920's the farm sector was in a depression while industry and the stock market boomed. Due to the fact that no single farmer, no matter how large his farm, could influence the market, agriculture looked to government to bring about a redistribution of national income through the market place or by special programs.

In the 1930's, farm policies, including the Agricultural Adjustment Act of 1933, were developed on the basis of establishing a farm-nonfarm price parity which it was hoped would restore the purchasing power of agricultural commodities to a 1910–14 level. This particular philosophy, though amended, is still with us. Marketing quotas, production incentives, acreage allotments, and efforts to raise the nutritional level of the poor (thereby disposing of surplus commodities) were also initiated at this time.

Price parity was not easily attainable, and so the 1930's and 1940's saw growing pressure for a parity between farm and nonfarm incomes as well as prices. However, the administrative implementation of this concept never materialized. During World War II, the need for maximum food production, the existence of higher farm prices, and a generally restored economy reduced the immediacy of the need to help farm people.

Also, during this same period school lunch and special milk programs were expanded. The concept of national emergency food and fiber reserves was reexamined. And the Nation began to stir to the challenges of increasing foreign trade.

During the 1950's, spurred partly by the lack of success in gaining a parity of either income or price, increasing attention was paid to a parity of return to labor and capital in farming compared to their returns in other jobs and uses throughout the economy.

Up to the mid-1950's agricultural payment policy had concerned itself almost exclusively with attempts at control of production. Compensatory payments were based either on production or on land use, not on the needs of rural people.

Although the ideas go back to the late 1930's, President Eisenhower in 1954 asked the U.S. Department of Agriculture (USDA) for a study of rural people, their needs and development opportunities. In 1956 the Rural Development Program (RDP), a nonfunded program, was established. In 1961 the Rural Areas Development (RAD) Program, now funded, superseded RDP. Since then increasing attention has been paid to policies directed at the needs of rural people.

A special note in the development of agricultural policy is that there has never been any extended social pressure against farmers because of high retail food costs, or because farm prices were judged too high. Consumers have generally believed that the Government is really trying to keep food costs relatively low while helping maintain a reasonable level of farm income. This belief has been bolstered by legislation concerned with full employment, minimum wages, increases and extension of welfare programs and Social Security, health and education measures.

Price and income effects of agricultural policies and the debate on how much we should rely on "free" markets are important. But factors showing perhaps more influence on policy toward the end of the 1960's are the social and economic costs of people and communities as they adjust to changes in farming, overall Federal budgetary expenditure levels, and a growing ability of people to identify and express desired social equity.

The polar positions of free markets versus mandatory production and price controls have been rejected by the majority of farmers and Congress.

Besides the pressures already mentioned, agricultural policies will be developed which will consider: How quickly should (or can) support price levels be reduced? How much mandatory production compliance or acreage diversion should be required for program participation? Is land retirement worth the cost? Will tenants, managers, and hired workers be helped or hurt by new policies? Should there be a limit upon government payments going to any one farmer? How can State or Federal health, welfare, and education programs best be coordinated with agricultural policies? And how can State and Federal employment policies be made more effective in rural areas?

Development programs have often been viewed as active competitors for limited budget funds by many people living where adjustment or poverty situations are not particularly evident. However, many urban residents concerned about their housing, education, welfare, health, and pollution problems recognize similar situations in rural areas.

Such recognition has led to increased pressures for more creative approaches to help people solve their "development-adjustment" problems. The Departments of Commerce, Labor, Health, Education, and Welfare (HEW), and Agriculture have been urged to coordinate their education and training programs as well as putting more emphasis into a broadened nutrition and food distribution program.

Growth and evolving roles of governmental agencies have also caused other changes in the development of agricultural policies. For example, the Bureau of the Budget and the Council of Economic Advisors must now counsel and advise with USDA on major price or program changes. Until a few years ago, the Secretary of Agriculture did not need to do this.

As another example, the Departments of State and Commerce may be vitally concerned about the use of food aid as a complement to foreign relations and international economic development. Continued massive food aid efforts and Public Law 480 which have only existed since the early 1950's, may have profound international and domestic implications.

133

The land-grant colleges feel they, too, deserve a voice in determining agricultural policy because of the increased professionalism and capabilities of their research, teaching, and outreach functions.

Fewer numbers of farmers with an accompanying concentration of production into fewer hands have caused an increased vulnerability of farmers and rural communities to changes in farm programs and reactions by consumers.

Focused power and better organization of farm lobbyists has led on the one hand to more efficient political and economic pressures for supported crops, and for favorable trade conditions with other countries on nonsupported agricultural items. But on the other hand, a more informed public has become aware that the rewards of "protectionism for agriculture" are not necessarily reaped by all of society.

For example, producer cooperatives have been joined over the years by consumer cooperatives, discount stores, and supermarkets. And since the early 1960's consumer interests have been explicitly represented at the White House or Cabinet level. But many people now think that food costs for the rural and urban poor still comprise "too large a share" of the family budget.

The influence of international opinion on the development of agricultural policies cannot be underestimated, whether it is a reaction to an isolationist protectionist trade policy, or whether it is for freer trade with all nations. Commercial exports of farm products have been increasingly important to the United States. In the 1960's we reached a point where the produce from one acre out of five was shipped overseas compared to almost no food trade in the 1930's.

Although the worldwide food scarcities of the 1950's have been replaced by forecasts of more adequate food supplies, at least for this century, trade and its impact upon our balance of payments is important policy-wise.

But on what basis should we trade? Do we want to trade for dollars or are we willing to take other currencies? Should we trade on a one-to-one country basis or through bilateral agreements or with blocs of countries? What about our attitude toward tariffs and food imports? Should we treat less developed nations of the world differently than we treat the more developed nations?

In summary, over the last 40 years we have seen agricultural policy move from mostly farm commodity oriented programs to an increased emphasis on farm people and community oriented programs. Since the mid-1950's more attention has been put on the income distribution aspect of agricultural policy, on the regional effects of programs, and on more analysis of who is helped by various programs, who pays the cost, and who bears the adjustment burdens.

Factors influencing the development of agricultural policy today include the changed political power structure. Reapportionment and continued fragmentation of the farm blocs of the 1930's and 1940's have rendered old groups and methods less effective than they once were in solving the problems of agricultural people.

The rise of an urban-dominated legislature makes it clearer than ever that the determinants of agricultural policy are interdependent, not independent, even though the scope and business of agriculture is growing and is much larger now than it ever was before.

While our society is increasingly aware of food needs and equity considerations of many kinds, there is also increasing skepticism of the individual's ability to influence the course of policy. So policy makers need to be surer than ever of the relevancy of the goals they espouse, more aware of the pressures that surround them, well grounded in their own philosophical approach to the problems at hand, and capable of critical analysis of their own proposals as well as those of their opponents.

Country and City—One Nation

RURAL AND URBAN,
THE INTERFACES

WHEN I WAS A FARM BOY, our mail was delivered from a rural village that has since ceased to exist. Our county seat was a town of maybe 4,000—a few more now. It claimed the grain elevator (on a railroad) to which we hauled our wheat, and the creamery where we took separated cream once a week—daily during the high school term.

The town also had the bank that held our farm mortgage, a "Carnegie" public library, the doctor who medicated our ills, and the little hospital you could get into without any advance appointment.

Country folks went to town on Saturday night to "trade" their eggs for the week's groceries and perhaps some gingham and jeans, and to visit with neighbors about crops and politics while the kids saw a movie, Mom traded kitchen recipes and gossip, and Dad bought an early Sunday paper.

On the way to town over a county road we passed by the "city" cemetery, the "city" dump, and a livestock slaughter plant, each using space in our open country.

Town folks, on the other hand, often drove into the countryside to buy fresh eggs and vegetables (in season), to attend a Wednesday night barn dance, or to accept an invitation to pick wild berries, or to hunt rabbits or pheasants in a friendly farmer's corn field.

Our township taxed its property owners for the maintenance of roads, for the support of its three one-room elementary schools (from grades one through eight), and to pay the tuition (about $125) of the rare farm boy like me who dared attend town high school. My nickname was "Farmer" from the first day. As I recall, we kids from the country numbered about 25 in a high school student body of about 500.

Our church was one of three in the open country served by the same minister.

My story could be duplicated by thousands of farm youth in hundreds of rural villages across the country.

In those days you knew that people who lived in the country were farmers, and those inside the city limits were town folk—and you could be comfortably sure of the difference—immutable facts to anyone. The interfaces between rural and urban were all neat and orderly.

Since that first brush with "urbanization," I have lived in increasingly urbanized settings—Madison, Wis., Milwaukee, Chicago, San Francisco, Washington, D.C.—and have observed the many interfaces between rural and urban.

But, what after all do we mean by the terms rural and urban? Jim Copp in a later chapter gives us several concepts of *rural*. I find others.

In *The Secular City* Harvey Cox, a theologian now at Harvard University, points out that the fortunes of rural man are closely dependent upon nature, which he takes as he finds it. And his misfortunes are dependent upon the elements—drought, hail, an early frost. Thus, his outcomes are not wholly dependent upon rural man himself. He can blame the weather, or fate.

On the other hand, cities—buildings, streets, business organizations—are wholly the creation of man, the sense Cox says in which cities are secular. If planning is poor or the streets acquire holes, man did it or let it happen. Thus, urban man is

✦

AUTHOR WARREN R. BAILEY is Deputy Director, Farm Production Economics Division, Economic Research Service.

pragmatic, does not deal in mystery, realizes that if he does not succeed he has only himself to blame.

A distinguishing concept I like, one that is functionally useful, has to do with our daily transactions. It goes like this.

Rural man's transactions are on a personal basis. He knows personally the merchant across the counter, his name, where he lives, which church he goes to, that his mother is doing poorly, his son is a star athlete, where the family came from originally, and so on. The service he gets—a quantity discount, an extension of "time," an after hour delivery—may depend upon his personal relationship with the merchant.

In contrast, urban man's transactions are on an impersonal basis. He knows not the name or the personal affairs of anyone he deals with. They are merely official agents—salesmen, claim adjusters, etc.—of the business firm or institution. But urban man does know the customary rules of daily business, and what treatment he reasonably can expect. Hence, on the whole he deals amicably, pleasantly, but firmly with others, not caring what their names are.

This view of urban society at least partly explains the difficulty of rural man when he first encounters the city, accustomed as he is to more personal relationships.

I once suggested to my colleagues that one could distinguish whether a community is rural or urban by where the people sit on a warm summer evening. Rural folks, of course, sit on their front porches so they can speak to passersby, most of whom they know. In contrast urban (and suburban) people sit on their backyard patios.

Later, I was told that ghetto people sit out front, too—possibly because they have no backyards, or possibly because they are recent migrants from a rural community. Ghetto folks, like rural man, deal more easily on personal rather than impersonal terms.

Are we two cultures—rural and urban? Not really! We have many degrees of urbanity and rurality. In a sense our suburbs are "rural" to the central cities, as are small cities to the large cities, towns to the small cities, and the open country to the towns. It is a matter of what or who is more urban or more rural than we are.

At this point we should observe that our whole society and culture is becoming more urban, whatever the criteria—that of the secular city, the impersonal transactions, or which porch people sit on.

A more mundane criterion of urbanity-rurality is density of population. For example, if we count as rural those people living in the open country and in "places under 2,500," then only a fourth of our people are rural. But they are so spread out and the urban people are so concentrated that our "land" is chiefly rural land. Let me explain.

A majority of the people in such States as New Mexico, Colorado, Wyoming, Utah, Nevada, and Arizona, actually live in cities, hence are urban. Yet, you drive across those States and they are mostly open country. Parenthetically, each State has two principal urban centers— Albuquerque and Santa Fe, Denver and Colorado Springs, Laramie and Cheyenne, Salt Lake City and Ogden, Reno-Sparks and Las Vegas, Phoenix and Tucson.

Interestingly, the number of rural people, defined as those living in places under 2,500, has changed very little in the past two or three decades. Their geographic distribution, of course, has changed somewhat but their total has not changed. Our recent growth has been wholly in urban population, an irrefutable sense in which our Nation has become more urban.

Make no mistake, the term rural is not synonymous with farm. Only a fifth of our rural population are farm operator families or farm worker families. The other rural people are shopkeepers, repairmen, school teachers, and the like, who serve farmers and each other.

Out of a U.S. civilian working force of almost 80 million, less than 4 million are classified as farmworkers.

Rural–urban migration accounted for much of the growth of the urban centers during the nineteenth and first half of the twentieth centuries. Rural migrants were welcomed by the city as willing workers, eager to learn, and generally trained in personal responsibility. Some of the rural–urban migrants were professionally educated but yet to be urbanized, such as the graduates of our agricultural colleges.

The city largely overlooked, as it easily could, the rural crudities and unsophistication of the rural migrant, made easier by the fact that most urban adults themselves had rural origins or were only one generation away from such origins.

Now there are whole urban populations with but a faint rural background or heritage or rural family relations. However, the interface between rural and urban people is made easier by the growing "urbanization" of the ruralite himself—urbanized in the sense of being able to function in his transactions impersonally, like the urbanite.

Today, the ruralites who are poorly educated, untrained, or indigent are not welcome as they once were in the central cities. In fact, they are often blamed for overcrowding, unemployment, crime in the streets, and the general deterioration of conditions of life there.

Whatever our degree of urbanity now, we have evolved from a rural society. When our people were mostly farmers, it was natural that farming and rurality dominated our economy, our society, our culture, and our politics. Presidential candidates traced their origins to a log cabin or a farm. Even villagers kept a cow, some chickens, and a horse or two.

Today the urban influence predominates in our society. This dominance, of course, is not easy because rural man has lots of time and space, a mind of his own, and has not yet quite accepted the reversal of his role,

feeling the way that he does about such basics as food and fiber.

Our Nation has, of course, become more urbanized in the social and the cultural sense because of the interaction—the interfaces—between "rural" and "urban" people, their communities, their economic activities, and their cultures.

One significant interface is that directly between individual persons—when rural man visits the city or urban man visits the open country.

My favorite example of rural man visiting the city is the cowboy named "Will" in the musical comedy "Oklahoma!" who "went to Kansas City on a Fridy" to see "what the modrin world was comin' to." To Will, Kansas City was magically, wondrously, totally urban—according to his account.

In past decades western Corn Belt farmers often rode in the train caboose on a drover's pass, as they accompanied a carload or two of their fat cattle to the Chicago market. Once there, they could take a day or two (no one need know) to see the Field Museum, a vaudeville show, a Big League baseball game—"the sights."

Rural high school students accompanied their athletic teams to the annual State tournament, held of course in a city. Rural youth were thrilled just to be there.

An example of rural man working in the city is my trash pickup man. He and two helpers drive the 40 miles of interstate highway from their rural homes each weekday to pick up trash in my suburban neighborhood and haul it back to a rural dump. There are lots of ways to earn a living.

Many rural people now commute daily from their homes in Appalachia to jobs in urban Pittsburgh, Philadelphia, Greensboro, Knoxville, Columbia, Nashville.

They continue to live in their rural (farm or nonfarm) residences because living costs are lower and "it's home." Their urbanization is now confined to the workday. Eventually they may become "urbanized" enough to move nearer their jobs, a decision hastened by the growing obsolescence of their rural family home.

Equally interesting are the interfaces in which urban man visits, works in, or moves to a rural area.

I remember well the unattached Detroit auto worker who, during the 6-week annual factory shutdown, came to our farm each summer to hire on for the wheat harvest. He ate with us, slept in the spare room, and on Sundays fished and washed his clothes in the creek.

He thought the auto assembly line was no more monotonous than driving a farm tractor. At either task your mind could drift to other things. We missed him when he stopped coming.

Somewhat earlier were the city schoolmarms who one by one migrated to the western frontier to fill the shortage of school teachers, and incidentally fill the shortage of single women. As they soon got married, the teacher shortage continued, but the education level of new frontier families was thereby augmented.

Untold numbers of urban traveling salesmen to the country are epitomized in the musical comedy, "The Music Man," whose star promoted the organization of a boys' band in River City, which (he argued) would keep the boys out of the pool hall, and incidentally let him sell band instruments and uniforms.

Let's not overlook the urbanizing influence—the interface—that reaches rural areas through the mass communication media. Rural people now hear the same radio programs, watch the same TV network programs, and read the same national magazines as urban people do. Many can and do read a metropolitan daily newspaper—though a day late. They too can listen to Arthur Fiedler and Lawrence Welk via stereo FM in their own homes.

Except in the remotest areas rural people now watch major league baseball, hear Walter Cronkite discuss the day's happenings, and see national personalities meet the press. The latest styles of the day—such as miniskirts, maxi-coats, and bellbottom slacks—appear in city shops and rural towns almost simultaneously.

In recent decades urban man by the millions has moved his residence to suburbs, rural areas, and the open country, where his presence, his affluence, and his urban attitudes have had an "urbanizing" influence.

Historian Frederick Jackson Turner credited the frontier with an assist to social progress. Man carried the customs and institutions (the only ones he knew) of his society to the frontier where some did not fit, were modified or replaced with new ones which were then carried back to be adopted by or to modify the older culture. Turner sagely observed that the original 13 colonies were once a frontier of England and the Old World.

Whether in this sense rural areas are the "frontier" of the urban is open to doubt—it could be the reverse. Today it may be the urban areas that are retesting our social institutions the most.

However defined, our urban and rural economies now maintain something of a symbiotic relationship—each complements the other, as we implied earlier. Each generates goods and services the other needs, thus becoming more interdependent. In that sense, surely, our society is becoming more integrated.

In this connection I find it useful to distinguish not two but three segments in our economic society—the farm and open country, the rural village, and the urban (city and suburbs). Let us see how the functional relations between these three segments are changing.

Of the three, the rural village is the most interesting because traditionally it has been the keystone, the connecting link between our farm and urban societies. It served both farm and city impartially and simultaneously. But its functional role is changing.

Traditionally, the rural village collected farm products and performed the initial processing, marketing, and transporting. This it still does in large degree but sometimes it is bypassed. For example, cattle and hogs are now hauled in tandem trailer trucks directly from farms in western Nebraska 350 miles overland to Omaha. Tomatoes and other vegetables in the West often are hauled directly from the farm to large processing plants a hundred miles away.

The rural village also served as a vendor of goods and services generated by the city, making them available to farmers. Farmers and villagers bought locally almost everything they needed. Increasingly this vendor function is migrating from the rural village to the regional city, where competition is keener and the choice of merchandise greater.

A farmer I know averages one trip a week via interstate highway to a city 90 miles—not much over an hour—away. That is where he does his banking, buys farm supplies, buys farm machinery and major household appliances, gets specialized medical and hospital care. While there, his family buys the week's groceries at a supermarket.

His new shopping habits are changing the function of his nearby rural village. It functions now much like the Pa-and-Ma grocery store once did in a residential neighborhood—where folks bought "what they forgot on the last trip downtown." Thus we have more rural villages than we really need, a fact now accepted in principle by many rural people as long as their village isn't the one to go.

Traditionally, the prosperity and viability of the rural village were assumed to depend upon the prosperity of the farmers it served. That was only partly correct because the rural villagers (the nonfarm population) outnumbered the farm population by 4 or 5 to one.

The Midwest is beginning to experiment with planned new rural shopping centers located in the open country—at least initially—that are equal in every respect to our modern suburban shopping centers. If this experiment succeeds as it surely must, eventually there will be 6 to 10 such farm centers per State. Those centers also could provide the locations for district or branch offices and services of State governments.

Likewise the function of our cities, particularly the central city, is also changing.

Most of our cities got their "shape" when urbanites typically had no private means of transportation . . . rode streetcars to shopping and other services "downtown." Between cities ran a train that discharged passengers in the center of the city. Ruralites of village and farm of necessity had their own private transportation.

Now the urbanite too has his private transportation—the auto. But it does not fit the city as well as the country—it needs parking space. So today we are moving many of the "downtown things" out to the suburbs and to the open country, things like department stores, doctors' and dentists' offices, and branch banks. This movement also brings the services to masses of suburbanites.

This migration most surely is changing the future role of the central city, particularly the downtown part. But is the city ready to accept the change? And who knows what the future role will be?

Our suburban shopping centers are large, well-planned, attractive, and convenient. The $50 million center at Tyson's Corner, Va., is across the highway from the gate of a dairy farm that operated up to 10 years ago.

Other facilities that need auto parking for the customers or employees, like hospitals, colleges, research and development labs, are also moving to the open country. Small cities and towns now often build their high schools out where there is space for athletic fields and for faculty and student parking.

Rural areas also provide space for superhighways with their cloverleafs, roadside picnic tables, and wayside rest stops. One might say the multi-lane highways are extensions of the city.

Massive system of freeways cuts through countryside to provide transportation and communication facilities needed in today's society.

The outmigration of urban type facilities and services has in the main brought new economic activity, prosperity, and stability to the rural areas it touches. But it has not touched all rural areas.

When urban industry moved to rural areas in search of labor, new surroundings, and "living space," it naturally was selective because it had much from which to choose. But in the process some rural communities, sometimes those that needed it most, got bypassed. They are the rural "drop-outs" of rural America. This problem is discussed in a later chapter.

Space seemingly is the most difficult concept for modern man to grasp . . . how to organize, manage, and use his space . . . not outer space but space on the earth we live on.

For example, man builds suburbs with residential streets adequate for the time, but fails to leave space for future corridors to reach future suburbs farther out . . . doesn't leave space for future parks which become necessary as the open country recedes . . . builds highways that are inadequate the day they open.

When our space-use becomes hopelessly obsolete we either bulldoze down the old and then rebuild, or we abandon the old and build anew elsewhere.

Rural areas are also grappling with the problem of adequate public services—roads, schools, medical, hospital, and so on. Rural people, like others, want and expect to have better services. The problem is more acute the sparser the rural population.

141

Some communities don't have enough people to support a good medical-hospital service system, not enough high school students to offer a diversified curriculum.

To improve the service and efficiency of services provided by local governments, we are beginning to think of multi-county units. For example, four (or six or eight) counties may cooperate in which each would administer a different service but to the citizens of all four counties.

Rural communities might also learn from what others are doing.

Some interfacing jurisdictions have developed cooperative arrangements. Cities often extend public utility services beyond their boundaries into suburbs or the open (rural) country. Or they may let adjoining (rural) jurisdictions "hook on" at the common boundary. Falls Church, Va., provides "city" water to many nearby areas in Fairfax County—an entirely separate jurisdiction.

Fairfax admittedly is an urban county. Where I live in the county, we get our water from Falls Church, our sewer service from the county, our gas comes from Washington, D.C., and we commute daily over highways built, maintained, and traffic controlled by the U.S. Park Service.

Another example is Fairfax City, Va. Recently incorporated, it has no high school of its own but pays the tuition of its students who attend the schools out in Fairfax County.

That, of course, is what the township of my boyhood has been doing for 45 years that I know of.

In the chapters of this section that follow you will find fascinating discussions on a number of topics . . . the changing character of rural communities . . . the search for new ways of providing public services . . . multi-county concepts . . . what makes a community viable . . . why some communities have been bypassed . . . the competition for land resources today . . . the quality of our rural environment . . . and many others.

Students at one-room school in Kentucky play dodgeball during recess.

THE MEANINGS OF RURAL—A THIRD OF OUR NATION

WE SPEAK of *Rural* America. What do we mean? Do we mean the country? The farms? Farm people? The answer seems obvious. But do we include small towns? If so, how small? Do we include people living in the country who don't farm? Do we include suburbanites? Is *rural* a place or a way of thinking and acting?

Answers to the last questions are not as obvious. Answering these questions has become increasingly troublesome over time, as distinctions between country and city have shaded over into each other. Yet, the questions continue to be asked and the answers are still important for public policy and the welfare of millions of citizens.

In the next few paragraphs I will attempt to define the word rural and explain why I feel the rural distinction is important and necessary for our country, despite the fact that we are living in an urban-industrial society.

Historically, the word *rural* has referred to the country. It comes from the Latin word *rus, ruris,* meaning open land. The origin of the word *rural* is closely akin to the words room and rustic. The word *rural* has been used to suggest open space, agricultural occupations, low density of settlement, isolation, and a slowness to make changes. Although these historical usages have faded, they are not entirely obsolete. *Rural* continues to suggest relatively open space, relatively low population density, and relatively greater reluctance to adopt new life styles.

Although our American society is commonly characterized as being highly urban, I would argue that the *rural* distinction is still important. Not all Americans live in big cities or densely packed suburbs. In fact, one-third of our Nation is still living in small towns and open country areas. For a highly developed Nation, this fact is extremely significant. Although our farm population has declined sharply since World War II, the proportion of our population choosing to live in the country and small towns has changed relatively little.

The very advantages of having more "elbow room" lead to some disadvantages for this one-third of a nation that are important for public policy. Dispersed settlement and low population density mean that the rural person spends proportionately more time in travel—getting to work, shopping, and in social activities. The rural person allocates more of his money and time budget to transportation. Certain opportunities must be foregone because of the cost or the time involved in getting from one place to another.

Delivery of public services such as water, electricity and gas, waste disposal, medical care, education, cultural activities, and social welfare, becomes more costly, more difficult, or even impossible. The rural distinction is important because of the peculiar spatial disadvantages falling on those who live in small towns or the open country.

Ironically, there is now another reason why the rural distinction is important. America is an urban society. Most of our recent Federal and State programs for improving the general welfare of our people have been designed primarily for the urban situation by urbanites, and require grant-seeking skills less frequently found among country and small town people.

An example would be the Com-

✦

AUTHOR JAMES H. COPP is Chief of the Human Resources Branch, Economic Development Division, Economic Research Service.

munity Action Programs that require frequent meetings of representatives from local areas. Transportation to a central meeting place has been a problem. Low-income people from various supposedly adjacent neighborhoods may not even know each other or have established patterns of cooperative action.

Communication back to rank-and-file citizens may be difficult and have to rely much more on word-of-mouth channels. Expertise in "grantsmanship" and organizing skills may be in short supply. Traditional social barriers between racial and ethnic groups may pose unusual difficulties.

The gist of the matter is that the delivery of social services, especially when these programs are urban-designed, is much more difficult in rural areas. Thus, for an unfortunate reason, the rural distinction is important in designing and administering programs.

Sign points way to rural welfare office. Providing social services presents more problems in country areas.

If, as has been argued, the rural distinction is important, how do we define rural? A number of definitions have been used and, for a number of reasons, found deficient.

Once, when our Nation was largely agricultural, rural and farm could be used interchangeably. Most of the people who lived in the country were farmers. Today, most of the people living in the country are not farmers (less than a fifth). Furthermore, a considerable number of farmers and farmworkers live in towns and cities (about 10 percent of the farmers and two-thirds of the farmworkers).

Some people would define rural as meaning open country. Then what are we to do about hamlets, villages, small towns, and scattered housing subdivisions? Most of these locations are isolated from cities, are unincorporated, and permit their residents the luxury of considerable open space. Residents of such places frequently explain they are living where they are "to get away from the city," the high costs of unwanted urban facilities, and the restrictions on pets, dogs, horses, livestock, automobiles, and other non-conforming interests prohibited in built-up areas.

How large can a place be and still stay rural? How small and still be urban? There are no precise answers. In this country, the U.S. Census has made the dividing line at 2,500 or more population (with special rules for built-up areas around cities of 50,000 or more). But other countries make the cut at 2,000, 5,000, or 10,000.

There is no convenient dividing line for separating rural and urban. The U.S. Census of Population vacillated between 8,000, 4,000, and 1,000 before finally settling on 2,500 in 1910. Today, most authorities feel 2,500 is too low. What do Diboll, Tex. (1960 pop. 2,506) and New York City (1960 pop. 7,781,984) really have in common? Suggestions for raising the cutting point run all the way from 5,000 to 50,000. Perhaps the cutting point should lie somewhere between 25,000 and 50,000.

Others have suggested that the distinction be between metropolitan (counties with central cities totaling 50,000 or more) and nonmetropolitan. This suggestion, though it has some merit, overlooks the fact that many people are living under rural conditions in metropolitan counties. In fact, one-fourth of our rural population, as currently defined, lives in the so-called Standard Metropolitan Statistical Areas. It is an interesting fact that much of our undeniably rural population, living under dispersed settlement, is located close to large

144

Like Grant Putnam family picnicking beside their farm pond in Ingham County, Mich., many farm people enjoy luxury of space and fine opportunities for outdoor recreation. But only one in five rural families lives on a farm.

cities. A good example would be the farm country in Lancaster County, Pa.

This last example is a good place to make the point that rural does not only mean low density of settlement and difficulty in providing public services, but it also implies differences in ways of life. In rural areas there is a preference for less government, less regulation, and more local control. This is fine, but it is not always the most happy arrangement. In many of our rural areas the machinery of government, which was designed in horse-buggy days, has become painfully obsolete.

In both areas where population has grown rapidly and where population has declined precipitously, present forms of government may be inadequate for dealing effectively with contemporary problems. The ideals of small government, local control, and local support, instead of enlarging individual opportunity, may actually restrict the development of human potentialities and the freedom of the individual to improve his condition.

The problem does not only lie with

government. Many of our other rural institutions—the church, the school, medical facilities, businesses—are also suffering from the problem of too small units, too small service areas, too small an economic base for support, and somewhat obsolete institutional design problems. Thus our rural areas today are the scene of conflict between traditional ideals and the need to revamp the institutional structure into more efficient, more economic, and more responsive units.

There is yet another meaning of rural that should be pointed out. This meaning lies in the area of culture, values, and preferences. It includes the preference for personal, face-to-face relations over impersonal, mass-media communication.

This meaning puts a strong emphasis on kinship ties, personal rather than highly theological religion, pragmatics over theory, performance over promises, personal trust over impersonal calculation, informal controls over legal regulation, open space over the crowded cities, growing plants and tending animals over manipulating

145

Above, church members in Millville, W. Va., boil apple butter, an annual event. Traditions and fellowship are important to rural people. Below, 4-H'er Deborah Tullar shows off prize Holstein in Orford, N.H. Growing plants and tending animals are strong rural attractions.

inanimate objects, a preference for nature and the outdoors, and a devotion to precedent and to established patterns. In a sense, all Americans are partly rural in their preferences.

However, the rural tendencies are most pronounced in our country areas. For instance an examination of voting patterns in State and national elections reveals these tendencies. Typically, there are sharp differences in voting

Rural is more than a place, it is an outlook on life.

So, what does rural mean? It means relatively lower population density, easier access to open space, fewer restrictions brought on by the pressure of people, somewhat different value standards in preferences and conduct, and a somewhat stronger commitment to the institutions and lifeways of an American past. It also means depriva-

Farm meeting near Warrenton, Va. Informality is valued in rural life. So is make-do.

patterns between the big cities and the downstate or upstate districts. These rural preferences are also reflected in responses to moral issues. People in our rural areas are much more likely to emphasize the traditionally established patterns.

Another instance lies in attitudes toward labor unions and membership in them. Rural workers are less likely to be unionized. There are differences in recreation, with rural people emphasizing fishing and hunting, rather than indoor pursuits. Differences in kinship interaction and size of family are also apparent. The above examples show that although the rural way of life may be muted, it is far from dead.

tions in terms of amount and quality of public services, the cost and time involved in transportation, and difficulties in relating to new urban-designed programs and services.

Rural, furthermore, means an important segment of our nation's population—one-third. It is a segment that is not decreasing in proportionate size, despite the alleged urbanization of our society. It is a segment that tends to be overlooked in these times of preoccupation with urban crises.

Although solving urban problems in our society should have top priority, the severity and magnitude of similar problems in the development of human resources and in the provision of basic

If rural problems are overlooked, what kind of future is there for children like these?

services and facilities are no less important in rural areas. The importance is for rural living itself, not just because rural areas contribute so many undereducated, unskilled migrants to urban areas.

Rural means people. It includes farmers, but it also includes men and women following every occupation known who choose to live beyond the city limits in housing subdivisions, in towns, and in the open country. It means people with a strong desire for privacy, living space, and self-reliance. It means people with a pride in home and family. It means people looking for opportunity who have left the country for the city. Rural means America, our history and much of our dreams.

Thus, the rural distinction is important because it represents so much of what America has been as well as what it hopes to be. Rural means life at a scale that is comprehensible to the individual. It is important that we preserve and strengthen this option.

THE TEAM HAUL COMMUNITY IN A JET AGE

. J. GALPIN in 1915 characterized the ural community as the "team haul" ommunity.

This concept implied that comunity boundaries extended no farther a any given direction than a team of orses and wagon could travel and eturn during the same day. The dayo-day interaction of those who lived a these rural communities was limited y the available transportation and ommunication to a small geographic rea and a very small number of eople.

In that day, little more than a eneration ago, the family was the rimary producing and consuming nit, particularly in the rural comunities. Each family was essentially elf-contained, producing most of the oods and services it consumed.

American communities—both large nd small, rural and urban—have lways been in a state of flux. However, change has been more rapid and ervasive in recent years than at any ther time in our history.

In characterizing the impact of ecent changes, Malcolm Knowles aid that a child born today will see complete change in culture in his fetime.

Change has included not only the naterial things of life but is challeng-ng even our way of life, including our asic values.

Powerful economic, technical, and ocial forces are reshaping our comunities, both rural and urban. among the major forces at work is ne tremendous growth in science and technology, industrialization, specialization, and automation. Besides all this, we are witnessing marked advances in transportation, communication, and new and improved sources of power. Rapid population growth and shifts in population also have made a real impact on our communities.

The consequence of these and other forces has been the increasing growth and complexity of many of our communities, which are intricately dependent upon each other and the total society. Urbanization, suburbanization, and metropolitanization have become bywords in describing today's trends. At the same time, many rural communities have been struggling for their very existence as farmworkers have migrated to the towns and cities in increasing numbers.

High mobility has become a characteristic of rural as well as urban society as more and more farmers migrate off the farm, or commute to work in the towns and cities, and enjoy vacations and recreational activities away from the farm.

Along with specialization in industry, agriculture, and the economic segment of our society has come a specialization in institutional services. Many of the services once provided almost exclusively by the family have been taken over by other institutions.

Change has been so dramatic and far-reaching that the traditional differences between rural and urban have largely disappeared as these communities have become mutually dependent parts of a total system. Throughout history, rural and urban areas have depended upon each other for products and services, but there has never been a time when the interdependence was so complete.

Urban areas are dependent upon the rural for daily sustenance in the form

✦

AUTHOR PAUL J. JEHLIK is Director of the Economics, Marketing, Rural and Community Development Division, Cooperative State Research Service.

COAUTHOR SHELDON G. LOWRY is Principal Sociologist of the Division. He is on leave from Michigan State University.

149

Left, machine harvesting potatoes in Michigan in 1960's. Right, hand loading sugar beets i wagon in Cache County, Utah, in 1935.

of food and fiber and related commodities. Rural areas, on the other hand, are among the major consumers of most urban products and services including such things as tractors, equipment, automobiles, trucks, gasoline, oil, electricity, clothing, and processed foods.

Many of the changes that occurred in recent years have been desirable and instrumental in increasing the level of living of individuals and families in our communities. Other changes have had undesirable effects. All have posed new problems to be solved and have brought new challenges to be faced.

A farmer gazing across that "team haul community" today sees quite a different picture than he would have seen in 1915. Many of the farm homes have been abandoned. Others are occupied by families whose breadwinner no longer farms but commutes to work in a nearby town or city. Still others live in town and commute to the farm. Some of these farmers combine farming with work in the city.

Numerous small rural villages are barely holding their own, while others are giving way to the competition of the larger towns and cities. Although the land is producing much more than it ever did, more and more people are leaving the farm for nonfarm work.

The vast majority of those leaving a in the younger, more productive ag group with the most training and ski

At the time of the first census i 1790, only one out of 20 residents this country lived in urban area Today 14 out of 20 live in urba centers.

As a result of this dramatic shift i population, 70 percent of our peop are living on about 1 percent of th land, while 30 percent are living o 99 percent of the land.

Our best population estimates in dicate that in just 30 years anoth 100 million people will be living the United States, a 50 percent ii crease over our present population. present trends continue, most of th increase will be added to the 14 million people already in urban area Rural communities likewise will ii crease but at a slower rate.

With the rapid growth and increas ing complexity of our society there ha been a proliferation of organization programs, and services. Much of th participation that was once in th home is now out in the organization and agencies in the community Family participation has been givin way to individual participation i specialized organizations like Bo Scouts, Girl Scouts, the 4–H Club church, school, and others.

150

Rural community in Northumberland County, Pa., with its relatively complete service center and modern farming, forestry, and conservation practices in surrounding area.

Despite the unparalleled growth of programs and policies designed to solve the problems and meet the needs of rural people, there are many communities in which rural schools, libraries, housing, roads, and most rural facilities and services often are inadequate and of poor quality.

Furthermore, reports prepared by the State Agricultural Experiment Stations and the U.S. Department of Agriculture indicate that water supply, waste disposal, and fire protection are often lacking in rural areas, and health and medical facilities are inferior and frequently inaccessible. Other services such as employment counseling and job placement are practically nonexistent outside of the larger urban centers.

While churches are attempting to provide a meaningful religious program for all ages, many are finding it necessary to merge with other congregations or cooperate with them in joint

Deserted farm in Caroline County, Va.

efforts to obtain a pastor and to support buildings and facilities for declining and aging congregations.

Business firms and professional people located in rural communities often are faced with a variety of adjustments. New products are displacing the old. Many customers and clients are migrating to other areas. The ever increasing and expanding shopping centers are attracting away customers and clients. And many customers, through rapid transportation, are travelling to centers outside the local community.

In addition, the demand for farm machinery, equipment, supplies, and farm-related services is being reduced due to government programs which are taking substantial acreages of land out of production.

Often without the opportunity or the ability to provide alternate employment opportunities, the local community experiences a further decline in population, particularly the productive age group. There is a tendency for those persons who remain in the community to be the older, more conservative residents who are less likely to adjust readily to change. Often they find it difficult to bring about retrenchments in the schools, churches, and other public and private services and facilities in keeping with the reduced numbers of residents.

Villages and towns experiencing declines in population and faced with the need for retrenchments also find that real estate values tend to remain relatively unchanged. But at the same time surrounding farmland values most likely have continued to rise, paralleling real estate values in the larger centers.

Thus, in almost any given community that has experienced a stationary or declining population, the social and economic forces of time have denied some of the residents a share in our rising affluence. This failure to share in the Nation's rising wealth is both one of the causes and one of the effects of the changing character of a large number of rural communities.

Some communities, in which new industries are being established, experience quite a different set of forces and influences. New occupations become available. Sources of income change.

Employees who accompany the new industry into the community become new members of the community. These newcomers may be accepted or rejected by the local residents. They in turn, may or may not like their new community, its schools, churches, medical services, housing, and other facilities.

The values and attitudes these individuals and families bring into the community may not be in conformity with the norms of the local community. Therefore, the chances of conflict often are present and there follows a period of adjustment and accommodation.

Among the more crucial concerns in community change is the ability of local government to cope with the increased demand for services in the face of limited sources of revenue. Federal, State, and local programs have multiplied in recent years. And many rural communities are faced with numerous uncoordinated programs operating simultaneously from two or three different levels of government. The resulting multiplication of governmental activity has made it increasingly difficult for community leaders to furnish the services needed by the local people.

Problems faced by former rural communities were largely internal local problems. They were the kind of problems that could be handled on the basis of past experience by people who were well acquainted and often related.

Many of today's problems have never been encountered before, and to a large extent have their origin and roots outside the local community. Furthermore, and particularly in growing communities, they must be solved with people who are comparative strangers.

Because the causes and the results of

change are complex and sometimes deeply rooted in past history, there is a need for continuous study and research so the people of our communities may have better information for use in determining their destiny.

What is required to strengthen the position of rural people and to insure adequate services, facilities, and opportunities needed for a quality level of living?

What are the essentials of a functional and effective community?

What kind of community can best provide these essential qualities?

And what are the modifications required from one community to another in order to meet the needs of the Great Plains, the Ozarks, the Intermountain Region, and the other parts of the country?

These are the kinds of questions to which people at all levels of decision-making are addressing themselves.

Families can build new houses with all the latest equipment and facilities. But modern living involves much more than simply occupying a new house. It includes a total environment with opportunities for work and with facilities to provide for the social, intellectual, religious, and physical needs of community members.

Such a community does not come about by the uncoordinated acts of separate individuals and families. It is developed through a careful process of planning, using the best in leadership and research information available to the community.

Specialists in community organization tell us there are about 40,000 communities in the United States, varying in size from small neighborhoods to large communities consisting of several counties.

Only about one in four of these communities is well organized to provide residents with the basic essentials of a quality level of living.

The few rural communities that are well organized have available to them the leadership, the know-how, the financial resources, and the access to services and facilities which are usually available only in the most urban areas.

In recognition of the advantages of organization and planning, there has been a growing emphasis in recent years on programs of rural development. Much effort has been directed at seeking the initiation of such programs at the "grass roots" level so they will be soundly rooted in the needs of the people.

There is no blueprint for all communities, since what may be good for one community may not be good for another.

However, it has been demonstrated that with sound local leadership and good organizational effort backed by adequate research information, communities can direct change for the benefit of all.

The hope of many concerned people is to develop in rural America a blend of well organized and functioning towns and villages, each with its own jobs and industries, its own educational, health, and religious centers, its own cultural, entertainment, and recreational centers, and with an agricultural and nonagricultural economy fully sharing in the national prosperity.

Such communities might cover a larger geographic area than many of today's communities. They may extend over two or more counties and include some small cities, towns, villages, shopping centers, and the open country in between.

The components of these communities—the villages, towns, cities, and counties—would be bound together in a natural geographic structure by roads, rivers, and other resources and provide a blend of needed economic, social, and cultural facilities and services for the area.

Thus, the day of the "team haul" community is gone.

In the rural communities of the jet age, farming is becoming simply one of many kinds of industries in a complex and totally interdependent society. The traditional distinctions between farm and nonfarm people have virtually disappeared.

STRUCTURE, CHANGE IN RURAL GOVERNMENT

AS WE DRIVE through a rural area we are surprised to see clusters of farm homes with common water supplies, television antennas, sewer systems, and a warmed waiting place where children from the farmsteads meet the school buses.

Special sewage treatment centers exist to care for the waste from homes and from large feed lots. Closed rural roads now serve as nesting places for pheasants, quail, grouse, and other wild game of the area. It looks as though the farmers have developed a hunting-recreation program using these formerly public right-of-ways, now closed by the consolidation of farmsteads.

Fire numbers identify each home for the fire department of the city serving this cluster of homes. In short, the urban benefits long denied rural people are there and the much desired benefits of living in open spaces are still available to those who want them.

This picture could be true some time in the future. Some of those things described above are being supplied to rural people. Yet many such services are demanded but not supplied due to, first, the sprawling nature of rural living and, second, inadequate rural government and lack of the necessary tax dollars.

Instead of the picture just described, the following is more near reality:

A multitude of roads leading to fields are publicly maintained with little or no use.

Individual farmers must drill new wells from time to time due to inadequate water supplies.

Many small units of government, overstaffed with elected and appointed officials, continue to carry on functions prescribed many years ago.

Let's take a brief look at structure and change in rural government.

Many students of rural government would ask if it is possible to include the word "change" with the words "rural government" because of the long term, relatively constant form of rural government. There are, however, some indications of change.

Historically, rural governments have served as general purpose governments. They have provided such services as recordkeeping for vital statistics, land ownership, tax records, mortgages, and the like. Many States use the rural government as the property tax collecting and disbursing agency.

Other traditional services include road construction and maintenance, care of the poor, a seat for judicial action, rural law enforcement, administration of elections, maintenance of rural cemeteries, resolution of agricultural boundary issues (in some States, township trustees still decide who should maintain a fence between two landowners).

And counties still administer rural schools. Rural governments have added services to include an administrative seat for Federal, State, and local social welfare services; plus construction and maintenance of parks, airports, and sanitary land fills.

Basically, the structure of rural government in most States is unchanged from a hundred or more years ago. Townships still have the organization of their earliest years. Counties have simply added committees or individual administrators to perform functions added over time.

Today we commonly find three types of general rural government in the States. The New England town, the township supervisor systems char-

✦

AUTHOR ROBERT I. WESSEL is an assistant professor, Department of Political Science, Iowa State University, Ames.

acterized by examples in Wisconsin and Michigan, and the county commission system typical of much of the South, Midwest, and West.

These rural government systems have some common characteristics such as no single executive leadership and a substantial number of elective officers to serve as administrative heads of segments of governmental services.

Perhaps the most significant problem is the lack of unified leadership and authority just discussed.

Variations among the three forms of rural government include the broader based participation in decisions in the New England towns, with their town meetings. Township supervisor governments are systems in which representatives from townships and villages make up the county legislative bodies.

Under the commission system, a limited number of commissioners are elected at large, or by district, as the policy-making body. The commissioners also tend to serve as administrators for some services, like roadwork. These systems include a number of appointed boards, commissions, and appointive officers to administer specific programs, such as social welfare boards, county health boards, and county engineers.

Most variations from the forms described tend to concentrate authority in some elected or appointed officer. A number of New England towns have town managers. New York has a few elected executives who serve as county administrators, similar to mayors in strong mayor cities.

Virginia counties have in many instances adopted some form of executive system similar to city managers, commonly called county executives or county managers.

The Virginia approach generally calls for a reorganization of county services along specialty lines such as police, finance, and utilities. In these counties only a governing board is elected. All other officers are appointed, quite in contrast to township supervisor and commissioner systems

where a number of administrative heads and the chief law enforcement officers are elected. But some commission type counties have found it useful to employ administrative officers.

There is an indication that townships are declining in significance in the commission type of county. For example, in Iowa the Census of Governments no longer counts townships as units of government.

One of the unique changes in local government occurred in rural South Dakota when one county decided to annex a neighboring county which had no organized government. Perhaps the most interesting reason for the annexation was the problem of taxing livestock that were driven to the unorganized county during tax assessment time. In order to assess and collect taxes from the cattle company it was apparently necessary to annex and provide a continuing government for the area.

Perhaps the greatest number of variations in rural government aimed at meeting contemporary needs have occurred in areas in which the county and a large urbanized area are the same or where the urban area covers a large part of the area generally thought to be under the county.

Places in which experimentation in forms of government in urban areas has occurred include States from California to Florida and from Louisiana to Minnesota. For example, San Francisco has lumped its city and county functions under one governmental unit. The city and county of Denver, Colo., has similarly combined functions. Los Angeles County, Calif., instead of combining city and county functions, provides services to municipalities on a contract basis.

Baton Rouge Parish and Baton Rouge City in Louisiana have a joint governing body to make area-wide decisions affecting both city and parish (county). A similar policy-making body is being used in Nashville and Davidson County, Tenn. Miami and other metropolitan cities in Dade County, Fla., have combined with the

155

county to provide for a county manager and county-wide services for incorporated and unincorporated parts of the county.

Minnesota's efforts have been multi-county in nature, due to the seven counties involved in the metropolitan area. Here a new level of government has been constituted called the "Metropolitan Council". The Council assumed an area-wide policy function and the planning role previously under a metropolitan planning commission. The Council members are appointed by the governor from the State senatorial districts in the counties involved.

An informal type of organization among local governments should also be mentioned here. The volunteer councils of governments, which include central cities, suburban communities, and counties on regional bases, provide a source for communications among units of government within the region. These councils could provide the possibilities for future regional governments.

Regional administrative units which are intended to provide locations for future State services are being considered in a number of States. Iowa and Minnesota have designated regions for future area-wide services. Regional schools and regional extension districts already operating in some States are indications of the change to regions as basic rural governmental units bypass townships, school districts, and counties.

Innovations in forms of government are numerous. Innovations, however, do not necessarily result in adequate government. Continued proliferation of cities in Los Angeles County, and the failure to resolve many significant public problems in the Twin Cities area of Minnesota such as airport location and metro sewer systems, indicate that a reorganization or new governmental units do not necessarily resolve problems. These examples do indicate, however, that changes are occurring in rural governments that include metropolitan areas.

Perhaps the most striking change in the financial situation of governments in rural areas is the significant influx of Federal and State aid. This aid has allowed rural governments to continue and expand services that would otherwise be cut or ended. Because services are continued or expanded, the total expenditures per person have risen sharply since 1950 in the low population counties.

The more populous places have seen a relatively constant level of expenditures per person over the same two decades. During this time period the populous counties appear to have expanded their services also. But, because of the large influx of population, their per person expenditure levels have generally held constant.

In contrast the rapidly rising expenditures per person in the areas of declining population appear necessary just to maintain existing services. In many instances, rural people are receiving lower levels of service than in the past while their costs of government have risen. The political control of rural government is changing.

In many counties with large central cities, the central city can have control of the county's governing body. But a typical way of avoiding city domination of the county is the slicing up of the city as parts of representative districts that also encompass a majority rural population. This is known as gerrymandering. An example of gerrymandering on the county level occurred in Itasca County, Minn., where three commissioner districts take part of the county seat population.

Election at large of county commissioners also tends to assure rural control of such policy boards due to the lack of knowledge and interest in rural government by urban people. Candidate recruitment for county boards tends to be rural even in counties with large urban populations.

The traditional rural control of the county government in Wisconsin through a requirement that each township have representation on the county board of supervisors was changed to break township lines. With representatives coming from multi-township districts, it is now possible for urban places to become dominant in Wisconsin.

Minnesota courts have ruled that the one-man-one-vote rule must apply to county commissioners. Now large populous areas in Minnesota counties will be able to control the boards of county commissioners.

General application of the one-man-one-vote principle indicates a continuing shift of power from the rural to the urban parts of local government. As rural population declines even more, political power will move to the populous points in the counties. This shift in power, of course, assumes an active effort on the part of urban forces to secure control.

At the State level the one-man-one-vote rule and reapportionment resulting from it has resulted in a shift in allocation of State resources. County boundaries which were considered limits to State legislative apportionment are no longer a factor. Before reapportionment, rurally dominated State legislatures tended to tax urban areas and to redistribute the taxes through State services to rural areas.

Some shift of public services to benefit urban areas has already happened. For example, cities are demanding and receiving larger shares of State road funds. Changing State legislatures to an urban orientation, along with a shift in control of county government from rural areas to urban centers, indicates a potential two-edged attack on resources previously allocated to rural areas.

This chapter began by describing some changes in rural demands for urban services. The future would indicate an expanded demand for urban type services in rural areas. Such services include water and sewer systems, more paved roads with urban type maintenance, and urban quality care for the aged in nursing homes, with county homes becoming obsolete.

Some States have already closed their county homes. Others are in the process of phasing them out. It should be noted here that the cost of providing urban services to rural people obviously will be much higher than

Filtration tanks of new water system in Denton, N.C.

providing the same services to concentrations of people in urban places. The future also holds a demand for more intergovernmental cooperation among counties and between counties and their central cities to provide airports, sewage, and refuse disposal.

Rural people have been demanding and providing urban type services for themselves. Rural governments have remained relatively constant in their structure while additional services have been added. Reapportionment is resulting in a power shift that is increasing the withdrawal of urban resources from rural areas, and probably will continue to do so.

PUBLIC SERVICES
IN RURAL AREAS

PUBLIC SERVICES in rural areas often are inferior to those provided in urban areas. This is especially true of services financed from local revenue. Among the most common areas of inadequacy are education and health.

In 1968, the National Education Association reported that in the 38 States which identified their need for teachers, all reported a shortage in rural areas. Because of these conditions, many rural areas have been forced to employ teachers with below-average or substandard qualifications.

Inadequate salaries are probably the major reason why rural areas have not been able to recruit qualified teachers. Some rural districts have paid their teachers only about a third as much as some metropolitan districts. In part, this results from lack of revenue due to a sparse population and the lower incomes of rural residents.

Other evidence of inadequate educational services is the fact that rural students have scored lower on standard tests than their urban counterparts. One recent report showed that when achievement tests on verbal ability, reading comprehension, and mathematics were given to students in 1965, nonmetropolitan youth scored considerably below the metropolitan youth.

Nonmetropolitan white 12th graders in the United States average about one grade level below metropolitan white 12th graders in the Northeast. Nonmetropolitan Negro students scored about one and one-half grade levels below the metropolitan Negro 12th grader in the Northeast.

It appears that fewer rural students than urban students are finishing high school. In 1965, 12 percent of the 16 and 17 year old children in nonmetropolitan areas had not completed school and were not enrolled. In comparison, 8 percent of the 16 and 17 year olds in metropolitan areas were in this category.

Rural health services generally are inferior to urban health services in several important respects. The first and most important is that there are fewer physicians and dentists per capita in rural areas. Also, there are fewer specialists.

Rural areas commonly have fewer hospital beds per capita than urban areas. When hospitals do exist in rural areas they often are very small and have limited equipment. And a smaller proportion of the rural population has hospital and medical insurance than is the case with the urban population.

Lack of these medical services and other reasons have led to the rural family visiting the doctor about three-fourths as often as the urban family, and the dentist only a third as often. The fact that the chronic disability

✦

AUTHOR THOMAS F. HADY is Chief of the Community Facilities Branch, Economic Development Division, Economic Research Service.

COAUTHOR RONALD BIRD is Assistant Chief of the Community Facilities Branch.

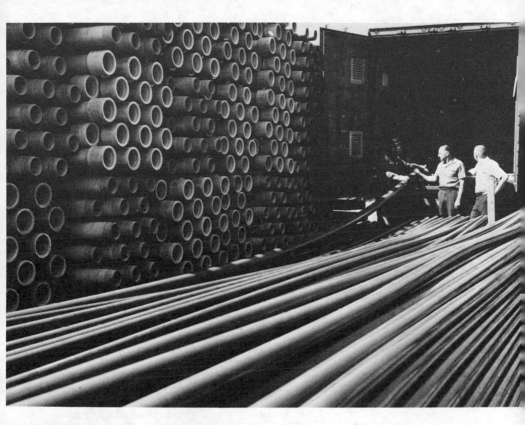

rate is twice as high among rural residents indicates the need for medical services in rural areas is far from being met.

Adequate public water and sewage systems are considered a prerequisite for maintaining community health. In 1968, about 33,000 communities in the United States lacked a public water system, and 43,000 lacked an adequate sewage system. Almost all of these communities were in rural America.

Of course, each region of the country does not need the same services, in the same amounts. An area with a large population of older people with

Above, some of nearly 60 miles of pipe for Umpqua Basin Water System in Oregon, financed with Farmers Home Administration loan. System serves about 800 rural families. Left, rural resident pumps water from cistern before new water system was completed.

159

low incomes, for example, needs more public health services than does an area in which most of the people are young, healthy, and working.

A lack of elbowroom produces another kind of need for services. Children shooting BB guns on a farm a mile down the road are not a serious problem for the typical rural resident; children shooting a BB gun in the lot next door are a problem for the typical small town resident. The town needs regulatory services.

A more subtle cause for differences in service levels is the differences in people's desire to meet their problems through public action. Decisions on tax levels and the size of the budget for various services are really decisions on the allocation of our incomes among the various goods and services that are available to us—both public and private.

In a democratic society, these decisions are made collectively by the citizens of each governmental unit, and the citizens of neighboring communities may reach a different set of decisions.

Nearly three-fourths of the money to finance local government services comes from two sources, State and Federal aid and the property tax. While separate statistics are not available for rural areas, it seems likely that these two sources account for an even larger part of the revenues of rural local governments. These governments typically have fewer alternatives available for obtaining revenue through other types of taxation and service charges than larger communities.

State and Federal aid to local governments has been one of the rapidly growing areas in public finances. This aid almost tripled from the 1957 level of $7.7 billion to $20.4 billion in 1967. During the same period, Federal aid paid directly to local governments rose from $0.3 billion to $1.9 billion— an increase of more than six times— Furthermore, the typical pattern of Federal aid programs is to channel the money through the States. Statistics

are not available to estimate the amount of the increase in State aid which was actually financed by increases in Federal aid to the States.

As our population becomes more mobile, and as we become more urbanized, the quality of the services which our neighbors in other parts of the State get from their governments become more important to us. Congress and the State legislatures have recognized this concern by providing assistance to local governments so that they are able to provide minimum levels of services to all citizens.

The property tax is the mainstay of local revenues, and it has proved an effective one. Property tax collections by local governments doubled from 1957 to 1967, to reach a total of $25 billion in 1967.

This tax has a number of advantages for local governments. The revenue it will produce can easily be predicted; property taxes fluctuate much less with business conditions than do sales taxes and similar sources of funds. Property, or at least real estate, is difficult to hide, so evasion problems are not serious. And, compared with an income tax, the property tax is easy for small local units to administer.

Nevertheless, the property tax has a number of problems which must be resolved if it is to meet the increasing needs for local revenue.

One of the most important problems is how to improve the quality of administration. Most of the property is assessed locally by a poorly-paid elected official. He is required to assess a multitude of properties in a short time period. Inequitable assessments often are the results.

When property tax rates rise, these inequities become much more serious, and public confidence in the property tax is undermined.

Sources of State revenues are more varied. A large element, however, is the aid the States receive from the Federal Government. This amounted to some $14.9 billion in 1967, four times its level in 1957. It is mostly for specific categories of functions.

160

In fiscal 1968, 30 percent of all Federal grants were for public assistance programs (to the aged, disabled, dependent children, etc.). Another 24 percent were for highway construction, 15 percent for education, and 5 percent for health services and facilities.

For a variety of reasons, States usually can administer income and sales taxes more easily than local governments can. Hence, many people now feel that a promising supplement to the local property tax can be found in the "piggy back" sales or income tax.

Under this arrangement, the local unit levies a tax as a supplement to the State sales or income tax, and the State collects the tax at the same time it collects its own tax. The local portion is then sent back to the local government.

These taxes can be arranged so that the local unit can set its own tax rate (collecting, for example, some percentage of the tax that's due the State), thus preserving the opportunity for local citizens to decide how much of their incomes they want to devote to local governmental services.

A second source of new funds for local services is increased State and Federal aid. As we noted above, this aid has increased rapidly in recent years. There appears to be no reason to expect that this rapid growth will diminish.

What some observers consider the greatly superior revenue raising ability of the Federal Government, coupled with large and growing needs for services at the State and local level, has led to another proposal to help finance local services—Federal revenue sharing.

Under this proposal, the Federal Government would earmark some portion of its income tax revenues to be returned, each year, to the States. The revenues would be apportioned among the States according to a relatively simple formula, and the grants would have few strings attached to them.

Many of these proposals, however, do call for specific requirements that the States, in turn, pass at least a certain fraction of the money on to cities, school districts, and other local units of government. Except for minimum requirements like these, the States would be free to use the revenue whatever way they felt would do the most good.

To sum up, the property tax continues to be the primary source of revenue for financing local government services in rural areas. But other sources are being investigated, to provide an equitable and adequate basis for financing improvements in these services. Whether one of the alternatives we have described, or some alternative not yet devised, will largely replace the property tax is a question only the future can answer.

If the future is to hold promise for rural America, however, it is clear that efforts must be intensified to provide adequate services to rural Americans. We can see that considerable strides have been made in public services in recent decades, but it is less clear that these strides have kept pace with the rapid strides in technology and the increasing complexity of our society.

Schools, by and large, are much better than they were 50 years ago in rural areas—but the amount that a rural child must learn in school to function effectively in our modern economy also has increased greatly.

Medical technology has learned how to cure many diseases that formerly were almost invariably fatal—but we have not developed adequate means of delivering this technology to rural residents.

Our highway programs have succeeded in paving thousands of miles of dirt roads—but many of these roads are inadequate for modern cars and high traffic densities.

Solving these problems will take cooperative efforts by many people. Social and physical scientists must develop alternative approaches that can be used to provide improved services. Public policy makers must develop the public programs that are needed. And, most important, both rural and urban citizens must think, discuss, decide what they want, and communicate those decisions to their elected representatives at all levels of government.

TOGETHERNESS FOR COUNTIES

AMERICANS can walk on the moon. Galloping technology is changing the lives of all Americans back on earth, too.

Multi-county areas help us make these changes.

They symbolize the way we harness technology to benefit all citizens. That way is cooperative planning. Neighboring local governments and communities plan together. They cooperate on projects and programs to cut costs and provide services they could not provide alone. State and Federal agencies help with money and with technicians.

"Thanks to school consolidation, my boys will have a much better chance in life than I ever had. And they need a much better education. Everything is technical now."

Jim Smith was making a strong pitch for multi-county planning and related multi-county program development to spell out the priority needs of local citizens and respond to those needs as rapidly and cheaply as possible. The one-teacher school still meets a basic need for education in sparsely populated areas. As recently as 1966, there were still over 73,000 of them.

Most of us know some outstanding people who started their education in very small schools. Still, many communities that can afford to do so have built larger schools to serve pupils from a wider area.

Experts have concluded that a high school can't adequately prepare its students for modern living and working unless it graduates a class of at least 100. Science and language laboratories and many other needs can only be provided if they can be used by a large number of students and so reduce the cost per student for modern education.

Communities that join together to provide these better schools can pay higher teacher salaries, since each teacher can usually instruct more students. And the teachers can specialize so that students are taught chemistry by a science major and not the English teacher filling in. Teachers also have more training and promotion opportunities. So there's a good chance a large school can maintain its standards of excellence.

Rural areas have a widespread need for joining together to provide better services to all their citizens. The need for school consolidation is one of the most general and most obvious. In some areas, it is one of the most difficult needs to meet. New ways of working together must be forged by individual districts and counties that have very little technical support and very limited budgets.

In some sparsely populated areas, school consolidation is not feasible. New techniques are needed to provide adequate services to citizens who must live there.

Jim Smith didn't have the advantage of a first-class education. And he's paying the penalty. Jim grew up in rural Michigan. It could have been rural Anywhere.

In 1912, the number of Michigan school districts reached its peak of 7,362. By 1943, there were still 6,239 separate school districts.

During 1944, the Michigan Public

✦

AUTHOR ALAN R. BIRD is Deputy Director, Economic Development Division, Economic Research Service.

Education Commission recommended steps for major improvements in education through reorganization of school districts. The key proposals were:

• Organize all primary, graded, township, and rural agricultural school districts into fourth class city districts with, generally, at least $3 million of state equalized valuation.

• Establish county school district reorganization committees to assist in the fourth class organization.

In 1955, the State passed landmark legislation to encourage school consolidation. At that time, three percent of the school districts in the state were educating 57 percent of the pupils. This law (Public Act 269 of 1955) reduced nonoperating districts from 533 on June 30, 1956, to 45 on June 30, 1958. Yet more needed to be done.

In 1964, 893 of the 1,438 Michigan school districts still did not offer classes from kindergarten through grade 12. So the State legislature passed another law—Public Act 289. This act set up State guidelines to help local communities to a common goal of school improvement. Key items were that each district offer classes for kindergarten through grade 12; have at least $12,000 State equalized valuation per pupil; and have at least 2,000 pupils.

Local progress in consolidating schools speaks volumes for the wisdom of the State guidelines and the ability of State and local leadership. With a relative lack of controversy, local communities have worked together until, by June 30, 1969, the State had only 650 school districts, fewer than at any time since 1837.

Jim Smith's sons and the many millions of other rural children are reaping the benefits of this kind of cooperative community development. They can look forward to promising careers of their own choosing. They do not plan to make a career of retiring on the small farm where they now live.

Their father had little choice. His education was limited. And his only technical training was in vocational agriculture. When his farm income didn't meet his family expenses, he was forced to sell his cows and commute to a janitor's job in a distant town. That was the best he could do.

Not all rural areas in the United States will be able to consolidate schools as successfully as Michigan districts. Special local conditions will govern what is feasible to ensure rural youth the best chance in life. These local efforts will, however, all require commonsense planning to make the most of public funds that will always be limited.

In one area, it may be that three counties each having one high school of 200 can join together and have one better high school of 600. That sounds good, at least for the county that gets the new high school. People in neighboring counties can benefit from that new high school—but not by any means automatically.

Special efforts will be needed to make use of former school buildings. They may be used for other public services. Careful planning (and money and a great deal of sweat) can result in better roads and bus services so that many more children can have access to a better school.

Specialist teachers may visit several schools to teach French or music, science or advanced mathematics. Classes from outlying schools may spend a day or two each week at a centrally located science laboratory.

Other facilities, such as a hospital, a library, or a vocational training center, may be centrally located to the benefit of all citizens in a multicounty area.

This need to provide better schools has a way of snowballing. As the schools seek to offer up-to-date vocational training, they have a better chance of recruiting good instructors if the firms that actually employ these skilled people are nearby.

Especially in the primary schools, most of the teachers are women. Many of these women are married and are the second wage earner in the

163

family. So good teachers can be recruited more easily if the school is located near businesses that employ other members of the family. It's so much the better for the businesses and for the schools if there are day-care centers nearby.

Good teachers want to upgrade their own skills. So, even at the same salary, they are likely to favor communities that have community colleges, other colleges or universities, and other community educational, cultural, and recreational activities.

Many forms of recreation will help attract higher-skilled, higher-income people. Rural communities may have promising outdoor recreational drawcards such as ski slopes, golf courses, and swimming pools. What they may lack are bowling alleys, indoor swimming pools, and other facilities now found increasingly in suburbia.

It helps both parents and teachers if shopping and other services are on the way to school. That includes the various kinds of dentists and doctors that an average family may need. And these services can typically be provided only near towns and cities.

Rural people have long been disadvantaged by lack of adequate access to good education, health, shopping, and other community goods and services that most Americans recognize as part of the "good life." These rural disadvantages are an ironic byproduct of exploding American technical know-how.

Take a prosperous farming area in Iowa. The commercial farmers who remain make more money because they farm many more acres than their grandfathers did. Today's farmer uses large tractors, hybrid corn, and the rest of the package we think of as modern technology.

Because this farmer is more productive, there are not nearly as many farmers in the county as there were in grandfather's day. So the gas stations, stores, libraries, and other facilities needed by farmers must be further apart. If they are too close, they do not serve enough customers to provide the range of services our modern farm family and their nonfarm neighbors need and expect.

Less prosperous farming areas have lost people, too. Many rural areas depended on other industries like lumber, mining, and railroads. They, too, have tended to lose population because local income and employment opportunities shrank.

Multi-county planning areas are one of the promising tools rural people are using to regain their mastery over technology. By pooling resources of money and technical know-how, rural people are better able to provide the schools and other services they need.

And because citizens of any area need a package of services and facilities, these multi-county development activities often face the need to concentrate services in one area and make parallel provision for adequate access to these services by all local citizens. This area where most services are located is commonly called a "growth center" or a "growth area" or "central city."

FOX'S BOXES

Dr. Karl Fox and colleagues at Iowa State University were some of the early champions of these multi-county development areas. Fox calls them Functional Economic Areas—now popularized as "Fox's boxes."

Dr. Fox suggests that the central city needs to have about 50,000 people. Communities with 50,000 or more people in relatively dense settlements are called Standard Metropolitan Statistical Areas. To date, there are 233 SMSA's deployed throughout the Nation.

About one in four Americans outside these cities does not live within convenient commuting distance of about one hour on a clear day without other commuters.

With all multi-county areas, it is important not to take growth center size too literally. For the more sparsely populated areas, it is even more helpful to think of a group or galaxy of smaller communities as the equivalent of an "exploded city." Thus, some rural areas may provide community services that meet the needs of local citizens although the high school is in one county, the hospital in another, and the factories in a third, for example.

Of course, some rural areas are so isolated that new techniques and new approaches are needed before residents will enjoy adequate opportunities for living and working.

Dr. Brian Berry, a geographer at the University of Chicago, is one of the scholars who has studied commuting patterns to cities and helped identify functional economic areas. He and other scholars, such as Dr. John Borchert of the University of Minnesota, have pointed to what they call a "hierarchy of urban places."

They recognize that cities and towns smaller than 50,000 provide some services needed by consumers. On the other hand, they point out that even a city of 250,000 may not supply all the services needed or wanted by most citizens.

Symphony orchestras, modern medical clinics, large convention centers, and many, many other services and facilities are most readily available in or near large cities.

Multi-county areas have existed for decades—as lines on maps. Some, such as State economic areas, have long been used for statistical purposes. The use of multi-county areas to plan and carry out improved programs for local citizens is relatively new.

One of the outstanding facts about modern multi-county areas is their widespread acceptance and support. More than 30 States now have a Statewide system of multi-county areas or districts for development and planning purposes. Both State and local agencies are using multi county programing.

In addition to Michigan, several States have been successful in school consolidation. The Office of Education (HEW) under Title III of the Elementary and Secondary Education Act provides explicit financial assist-

ance for multi-county planning of education and training.

Some of the earliest multi-county planning areas were created as State planning areas under sponsorship of the Department of Housing and Urban Development (formerly HHFA). Notable later ones are the Local Development Districts of Appalachia and the Economic Development Districts sponsored by the Economic Development Administration.

The U.S. Department of Agriculture has sponsored 56 Resource Conservation and Development Districts, most of which are multi-county in scope. And most recently the Department of Agriculture has cooperated with the Department of Housing and Urban Development in creating special rural (nonmetropolitan) districts for overall development planning purposes.

Students of development like to think of the United States as a patchwork of development districts each with at least one growth center. The growth center is the connecting point to the rest of the United States and the world beyond.

If we think of the United States this way, we can picture the 3,000 or so counties grouped into some 300 to 500 districts. We can think of each district as producing goods and services and selling them to the rest of the United States. From the income they receive, they can provide the needed services to educate and train local citizens and provide the necessary luxuries of life.

We can think of well-trained young men and women moving among these districts and particularly among the growth centers in response to better job and income opportunities or simply in search of something new or different.

This picture is, of course, what technicians need so that they can make a realistic appraisal of development opportunities for various areas. They can also look at possible changes in migration patterns and provide needed technical backup on related questions, such as the scope for "new towns" and the effect of Federal policies on

Fires are stoked in outdoor ovens (ornos) used to precook corn for Mexican food products, a resource-based rural industry in the Northern Rio Grande Resource Conservation and Development project in New Mexico. Foods are grown and processed locally and distributed throughout northern New Mexico and southern Colorado.

the location of population and on employment.

Local citizens have the opportunity to create multi-county areas that will best serve their purposes. It is quite reasonable to expect that several kinds of areas can exist together to perform functions needed by one group of citizens. Some functional areas may continue to be less than a single county and for good and sufficient reasons.

When we talk of multi-county areas, we face the temptation to assume that each county presently has a well-defined and fully coordinated system of government. The facts of life are startlingly different.

As recently as 1967, the United States had 81,248 separate units of local government. Over 70,000 of these units had property taxing authority. That's an average of about 23 separate local taxing authorities for every county in the United States.

There were more than six operating school districts per county. And that doesn't count the private and parochial schools that together employed

some 242,000 teachers, compared to 1,917,987 public teachers.

Multi-county areas are a proven form of local cooperation that often enables local citizens to enjoy services they could not otherwise have. Providing these services in such fields as health and education is a "must" so that rural youth can develop their talents.

The needs of rural youth, even farm youth, in a rapidly urbanizing, technological America are generally the same as the needs of city and suburban youth, so there is much sense in combining town and country resources to provide improved packages of services for all citizens of a multi-county area. However, a multi-county approach is no automatic panacea to local development problems.

Alert and dedicated local leadership backstopped by adequate technical support and citizen commitment have already shown that multi-county planning and development can help define and meet local goals. The seventies will see increasing needs and opportunities for these efforts.

166

Above, logs are assembled into rafts to be floated down Ohio River to wood veneer mill, as part of Tradewater RC&D project in Kentucky. Below, poultry operation in rural multi-county Cherokee Hills RC&D project in Oklahoma.

THE DYING TOWN AND WHY TIME PASSED IT BY

EMPTY STREETS. Store fronts with paint that is faded and peeling. A scattering of frame houses and two- or three-room bungalows.

A small railroad station with doors barred and windows broken. Other buildings standing mute and empty, windows shuttered, doors locked. A stillness in the air, notable for the absence of children's voices.

These are the visible signs of a bypassed community. They are signs that few of us see. They are rarely evident to the suburbanite who commutes to the job "downtown" or to the interstate highway traveler.

They are up the hollers and down the creeks of Appalachia; they are at the intersections of the dusty side roads of the Southwest; they are scattered across the vast expanse of the Great Plains. They are the truly bypassed places that dot the American landscape.

One should not of course assume that *all* villages and small towns are bypassed. Size alone is not the determining factor in whether a place prospers or withers. If there is a single lesson of our development history, it is that development is a function of many interrelated factors.

Not all small communities evidence the symptoms of decay and stagnation. Many are vibrant and growing. Evidence for the 1960's suggests that overall trends in several important indicators—outmigration, growth in nonfarm employment, and personal income, for example—have undergone basic change for the better.

The rate of growth of nonfarm jobs in rural and semirural areas during the period 1962–67, for example, jumped ahead of the rate for metropolitan areas. Though a higher rate is not necessarily the equivalent of a large absolute increase, in some areas the turnaround has been of sufficient scale to result in sizable numbers of new jobs.

Related to the changes in job growth are changing patterns of population movement. In the 1950's, nearly half of all counties in the Nation lost population, principally through outmigration. Since 1960, the magnitude of this outmovement has diminished.

The annual net outmigration from nonmetropolitan to metropolitan areas fell from 670,000 in the 1950's to 216,000 in the period 1960–65. Surprisingly, foreign nations now add more people to the metropolitan area growth from migration than do our own rural areas.

Thus, conditions are changing. Some outlying rural areas are visibly benefiting, many others are not. This chapter addresses the condition of those that are not.

The full dimensions of the problem are not well documented. Evidence must be garnered from a variety of sources. There are around 18,000 incorporated towns in this Nation, over half of which had a population of fewer than 1,000 in 1967. A far larger number are unincorporated; the total is estimated at over 50,000.

Of our 3,049 counties, two out of three were outside metropolitan areas and contained no urban places with as many as 10,000 persons in 1960. Over half of these essentially rural or semirural counties experienced a loss in population between 1960 and 1966.

Several recent studies of the subject indicate that population trends are related to both town size and proximity to cities. The larger the town and the nearer it is to a city, the greater

✦

AUTHOR LYNN M. DAFT is a Staff Economist in the Office of the Secretary of Agriculture.

its likelihood of population growth. Towns of less than 500 appear particularly vulnerable to decline.

Beyond the loss in population stemming from outmigration, an estimated 300 central and south central counties had fewer births than deaths in 1966, resulting in a "natural decrease" in population. This is an unheard of demographic phenomenon in contemporary American history. For those areas affected by it—and it has been predicted the number will grow to 600 by 1970—this is indeed an alarming trend.

Absence of job opportunities in these areas is yet another indication of the seriousness of the problem. While trends taken for rural areas as a whole are improving, more than 250 rural and semirural counties actually lost more nonfarm jobs than they gained between 1962 and 1967. And many of these are the same counties that are rapidly losing population.

Another 750 counties added fewer than 50 jobs per county, per year. In many cases this does not even compensate for the jobs lost in agriculture, not to mention those being lost in other industries and the excess of new job entrants over retirees.

To appreciate what has happened to these places, it is useful to consider the how and why of their origin. Communities come into being for a variety of reasons. In the more sparsely populated agricultural regions, settlements sprang up around farm supply and marketing facilities. It has been estimated that nearly three of every four communities in the Nation today originated as a service center for agriculture.

Their location was often determined by the existing pattern of transportation linkages. The early railroad, with its dependence on fuel and water stops every few miles, exerted an important influence. So also did the constraint of transporting products and supplies by horse-drawn wagon. A distance of 20 miles by such conveyance could easily take as long as 4 or 5 hours.

Towns and villages in nonagricultural regions were associated with other forms of economic activity—the mining towns of Appalachia and the Mesabi Range, the logging centers of the Upper Great Lakes and the Northwest, mill towns of New England, the assembly points along barge canals of New York, Pennsylvania, and Ohio.

Each town contained the rudimentary economic and social institutions: general store, bank, grain elevator, railroad station, church, and school.

At the turn of the century, most social, economic, and political activities occurred within boundaries that were roughly the same. For the most part, the activities were focused on the local community and its adjacent open country. In many respects, these communities were autonomously functioning units, largely independent of their neighbors.

But with time these conditions changed. New, more rapid and more effective means of transportation and communication laid the basis for part of the change. Faster steam driven railway engines with much greater range replaced the wood burners. These, in turn, were replaced by the diesel.

Horse-drawn transportation gave way to the motorized vehicle and all-weather highways. In terms of travel time, the range a person could travel in one hour jumped from 4 or 5 miles at the turn of the century to 50 miles or more at present.

The production process of every major industry, including farming, became more specialized. Coincidentally, the process became more segmented. Fewer factors of production were produced within the firm. The labor input became separated from assembly of the final product by greater and greater distance.

Though this has often been viewed as a replacement of labor with machines, the more important result was the stretching out of the production process and the increasing demand for specialized labor at all the stages of production.

Increased tilling capacity associated with replacing a mule drawn plow with one that is tractor powered, for example, reduces the demand for labor in the field several fold. At the same time, however, it increases the demand for labor in the steel mills of Pittsburgh, the rubber plants of Akron, and the oil refineries of Tulsa. The same is true of other "labor-saving" innovations, of course.

The changing pattern of labor requirements that were associated with this phenomenon redistributed labor geographically as well as occupationally. The major considerations in locating a steel mill or an automobile assembly plant are not the same as those guiding the location of a wheat farm or a sawmill, for example. While land is the determining factor in the latter case, in the former it is large quantities of labor, capital, and accessibility to markets.

Thus, as labor changed occupations it also changed its places of residence. In most cases this resulted in shifts of the population toward more densely settled areas.

In the wake of these changes, many small towns simply lost their reasons for existence. There was no longer a need for large numbers of small settlements scattered over the countryside.

The principal patterns of economic and social activity changed rapidly. But the institutional framework did not. Political boundaries remained fixed. The number of county governments declined by only one between 1957 and 1967.

Although school consolidation has moved at a brisk pace ever since 1940, nearly a quarter of our school systems

Business district of a southern town that once thrived on cotton trade.

Closed-down theater in Kentucky town.

still had an enrollment of fewer than 50 pupils as recently as 1967.

While the small settlements that have suffered from this process are often characterized as bypassed communities, the term itself is somewhat misleading. It is misleading because it defines community in a static rather than a dynamic sense. The community, when viewed as an area within which prominent socio-economic forces interact, has changed drastically.

It is the institutional settings that have failed to keep pace with the changing times. Our attachment to these institutions has inhibited our making many needed adjustments.

In the absence of this adjustment, there has arisen an incongruity in what we call a "community" and what in practice serves as a community. We continue attempting to deal with each crossroads settlement and village hamlet as though it were an autonomously functioning unit for which separate community decisions can be made.

We count the number of "communities" that lack water systems and the number whose population grows or fails to grow through time. We lament that the standard of living within these places is shockingly low in comparison with the remainder of our society.

In all too many instances our solution is to attempt rejuvenation of a totally obsolete institution. It is becoming clear that this won't work. It hasn't in the past and it won't in the future.

But if these solutions won't work, what will? Is there no hope for bringing the people who live in these places nearer the mainstream of our contemporary society? I believe there is, but only after a rather careful look at the fundamentals of our social organization. Three facets that seem

171

to me to be in particular need of a re-examination are our systems of: institutional flexibility, social compensation, and policy rationale.

• Institutional Flexibility. Failure of our social institutions to maintain relevancy in the face of constantly changing needs is a key ingredient. By perpetuating a system of governing institutions based on past patterns of population settlement, for example, the adjustment to changing conditions has been seriously hampered.

It is totally unrealistic to view many of these small places as entities in their own right, capable of providing their citizenry with the full array of public services and facilities consistent with contemporary standards.

Thus, if the people of these villages and hamlets are to share more fully in the fruits of contemporary society, one must view their settlements for what they are—highly dependent parts of a much larger system. They are dependent upon the larger area for jobs, specialized health services, entertainment, consumer goods, higher education, and for a long list of other service items.

Though many of the activities associated with the private sector have already transcended these illusionary boundaries, this dependence has not yet become institutionalized within the public sector. And, since it has not, several of the more vital community functions continue to be performed along the old institutional boundaries—if, indeed, they are performed at all.

It is time, therefore, for us to revise our institutions to accommodate these changes. Some efforts toward this end are already underway. The Federal Government, through the Bureau of the Budget, has asked State governments to delineate these larger "communities" and to begin developing an institutional framework through which each can function with some degree of autonomy. To date, some 30 States have designated over 270 sub-State districts.

But beyond the need for recasting and modernizing present institutions lies an even more fundamental question. Namely, how do we avoid replacing one inflexible institution with another which is equally rigid and recalcitrant? Not only do we need institutions that are more responsive to contemporary needs but we need institutions with a built-in capacity to identify change and to adapt to it.

• Social Compensation. It is a natural outgrowth of a rapidly changing society that some individuals benefit at the expense of others. The costs of change are particularly evident in the small depressed rural settlements.

Thirty or 40 years ago the private market signaled that society valued employment and investments in these areas. In response, many people committed their capital and, in a sense, their lives to these places.

Their commitments took many forms: investments in facilities and equipment, homeownership, the development of personal relationships (family and friends), the learning of specialized trades, etc.

With changes in technology, the market value of many of these activities diminished. In part, this was a direct result of public investment aimed at improvements in the efficiency of production. It was also due, of course, to the forces of the market economy.

Regardless of the sources, however, the results of change have usually worked to the net advantage of the larger society. This is not to say that our blessings have been unmixed; greater industrialization has been accompanied by further pollution of the environment, for example. But even after allowing for these negative effects, I think one must conclude that the net result has been an overall net improvement.

We are faced, therefore, with a net gain for the whole of society while a small segment of the population incurs financial loss, if not hardship. Despite the absence of precise measures of the distribution of these benefits and costs,

172

there is substantial evidence that a disparity exists.

The conventional approach to the distribution of the results of change has been to leave it to the market mechanism and, when that fails, the political process. Limitations of this approach are becoming increasingly apparent.

Two of the limitations are particularly glaring: (1) it has provided those who stand to suffer from the adoption of change with a motivation to resist it; (2) it has often left those who suffer loss without the capacity to adjust.

As our society becomes more highly interdependent with further increases in specialization and urbanization, and as the public sector grows in relative importance, these limitations will become even more apparent.

• Policy Rationale. Finally, one senses a growing need for a rationale to our public policies.

Daniel Moynihan, Counselor to the President, estimates that the number of domestic programs of the Federal Government increased from 45 to 435 between 1960 and 1968. It is little wonder that the growing complexity surrounding this proliferation of programs has made it difficult to discern a sense of national purpose. Comparatively few of the programs are tightly coordinated; some work at cross purposes.

As a Nation, we are in need of a communality of purpose. Not a regimented, federally imposed plan but a coherent and mutually consistent approach to the satisfaction of diverse objectives.

Absence of an overall strategy has been a special handicap to the small towns that lie beyond the metropolitan fringe. Too weak to set forth a plan of action of their own and too isolated from the influence of urban areas, these places have become dependent upon assistance from higher levels of government. Until they can become effectively integrated into the affairs of the larger community, one of their best hopes will lie in formation of a national development strategy.

TOMORROW'S VISION SAVES MANY OF TODAY'S RURAL COMMUNITIES

THOUSANDS OF BUFFALO moving across the landscape in early daylight and at late sunset make a familiar sight to all lovers of western sagas. These animals were constantly on the move.

In a new saga of our land, millions of rural Americans have been on the move too—first like a few drops of water and then like a mighty river, across the face of America.

The buffalo were simply in search of food, but the youths (and they were mainly young people) of the rural communities were searching for jobs, searching for a bright tomorrow.

These great human migrations began with a few from the caves and the hollows, flatlands and hills, river basins and mountains, ghost towns and prosperous farming communities—tricklets flowed, merged, and swelled, and overflowed into the burgeoning cities of America.

Beginning who knows where or when, the rural migrations were beginning to reach multitudinous proportions around World War I—continuing the overflow of the small dams up to the great economic dam of the Great Depression of the 1930's.

Then came World War II; and the great economic dam broke and unleashed millions of rural youth to Europe, Asia, the great cities of this

✦

AUTHOR SELZ C. MAYO is Head of the Department of Sociology and Anthropology, North Carolina State University, Raleigh.

Nation, and the newly established war plants. Thus the scene is clear: youths, millions of rural youths moving, ever moving toward jobs and expanding opportunities.

As a result of accumulated research, science, and technology, there was no reason to even attempt to build or rebuild the human dams in order to provide labor for the farms and ranches across the Nation. The tractor, the reaper, the combine, new seeds and new breeds, insecticides and herbicides—all these and many more have contributed to the life and labor of all the people.

A new era—a new time—had come to rural America. Many rural communities appeared prostrate in view of the heavy migration of young, potential leaders. Pessimism was on every hand and showed itself in locked doors, boarded up windows, abandoned dwellings, depressed spirits, and a good deal of longing for the old days—the good days that really never were.

Rural people continued to produce the food, the feed, and the fiber—both in quality and in quantity—necessary for a rapidly expanding urban nation as well as for our manifold commitments to people abroad.

But the decade and a half from 1945 to 1960 may be looked upon by many as the apathetic years for rural communities across the whole landscape. This was a period in which there was a beginning of the realization that the old order—the older ways of life and labor—could not be restored. New techniques, new procedures, expanded aspirations, needs, wants, and desires— all these and more would be required for the period ahead.

The 1960's represent a different picture of community living. This was a decade of change—trial and error, adjustment, arousal of spirit and will, emerging new patterns of man's distribution across the landscape.

The future rural community will be neither a duplicate of the rural community of the past nor a copy of a large urban center. Its quality will depend upon the extent to which local imagination is combined with the results of research: The scientific-imaginative approach to development and planning.

A quick glance across the rural landscape reveals that former communities have disappeared, others are in a state of atrophy, while some are growing. Another way of stating this story is to point up the tremendous redistribution of the population across the rural landscape during the past one or two generations. It must be assumed that this dynamic process will continue. At the same time, it is not unreasonable to look forward to the building of complete, new communities in the future.

In any case, the search is for quality living for all citizens in these rural communities. How will this quality be achieved? For purposes of this brief analysis, I believe that the following five conditions—elements, factors, or techniques—will set the tone of the future rural community:

(1) Extensive use of professional assistance; (2) community leaders who are both future and outwardly orientated; (3) recognition that each rural community is a part of some larger whole; (4) new relationships with governmental structures at all levels; and (5) a quality educational establishment which conditions people for change.

Rural communities of the future must make extensive use of professional assistance in areas like budgeting, purchasing, taxation, valuation, planning for water and sewage systems, fire protection, and police services. There are many ways that such services may be obtained if the specific community cannot go it alone: two or more communities combining resources, cooperation between county and community, purchasing services from larger communities, and contracting with private consultants.

Leaders in the new rural community must be oriented toward the future and the outside world. This has not generally been true in the past. Citizens must recognize that leadership qualities come from many sources—the young and the old, black and white, females and males, rich and poor, farmers and professionals, and a host of other sources. Leadership potential is extremely broad based in every community if it is cultivated and trained.

Isolation is not a virtue in community living and complete community autonomy is no longer possible even if it ever was. Each new rural community must be viewed, and it must view itself, as a part of several larger wholes. Many problems cannot be solved by a single community regardless of resources available, as problems of land use and air pollution. They must be attacked on at least an area or multi-county basis.

Some rural communities cannot grow. It appears necessary, therefore, that decisions be made and carried out relative to potential growth points. Based on the best possible research, an entirely new system of resource allocation must be instituted by several levels of government. Major governmental inputs will be made at the growth nodes selected; but this does not eliminate services to all individuals.

Quality of the educational establishment in rural communities must be second to none. The curriculum in each school should include comprehensive programs in so-called general education as well as in occupational education. In my view, every high school senior should be graduated with a salable skill. Also, quality programs must be available to adults to meet their needs and interests.

Several brief North Carolina case studies follow which are examples of how some communities have accomplished their thrust forward.

A NEW EDEN

One change or one potential pattern of change in some situations is the merging of villages and rural towns. Continued existence even, but revitalization certainly, is a possible consequence. This, then, is the story of Eden.

On September 13, 1967, three small rural towns merged officially and legally to become the "new city" of Eden. The consolidation did not just happen and it took place neither quickly nor easily. Leaders had to grow and develop and legal tangles had to be unwoven. But merger did happen.

Eden is now a 25 square mile area including three separate rural towns and, prior to the merger, considerable open country area. Leaksville, largest of the three rural towns, had a population of about 6,400 in 1960. Spray had a population of approximately 4,500 in 1960, and the smallest of the communities contained a population of 3,400. In 1967, the population was estimated at 17,500.

The economy of the communities was mutually competitive—the same agricultural base, similar agribusiness associations, manufacturing textile plants, a host of similar manufacturing establishments, and the usual complex of service industries. Residential areas had become confusing and in some cases overlapping; and mail services were often confusing.

Economic development was stifled in many respects and numerous industrial prospects had passed by due to lack of clarity about responsibility for community facilities and services.

All of these and many other problems faced the three communities. Arguments mounted in terms of more adequate services and facilities for all the citizens: police protection, fire protection, water systems, a unified front for the attraction of industry, efficiency in government, and—perhaps above all—a more cooperative spirit among the citizens.

Changing traditions and attitudes is sometimes a slow process and the merger of these three communities is certainly a case in point. The first attempt at consolidation was a failure as the citizens of Leaksville and Spray voted against it in 1959.

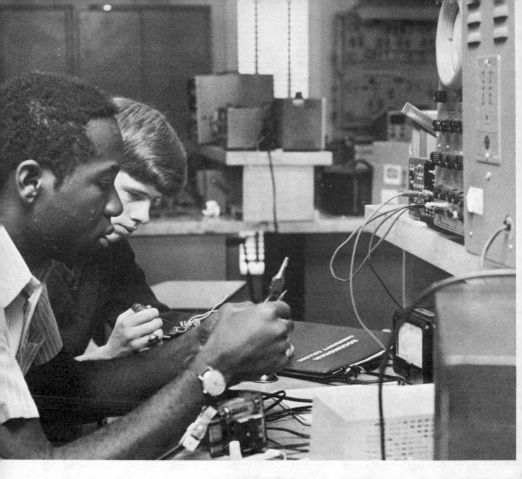

Above, students in basic electronics course at Rockingham Community College. Right, nursing class.

Changes had demanded other changes, however. A single consolidated high school was serving the three rural communities, while a consolidated junior high school was under construction at the time of the merger. A tri-city Chamber of Commerce commenced an aggressive campaign for merger—the idea was very appealing to the young businessmen of the three communities.

Legal mazes had to be conquered. Legislation at the State level was required and this was subject to approval by a vote of the people in the three communities. The climax was reached as the vote went for merger. So one day in 1967 the three communities, including fringe areas, became Eden.

Along with the idea of merging the three communities into the new Eden grew the concept for a community college. Thus, local leaders reasoned, their young people could be properly trained for professions with the long-range goal of attracting industry and providing them jobs locally within the area.

A $922,750 Farmers Home Administration loan was obtained in 1965 to form the Dan River Water Association, Inc., and provide water for 1,000 houses and businesses in and around Eden. As construction began on the new college, a second Farmers Home Administration loan of $154,000 was secured in 1967 to provide water for the new volunteer fire department, and the surrounding community.

Today, 1,500 students from Rockingham and surrounding counties are enrolled at the 2-year college.

Perhaps Eden is not yet the complete garden, but the people are working toward that objective. A substantial new industry has begun construction while several others have expanded. New jobs have been created. Young people have opportunities which did not exist prior to consolidation.

WATER IS CRUCIAL

Water, water everywhere but not a crop for rural community development! Many rural people have always been without the public services usually taken for granted by the city resident. Often such facilities and services require more resources in a rural community. In many instances, the raw material is at hand but organization of the leadership resources is necessary before the physical resources can be exploited.

This is the story of several communities in a rural county pulling together to obtain an adequate water supply for all the citizens—town, village, and scattered farmsteads. Farms and agribusinesses have been and are the very foundation of the county. The communities are very small indeed, including several that are legal entities and several that are open country communities.

In the early 1960's, a community development program was inaugurated, community by community, across the county.

Shortly thereafter the leaders began to analyze their situation, potentials, and prospects. With the help of some professional educators, they began to discover themselves.

The county had been losing population by outmigration, at least since the decade of the 1930's; and estimates indicated that the loss would continue.

As was typical across the Nation, Anson County was losing its better educated young people—those just on the threshold of their productive lives. The number and proportion of elders were building up while the most productive population sector was thinning out. And, in a community poll, it was found that those who had left in order to continue their formal education were not coming back to this rural county.

Thus a reassessment of natural resources was in order.

Flowing on the east side of the county, the Pee Dee River with a supply of more than five billion gallons a day was "rediscovered" and several questions and answers emerged in sharp focus. Additional investigations revealed communities in the county had almost everything going for them except water.

Visions began to take shape—water was a crucial item in the revitalization and future development of the county. Initial planning began in 1963 with the cooperation of the Corps of Engineers. About this time, the Anson County Resources Committee was formed. Concurrently a county manager was employed and he devoted almost full time to this project.

A community and a rural county need assistance, but they must be organized to accept such assistance. In this total effort, 28 governmental agencies were involved one way or another. Here are a few of them: Local Government Commission, State Board of Health, Division of Conservation and Development, Water Resources Board, Soil Conservation Service, Cooperative Extension Service, Farmers Home Administration, and Economic Development Administration.

Grant funds, loan funds, and local community funds voted by the people are making this project a reality.

The community of Ansonville has a new water system financed by the Farmers Home Administration. A new textile fiber plant immediately set up operation there as soon as the system became operative.

The towns of Peachland and McFarlan have water system loans approved by Farmers Home. Industry is expected to follow.

Several other communities are planning water systems to tap on the main line of the county system. New brick homes are popping up almost daily along these new water lines.

The community by community, countywide water system now represents a beginning. A comprehensive sewage system is being planned. A comprehensive recreation study has been completed, and it looks good. Cooperative arrangements for water have already been made with a number of communities outside the county. Other industries are interested and new job opportunities are emerging in this rural county—in these several rural communities.

Some of the small, open country communities can become revitalized but it takes a lot of effort. A fine working partnership must be developed between the people and a host of agencies and organizations. This is the story of one such community and its long struggle for more adequate housing. In the process, many changes occurred, not the least of which is the increasing ability of the people to solve other problems and meet other needs.

With the efforts of a few leaders and the help of the Cooperative Extension Service, community development clubs were organized several years ago in the Young Zion community and in Greenwood. Later the local schools were consolidated and the students bussed about 13 miles to another community. At this point, the leaders joined forces to form the Young Zion-Greenwood Development Association.

Young Zion-Greenwood is a small, open-country community covering an area of about four square miles. The citizens are Negro and they have had a long history in agriculture, largely as tenants and sharecroppers. Today there are few full-time farmers, but most of the adults combine part-time farming with other employment.

As part of their development efforts—a collective method of solving problems—they began to study and analyze their community. They soon discovered their problems were both deep and wide; and many appeared insurmountable. Some of the more pressing problems were:

• Many basic living items were not available in the houses; in fact, 95 percent of the families were without bath, running water, and telephones.

• Over half the houses in the community were classified as dilapidated, and most of the remainder needed major repairs or renovation.

• Over 50 percent of the families were renting their homes in some form.

• Average total cash income per family was estimated to be under $3,000.

Along with kibitzing neighbor boy, Samuel Roach family checks out a planter in front of their new home in Rockingham County, above. Home was financed with $11,500 Farmers Home Administration loan, and is served by Dan River Water Association. Below, Mrs. Roach and daughter Gwendolyn do dishes in new home. Right, house with no running water or bath, formerly occupied by family; in foreground is shallow well. Below right, old privy.

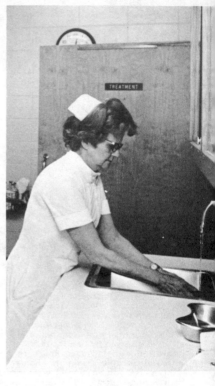

New industries and hospital served by Anson County Water System. Left, textile plant; below, shirt factory. Above, nurse at county hospital.

• There was heavy outmigration of youths and young adults into the urban areas.

Today 90 percent of the families in the community are homeowners. This did not just happen. It was a long educational process for the people. At their regular community meetings, educational and/or technical information was presented by invited representatives of Farmers Home and other agencies.

Some of the agencies and enterprises which cooperated in this great educational adventure were the Agricultural Extension Service, Farmers Home Administration, Public Health Department, the local newspaper, county government, highway department, and private industry as represented by construction companies.

What is the result of this effort? The consequences are quite startling and rewarding.

Over 50 percent of the family-owned homes are new or have been extensively renovated. A third of the families have new homes, complete with baths and running water. New job opportunities are available. Incomes have about doubled. And 10 youths from the community are presently enrolled in college.

These case studies are examples of the infinite ways that cooperation and collaboration are the prerequisites to developing a new rural community.

Ingenuity and imagination by lay leaders must be coupled with the knowledge and skills of a host of available professionals. In turn, these two ingredients must be mixed with a bundle of other resources both from within and from outside the local community. A rationally designed plan of action for orderly development must be prepared, community by community.

On the other hand, disintegration has already caught up with many rural communities. And disintegration stalks the very heart of others as real functional systems. There are many reasons for this, not the least of which is the lack of planning—a plan for the development of the people and their resources.

Planning as visualized here does not mean an attempt to restore the old order, a former way of life and labor. Let the old way of life rest in peace; it served its purpose.

Development means the creation of something new and vital. Everything old will not—need not—be eliminated or destroyed, but the old will be blended with the new. Hence, a new and dynamic way of life will be created in the process.

The emerging rural community will be neither a copy of the past nor a duplicate of the large, urban community. It will contain some of the elements of both, but it will be different. The emerging rural community will provide new and expanded facilities and services, both in terms of quantity and quality.

The old gaps and gulfs, which have been documented time after time, will be torn away. These gaps and gulfs between rural and urban, between need and reality, between possibility and availability must be eliminated in this decade.

Quality of life in the new rural community will be dependent upon the availability and "reachability" of facilities and services for all the citizens. Participation in every aspect of community life is a key element.

Translated in everyday terms, this means that the emerging rural community will have more adequate educational establishments, improved health care facilities and services, recreational services in keeping with a modern society, an economic base which will provide job opportunities, and a governmental structure geared to the expanding needs of the people. Yes, all of this and much more.

Optimistic as it may sound, one may crystal gaze and point up the calculated belief that as the decade of the 1970's closes, rural people will no longer be characterized as either *Yesterday's People* or *The People Left Behind*. Rather, they will be people with tomorrow's vision and life style.

PHILOSOPHIES
OF RURAL LIFE

A PHILOSOPHY OF LIFE is what anthropologists call a *world view*. That is, it is a generalized perspective made up of beliefs, values, and customary ways of solving life's problems.

There have been no systematic large scale studies and few small ones designed primarily to identify different philosophies of life among various residential segments of the population of the United States. Consequently, there is little "hard" evidence concerning the subject.

Thus, we are forced to rely on indirect evidence from behavior and on the comments of knowledgeable students of rural life.

Information from these sources generally supports the proposition that many traditional rural and urban differences in life styles and philosophies have disappeared as rural people have become more urbanized. This does not mean that variations in world view no longer exist between individuals, families, or ethnic groups.

Specialization, diversity, mobility and individualization are characteristic of contemporary America, both rural and urban.

Despite the great heterogeneity that stems from the diverse ethnic, religious, and racial origins of our population, some common beliefs, values, and goals appear to be generally agreed upon by most American adults, regardless of residence.

Robin Williams, in the 1960 edition of his book *American Society*, listed the following typical American values:

"Achievement and success, activity and work, moral orientation, humanitarian mores, efficiency and practica-bility, progress, material comfort, equality, freedom, external conformity, science and secular rationality, nationalism-patriotism, democracy, individual personality, racism and related group-superiority themes."

To this list, I would add the belief that education is not only the channel for upward occupational mobility but the key to solution of all or nearly all contemporary problems.

Not long ago men with college degrees were scorned by farmers and by many others as impractical. Now, advanced education is seen as crucial to successful careers, even in farming.

So, from a position of extreme skepticism about education, rural people have moved to the other polar extreme. Many now have a naive belief that more education will solve poverty, crime, marital unhappiness, and all other problems. There is mounting evidence that the outcomes may be less utopian.

Williams' list identifies values that appear logically inconsistent with other values in the same list; for example, freedom and conformity. Many other examples could be given.

Francis L. K. Hsu, in his 1961 book, *Psychological Anthropology*, has suggested that the element in the American world view which explains these contradictions is what he calls the core value of ". . . self-reliance, the most persistent psychological expression of which is the fear of dependence."

I am not prepared to take as strong a stand as Dr. Hsu with respect to the overriding importance of self-reliance as the core value in the American value system, but it does seem to me that it is one of our most important values and I believe it is generally accepted by the majority, both rural and urban.

In the world of work, the emphasis of self-reliance appears in the Puritan work ethic which stresses the necessity of hard work, long hours, and devotion to duty as a formula for success.

✦

AUTHOR WALTER L. SLOCUM is Professor of Sociology and Rural Sociologist at Washington State University, Pullman.

In the family setting, this is manifested in the common desire of parents to have their children develop into adults who can make their own major decisions and become economically independent.

The idea that society should support able-bodied persons in idleness is clearly repugnant to the majority of Americans, including those who live in rural areas.

Hsu also suggests that the unrelenting competition engendered by the necessity to be self-reliant and successful may contribute to feelings of insecurity, with subsequent negative consequences.

Racial and ethnic prejudice in both rural and urban areas may be due in large part to fear that competition for jobs from people of other races and different ethnic backgrounds threatens the security of white workers.

But even though self-reliance may be a core value, it is not generally pursued to the ultimate of "every man for himself and the devil take the hindmost."

Cooperation to attain mutually desired goals is characteristic within organizations and communities. Furthermore, most Americans have a basic orientation of friendliness and kindliness, a human rather than an animal perspective.

These humanitarian aspects of American philosophies of life have their source in the religious ideology of western civilization. In fact, religion is generally acknowledged to be one of the great character-building forces in our society.

The influence of the Golden Rule and other religious precepts enters into the philosophies of many who do not belong to or attend a specific church.

Growing emphasis in American society on the individual's right to "do his own thing" appears to me to be closely related to the value placed on self-reliance. Paradoxically, while stressing individual freedom and the right to self-determination for ourselves, most of us also believe that freedom to take many types of actions should be restrained.

"There ought to be a law against that" we say, and soon there is such a law.

In my opinion, the idea that the typical American makes his decisions without reference to other persons and groups is largely a myth. Few major decisions are made without reference to the reactions of other people who are important to a decision maker.

Thus, people tend to be guided by the norms, beliefs, and values shared by their close associates.

This does not mean that the idea of self-determination is unimportant. The fact is that it is a shared value and many antisocial actions are justified in terms of it.

"It's his and he has a right to do what he pleases with it" is still heard. But, of course, we all know that an individual is not free to do anything he wishes with his property even though property is highly valued. That is because we recognize that the welfare of others, the interests of society, may be a higher value.

We do not accept the Potlatch custom of the aboriginal Northwest Indians, a ceremony during which chiefs destroyed valuable property to gain prestige. We would send a person who tried to follow this custom to a mental institution. Yet we do approve of certain types of waste such as new fashions in clothes and new models of cars every year.

Writing in the 1940 Yearbook of Agriculture on "A Philosophy of Life for the American Farmer," William Ernest Hocking characterized the farmer as a conservative hard working property owner with an opportunity for a superior family life. He thought of the farm family as the bastion of society and expressed concern that fundamental values would be lost if the urbanization of the countryside continued.

Said Hocking, "No civilization survives when the urbanite becomes the model for all groups." I hope he was

Above, dairy farmer Arthur Litton balances books as family relaxes in their home in Washington County, Md. Below, Littons tend their cows.

wrong, because the pace of urbanization continues to accelerate.

Values and fundamental beliefs change slowly. Changes in core values may take a generation, sometimes longer. Thus, we do not feel the full impact until a new generation of leaders takes over.

There is such a thing as a generation gap. Our own children live in a different world of values from ours. And a small but highly vocal, mainly urban minority apparently rejects many of the values accepted by the great majority of Americans.

Certain identifiable segments of the rural population have distinctive life styles and presumably also have distinctive philosophies of life, although all share to some extent in the major American values discussed earlier.

Commercial farmers are not a homogeneous group that shares a set of values, beliefs, and norms that are distinctive and unique. There are important differences among farm people engaged in different types of farming. Even within a specific type of farming such as wheat ranching, apple growing, beef cattle ranching, or dairying there are regional, local, and individual differences.

A friend who was raised in the ranch area of Montana once told me that the typical attitude toward work of local cowboys could be expressed by the statement: "I can do anything, I mean anything that can be done on horseback."

Nevertheless, all the commercial farmers—or at least all who are economically successful—share with other businessmen a common set of beliefs, values, and norms about private enterprise, including emphasis on the importance of profits, the privileged position of owners of private property, and tax incentives for business.

I do not mean to suggest that commercial farmers do not have a desire for rural living, even though some of the most successful actually live in cities. However, it seems to me that the one common distinguishing aspect of their philosophies of life is allegiance to what might be called the business ethic.

The situation appears to be quite different for part-time farmers and for open country residents who do not farm. For the most part, these people work at nonfarm jobs but live in the open country because they place a high value on rural living.

Many of them believe that the countryside is not only a healthful place to live but a morally wholesome setting for their children to grow up in.

Most of the breadwinners in these families are employees, in contrast to the commercial farmers, most of whom are self-employed. Consequently, while they may share some of the attitudes of the latter concerning property, relatively few are profit-oriented in the same sense as a businessman.

Although there is little objective justification for such a belief, many feel that their part-time farms give them security in case of layoffs. Thus, their farming operations reflect their desire to be self-reliant and independent.

Large local concentrations of subsistence farmers are found in Appalachia and in other areas of the Southeastern United States. In addition, they are interspersed among more prosperous farmers in other parts of the country.

Many are former sharecroppers who have been displaced by cotton picking machines or other new technology. Some are displaced miners. All of them are poor unless they have other sources of income, some because they are ill or too old to compete for nonfarm jobs, others because they are uneducated, and some for additional reasons.

With a few notable exceptions such as the residents of Marks, Miss., many of whom participated in the Poor People's March on Washington in 1968, these disadvantaged rural people do not demonstrate or plead for their rights in the fashion of their kinfolk who have moved into the so-called urban ghettos. Their apparent apathy is a reflection of their philosophy of life.

Many who once had greater aspirations have resigned themselves to their lot, apparently believing that any improvement in their living conditions cannot come through collective action. Yet it is clear from studies in the Southeast that a large number of subsistence farmers have aspirations for their children to rise from poverty.

Lots of the people who live in Appalachia apparently embrace the same values, beliefs, and norms as their ancestors of colonial times did. Although television is now bringing them into vicarious contact with the outside world, they still live in relative isolation and have a world view that emphasizes kinship, membership in small friendship groups, and fundamentalist religious beliefs.

According to the Rev. Jack E. Weller, who resided in Appalachia for many years, the mountain folk tend to be introspective, fatalistic, individualistic, and traditional.

Another major difference from people in the mainstream of American life emphasized by Weller is a tendency to "live for today" rather than being future oriented.

In his words, "The mountain man . . . has a 'regressive' outlook for he does not look forward to tomorrow with pleasant anticipation. For generations his life has been hard and uncertain.

"(Life is) . . . geared toward achieving only the very basic goods needed for survival—food, shelter, and a minimum of comfort."

The competition and anxiety of modern technological society is not characteristic of mountain folk in their home communities. Thus, when they migrate to urban areas they tend to have problems adjusting to new social environments.

This same dedicated adherence to a unique social subsystem and its traditional values is also characteristic of groups such as the Amish, for whom the dominant values are religious.

A 65-year-old farmer works part of his 30 acres of land in Morgan County, Tenn.

Indians preparing to stack hay with tractor stacker in a hay guard chat with USDA man. Thirteen families on Fort Berthold Indian Reservation, N. Dak., formed a livestock association and borrowed funds to buy equipment and breeding stock.

Even today, in the last third of the twentieth century, according to John Hostetler, the Old Order Amish have the same beliefs, value the same ideals, observe the identical social norms, and use the same farming practices as their great, great grandparents.

The noted anthropologist Clark Wissler in his 1940 book, *Indians of the United States*, said "One of the first things to learn about Indians is that there are many kinds of them."

Originally independent, all of the Indian tribes and nations were overcome by the invading whites. Descendants of these proud aboriginal warriors have lived in poverty on rural reservations for several generations. However, few tribes have been willing to abandon all of their traditional values and beliefs even though they were obliged to adopt new patterns of behavior.

Until recently most Indian Americans apparently had accepted their circumstances with the fatalistic philosophy that nothing could be done to change their lot. There are indications that this perspective is changing. Indians in many parts of the United States are beginning to challenge existing arrangements that they now regard as unacceptable.

The perspectives of life of Negroes living in the rural South have grown out of their long history of slavery followed by continued white domination. If we can judge by their apparent reluctance to take direct action to challenge local arrangements, their philosophy of life has changed less than those of their kinfolk who have migrated to the metropolis.

Nevertheless, it seems clear that their perspectives, especially those of younger people, have been changed materially by events of the past decade. Tangible expression of this can be observed in the election of Negroes to local offices and in collective action in some communities

187

Above, Spanish-speaking couple
confer with builder of their new pre-fab
home in Oakley, Calif. Right, husband—
who did good bit of work on home himself—
shows kitchen cabinet to one of his children.
Below, Mrs. Louise Miller and her
15-year-old daughter put finishing touches on
their new home in Madison County, Ala.,
while Mr. Miller is on job as a truck driver.
The family put in about 1,000 hours
assembling and finishing home. Both homes
on page were financed by Farmers
Home Administration.

designed to change school policies and practices.

Rural Mexican-Americans have clung tenaciously to their own value systems and to the Spanish language. In the past, they have proved less receptive to assimilation into the larger society than have immigrants from northern European countries.

In 1954, Lyle Saunders described some of the major aspects of the world views of Spanish-speaking people that differ from the perspectives of Anglo-Americans:

1. They tend to have a different time orientation, instead of being oriented toward the future they are oriented to the present and the immediate past. 2. They do not have a concept of progress and hence express little desire for change. 3. They do not accept the Puritan work ethic, rather they think of work as something which is necessary but not important in itself. 4. They do not stress independence and success for the individual. And 5, they tend to be fatalistic, being ". . . more likely to meet difficulties by adjusting to them than by attempting to overcome them."

For the substantial numbers who are still employed as migratory agricultural laborers and in other unskilled occupations, the foregoing views may still be prevalent. Others have moved out of their native communities in the Southwest and entered actively into competition with Anglo-Americans; these apparently have accepted many of the values and norms of the dominant group.

We may conclude from this brief review that the perspectives of rural residents are characterized by diversity rather than unity, except to the extent that they share with all other Americans certain common values, beliefs, and norms.

Although there are notable exceptions, most people who live in small towns or in the open country are highly urbanized. They do not live in the past but are full partners of their urban contemporaries in meeting the problems of the times.

ENOUGH LAND FOR TOMORROW

WE ARE LEARNING to produce more and more on fewer and fewer acres.

There are several reasons for this. We are applying research findings about genetics, fertilizers and other soil amendments, and controlling insects, weeds, and plant and animal diseases. We have learned to mechanize an increasing number of farm operations. Farmers and ranchers, individually and in groups, are better managers than ever. And we have learned more about conservation— about managing and using our soil and water.

Phenomenal production, especially in the last quarter century, makes it possible to use land for purposes other than production of food and fiber. Demands for other uses which doubtlessly will increase in the future will be met only if we accelerate our program of natural resource conservation, development, and management.

Our natural resource base not only is the strength of our agriculture, but also provides space and conditions for many other uses wanted and needed by the whole population. Thanks to the most efficient agriculture ever developed, we can provide land for purposes besides producing food and fiber.

We have the land for recreation development and use; for parks and wildlife refuges; for wilderness; for second homes in the mountains, in the woods, on a lake, or at the seashore; and for the other amenities of

✦

AUTHOR LLOYD E. PARTAIN is Assistant to the Administrator for Environmental Development, Soil Conservation Service.

living an affluent society demands. Land can be made available to disperse industry, for highways and other travel facilities, and for military and other national defense and special uses.

But we must realize that as competition for land and water increases, food and fiber—people's vital needs—will always have first claim upon these resources.

Obviously, using farmland indiscriminately for purposes other than farming can prevent us from producing

must consider that the conservation job is not done so long as we keep using these resources more and more intensely.

For a future program to be effective, we must know about the availability and condition of our land and water resources. Fortunately, data and information are available in the National Inventory of Soil and Water Conservation Needs, which describe the use and condition of our privately owned rural land. Revised data as of base year 1967 were being prepared

Citrus grove on choice land in Arizona is invaded by housing.

enough food and fiber. By doing more research and using resource management and conservation practices on land, including using water wisely, we can be sure of meeting the increasing and varied demands on our resources. We must also consider that farm, forest, recreational, residential, industrial, and other land is being used more and more intensely. This helps meet resource demands but increases the need for conservation treatment.

In view of resource demands, our future depends on policies and programs for conserving, developing, and managing soil, water, forests, and related resources. In determining policies and setting up programs, we

for publication as this article was written.

U.S. Department of Agriculture agencies participating in this 3-year study are: the Agricultural Research Service, Agricultural Stabilization and Conservation Service, Economic Research Service, the Farmers Home Administration, Extension Service, Forest Service, Soil Conservation Service, and the Statistical Reporting Service.

The Soil Conservation Service has the leadership for this inventory.

Representatives of land-grant universities, State agencies, and interested county organizations also participated, as well as the Bureau of Indian Affairs of the Interior Department.

190

The study is a county-by-county inventory of land use and conservation treatment needs of non-Federal rural land, including watershed project needs. Some of the figures listed here from the inventory may be changed slightly when data have been analyzed completely.

The current inventory shows a total of 1.4 billion acres of non-Federal rural land in the 50 States, of which 437.6 million acres are cropland, 481.9 million pasture and rangeland, 462.3 million forest, and 56.2 million in other miscellaneous uses.

Comparing these figures with a similar 1958 inventory, we find that we now have 10.1 million fewer acres in cropland, 3.5 million fewer in pasture and range, 9.6 million more in forest, and 10.8 million fewer in "other" uses. Almost 15 million acres have been shifted from farming to nonfarming uses in the last decade. Most of this land has gone to urban and other built-up uses; some has become Federal nonfarm land; and some has been covered by ponds, lakes, and reservoirs.

Cropland acreage has been decreasing since 1950. It had risen to 480 million acres by 1920 and stayed near that level until 1950, except for a brief drop in the late 1930's and early 1940's associated with drought and a wartime manpower shortage. Cropland acreage decreased from 478 million acres in 1950 to 437 million in 1967 and is still decreasing. The average annual decrease in cropland has been almost 2.5 million acres per year since 1950.

During this time production per acre has increased about 3 percent a year due to such things as fertilizers, pesticides, better technology including soil and water conservation practices, and less use of lower grade land.

Some of the significant changes in land use have resulted from the Nation's resource conservation program. This aspect of recent land use history is not as well known or generally understood as are figures about decreased acreage in crops.

These changes have come about because better crops and pasture can be grown on land where good drainage, erosion and flood prevention, irrigation, and weed and brush control practices have been applied.

There have been substantial shifts in land use in many areas, such as concentrating crops on fertile, more

Once fertile valley in California spawns jumbled, crowded housing amid land aplenty.

Well-drained site with homes built in harmony with natural landscape, on wooded area in Montgomery County, Md.

level, productive soils, and growing grass and trees on hilly, less productive soils once used for crops.

The amount of food and fiber we can produce on fewer acres seems even more impressive if we consider that we have been meeting the needs of an ever-increasing population with an improving standard of living. Moreover, we can export a substantial amount of what we produce.

Few will doubt that we could not have made such records without public programs including research, extension education, technical assistance, cost-sharing and loans, and stabilization of the production and marketing processes. And industries supplying man-made inputs needed in modern agricultural production, processing, and distribution have contributed a great deal to the most efficient agriculture ever known.

Perhaps the greatest benefit of this efficiency goes to the American consumer, whose real food cost not only is lower than that in any other nation but is the lowest in history. Today we

spend on the average less than 17¢ out of each dollar of take-home pay for food. We spent more than 25¢ a quarter of a century ago.

Efficient agriculture, made possible by public programs and the American farmer's ingenuity, deserves the interest and support of every citizen.

As we look to the future we must remember that our land and water space is finite. For the most part all land suitable for food and fiber production is being used. This has happened relatively recently.

Since, from all indications, demand for the products of the land will increase, natural resource management of the future must be more selective and often more intensive. Even after years of enlightenment and experience in conservation and resource management, much remains to be done and it must be done quickly.

Details of the current National Inventory of Soil and Water Conservation Needs show where we have been and where we must go in managing resources.

192

A LOOK AT THE RECORD

The first modern conservation era in this country came into being in the first decade of this century. President Theodore Roosevelt warned Americans that ". . . to skin and exhaust the land instead of using it so as to increase its usefulness will result in undermining, in the days of our children, the very prosperity which we ought, by right, to hand down to them amplified and developed." A program to conserve and safeguard vast areas of forest, range, and other public domain lands followed.

Agricultural lands of the humid East continued to erode and wear thin. "Bread will win the war" became a slogan during World War I. Too much of the grassland of the Plains was plowed and put to wheat. In a few years the Dust Bowl stirred the concern of everyone, from the farmers who had to leave their land to the ravages of the wind to the Nation's representatives in Congress.

A second conservation era was born. Legislation was enacted giving responsibility to the U.S. Department of Agriculture for providing technical and financial assistance in a program of conservation and use of most of the Nation's land, water, and related natural resources.

In the last 35 years the program of conservation agencies of the Department has healed the gullies and eroded clay hills of much of the Southland, helped the amazing recovery of the Dust Bowl of the thirties, and literally changed the face of the American landscape from coast to coast. But the conservation job is never done because of modern man's many necessities for using the land.

The Department's conservation accomplishments have been made possible through the cooperative efforts of 2 million individual farmers, ranchers, communities, and other land users, who have voluntarily put their conservation plans into effect. The total land involved amounts to three quarters of a billion acres.

In a great measure the success of the Nation's soil and water conservation program is due to its local leadership and control provided through more than 3,000 local soil and water conservation districts covering practically all the land in the United States. Technical assistance from the Department of Agriculture is provided through these districts which are organized under State law and operated by local people. Space here limits recounting but few of their accomplishments:

- Strip cropping covers more than 20 million acres, preventing erosion and pleasing the eye.
- More than 45 million acres are contour farmed.
- Nearly 2 million farm ponds dot the countryside.
- Thirteen million acres of rangeland have been reseeded.
- More than 17 million acres of trees have been planted on farms.
- Wildlife habitat has been improved on another 16½ million acres.
- More than 20 million acres of cropland have been converted to grassland, 3 million acres to woodland, more than a million acres to wildlife and recreation, and some 4 million acres converted to other beneficial uses.
- Some 50,000 land owners and operators have established income-producing recreation enterprises on their lands.

Since the beginning of the watershed protection and flood prevention authorized by Congress in 1954, watershed projects have prevented an estimated $142 million in property damages. More than 11 million tons of sediment have been held out of streams and off lowlands.

Watershed reservoirs provide municipal water supply to hundreds of communities and for industrial development. Planned recreation development for more than 250 reservoirs in 40 States will eventually provide 12½ million visitor days annually.

This relatively new phase of the conservation program should expand rapidly in the future to meet the needs of rural and urban people alike.

Pond designed to prevent water damage and beautify factory site in Ontario County, N.Y.

Only 36 percent of the land in the inventory has been adequately treated with soil and water conservation practices and measures. By major uses, the amounts adequately treated are: 36 percent of the cropland, 29 percent of rangeland, 28 percent of pastureland, 38 percent of forest land, and 71 percent of "other" land.

Of the 278 million acres of U.S. cropland needing soil and water conservation treatment, about 4 percent should be used for other purposes. This is land that is too steep, has soils that are too thin, or has other characteristics that make it unsuited for crop production.

Cultural and mechanical practices are needed on 64 percent of the cropland to hold soil losses to an acceptable minimum. Terraces, stripcropping, and water diversions are needed on 22 percent of the cropland to reduce erosion by wind and water.

About 29 percent of the 40.5 million acres of irrigated cropland is adequately treated, and 12 percent needs only cultural measures such as effective use of crop residues and good tillage practices. This means that on 41 percent of irrigated cropland, irrigation and water management are good. Most needed on the remaining 59 percent is better irrigation, primarily to prevent too much water loss and to use water more efficiently.

About 29 percent of non-Federal rangeland is adequately treated according to current conservation standards. Five percent of the remaining land cannot be treated because of soil, topography, or climate conditions.

The many different plants on native rangeland make it valuable for several secondary uses compatible with producing forage and grazing for domestic livestock. Well managed range benefits big game animals and other wildlife which find a large part of their habitat on rangeland and related grazing land.

Often range treatment and conservation practices can be changed to improve wildlife habitat yet still meet the primary objective of livestock production. For many rangeland owners and managers, producing game is a primary objective and livestock grazing is secondary. Livestock and game usually can be companion crops.

Our wide expanse of native grazing land—interspersed with ridges, escarpments, and water courses, and having many different kinds of plants, topography, domestic animals, and wildlife—invites a growing number of

Grass reseeding to rejuvenate wornout range land, Garfield County, Wash.

recreationists. More and more range-land owners and managers operate their enterprises as guest ranches for part of the year. Some provide lodging and guide services to earn extra income from hunters and fishermen.

In determining conservation needs and in applying practices, both primary and secondary uses of grazing land should be considered.

Of the nearly 102 million acres of pastureland, 70 million need conservation treatment to improve vegetation and to supply forage needed on farms and ranches. About 28.2 million acres are adequately treated. Nearly 3 million acres should be converted to forest or to another noncropland use, and on another 1.3 million acres conservation treatment is not feasible. Most pastures are on soils that can be treated and managed effectively.

The Conservation Needs Inventory covers forest that is not in National Forests or on other public land of the United States. The Nation's private forest resources are 2½ times as large in area as all public forest land. Of the total 462.3 million acres, 398.2 million acres are called commercial forest and the remaining 64.1 million acres noncommercial. Conservation treatment is needed on 71 percent of the privately owned commercial forest land.

On some privately owned noncommercial forest land, forest needs to be reestablished or reinforced to protect watersheds, benefit wildlife, or hide the scars of past misuse.

A part of the National Inventory of Soil and Water Conservation Needs deals with watersheds. In this part, 19,194 upstream watersheds ranging up to 250,000 acres were identified.

In some of these watersheds the U.S. Department of Agriculture is assisting local sponsoring organizations under authority of the Watershed Protection and Flood Prevention Act (Public Law 566 as amended—83rd Congress). The kind and extent of upstream watershed problems needing action—beyond land conservation action discussed earlier—were estimated for each watershed.

Flood plains in these 19,194 watersheds comprise about 134 million acres, of which 129 million are rural and 5 million in urban areas. This kind of information about flood plain land has not been available before.

Problems needing project action include floodwater and sediment damages on 92.7 million acres of agricultural land and 2.8 million acres of

195

urban land. On 72.8 million acres project action is needed to treat severe erosion damage. Better drainage is needed on 65.4 million acres, and another 16.7 million acres need to be irrigated.

Multiple-purpose development is an effective way to meet resource needs in a watershed area: water supply and control facilities are combined with flood-prevention measures. There is a need and potential for developing rural water supplies in 5,540 watersheds, recreation in 12,396, better fish and wildlife in 13,059, and water quality control in 8,778.

The significance of these data and this information about conservation needs on rural land goes beyond problems of producing food and fiber. This information and similar studies—such as timber resource inventories, water supply and water management investigations, and other studies of basic natural wealth—show the importance of resource management. From these studies it is evident that resource management can be the key to solving many problems of future competition for land and water.

Competition for land and water becomes stiff as more people demand more parks and playgrounds, more wilderness and wildlife sanctuaries, and other uses which seem essential and desirable for modern living. Tomorrow's resource management must try to meet these demands so far as possible. We are fortunate that to a great extent we can allot resources to these and other uses. In many situations these uses are compatible with farming, ranching, and commercial forestry.

To best satisfy the interests of all people concerned, resource management must be considered fully in community, area, regional, and national development plans and action programs.

People must realize that to meet the needs of a growing population at a higher standard of living, we must limit the areas of natural resources that we lock up merely for preservation. In many situations, multiple use will have to prevail over single use. As demand for land and water resources grows, the price we pay for limited use or nonuse will be greater.

Fortunately, with our stewardship, scientific know-how, and resource management, we can meet most of the foreseeable demands for our land and water resources in an orderly manner.

Multiple use—grass, cattle, trees, recreation—all in harmony with the land's capability, in Laurens County, Ga.

A BETTER LIFE
ON THE PLAINS

MY OWN HUMBLE OPINION is that, with the exception of a few favored localities, the whole Great Plains region is already a desert that cannot be reclaimed through the plans and labors of men.

With these words, written in 1938, Lawrence Svobida closed his book entitled *An Empire of Dust.* Yet before the next decade had passed, the area was an abundant supplier of food to "win the war and write the peace."

What brought about the change? It was a unique combination of science, economics, engineering, and the resilient resourcefulness of the people on the land which reversed Svobida's evaluation of the future of the Plains.

Svobida was a young farmer who had come to Meade, Kans., in 1929 and after 9 years of hardship in the heart of the dust bowl, it was only reasonable that he should sum it up as he did. Elsewhere in the region the experiences were also extremely distressing—not as completely devastating but more prolonged.

The future seemed to hold little promise for those who had lived through the 10 years which Svobida described in his book. Adverse climatic forces had joined with a nationwide economic debacle to make the thirties a decade of disaster for America's semi-arid agriculture.

It must be recognized that the situation was not altogether the product of sudden disaster. As a matter of fact, symptoms of distress were plain during the early twenties. By the early thirties, the Great Plains was recognized to be a major problem area. The economic and physical decline which preceded the dust storms was caused, in large part, by lack of information about dealing with a semi-arid environment.

Theoretically, if the scientists and the economists of a later day could have preceded the frontiersmen into the semi-arid zones, many mistakes could have been averted.

The scientist could have worked out production methods which were compatible with the soil and climatic characteristics of that newly-occupied region.

The economist could have advised the settlers as to how much land and what types of equipment were needed to sustain a family. Also, he could have told all the members of the new community that variable income from year to year would put an unusual strain on the local financial and commercial structure.

And, of course, if there had been such a thing as a modern-day sociologist, the problems of community organization, such as public and commercial services and neighborhood relationships, could have been put into better perspective.

In actual experience, however, the adversities encountered by the settler far outran the accumulation of scientific and economic knowledge. However, the researchers were by no means idle. In fact, research in the physical sciences was begun before the turn of the century by experiment stations in most of the Great Plains States. The work was augmented by special dryland experiment stations, which were established through funds authorized in 1906 by Congress. But not until after World War I did the findings become available and begin to be taken seriously.

By that time, the scientists were suggesting some startling changes in crop

+

AUTHOR ELMER A. STARCH, now retired, worked from 1926–50 in semi-arid agriculture in the United States, as a coordinator of programs for its redevelopment, and served for 12 years in similar activities in several developing nations.

197

Above, wind sweeps soil off Iowa farmland in 1930. Below, a desert type landscape in Wyoming in 1967, with sheepwagon house and herder.

Wind-blown soil buries farm machinery and automobile in barn lot, Gregory County, S. Dak., 1936.

production methods in a moisture-deficient environment. For instance, they said "don't plow." Plowing turns under trash which ought to stay on the surface. The practice exposes too much soil to rapid evaporation and worst of all, it is too slow. This, they said, is in itself a handicap to good farming where timeliness of operation is a very critical factor.

The soils scientists found that unleached dryland soil was a great reservoir of plant food. They said that lack of moisture rather than fertility was the limiting factor. Therefore, moisture preservation should be the prime objective of dryland cultural practices. These were only some of the findings which would make life in critical moisture areas unique.

Taking note of the scientific discoveries and of the farmers' experiences, some leaders thought there was need for a revised system of management. M. L. Wilson of Montana State College pointed this out in a management survey published in 1923. Wilson's findings were carried further by the Montana Experiment Station through a most unusual system of research.

This new research approach was made possible by a reorganization of the work of Montana's Agricultural Economics Department in 1926 under

M. L. Wilson's direction and two new sources of funds.

The first source was Federal funds provided under the Purnell Act adopted by Congress in 1925. Purpose of the legislation was to stimulate economic research for agriculture. The second source was a grant by the Laura Spelman Rockefeller Foundation in 1924, for establishment of a special research unit looking toward agricultural recovery.

The special research unit was called the Fairway Farms Corp. It worked on farm financing, farm reorganization, and farm management, and facilitated adoption of new developments in science, engineering, and other areas.

Under the aegis of Fairway Farms' experimentation in the economic area, findings of the physical sciences were also brought together so that the pieces could be assembled into an effective whole. The testing period for bringing everything together into a scheme of operation was short, but the work was intensive. It began in 1924 and by the end of the 1928 cropping season, a set of revised principles of management had been developed as a standard procedure for semi-arid agriculture.

The experimental processes which preceded the rewriting of the rules of

199

management were preceded by projections. A series of theoretically constructed farm and ranch organizations was designed, and an operational formula fitting the physical environment was outlined.

An assumption was made that specialization and mechanization would be the dominating features of an agricultural renaissance. The formula also had to meet the stresses and strains which were occasioned by the rapidly changing economic situation following World War I. For example, wheat would probably be sold for 80 cents a bushel. The old standard had been one bushel—one dollar.

The management research of Fairway Farms from 1924 to 1928, which incorporated the findings of the scientists and the experience of farmers into an operating unit, proved that both mechanization and specialized production would play a big part in making the farms and ranches of the Plains country viable. After 1928, complete reorganization of spring wheat farms was recommended by the Montana Extension Service.

Today, a visitor to the semi-arid zones of America will find an almost universal adjustment of farm operation in accordance with the criteria upon which the recommendations of 1928 were based. It is remarkable that so much adaptation could take place within one man's lifetime.

There are thousands of the new Great Plains farms which one could visit to see the change. However, the farm of George Rubin of Whitetail, Mont., is a good illustration.

Rubin began farming in 1928. His community was subject to dust storms and distress but it did not suffer the complete devastation of Svobida's community. For that reason, recovery could come more rapidly in his area than in other places, but the principles underlying the recovery and redevelopment are similar for the entire area.

Rubin and most of his Plains neighbors began adjusting their operations according to the new rules set forth by the Montana Extension Service by specializing in what they could produce to best advantage, increasing the productivity per man by mechanization, protecting the land surface through suitable methods of cultivation, trying to level off year to year variation of yields through land management practices, and other adaptations.

It is the product of these multiple adaptations that one sees within relatively prosperous semi-arid zones today.

The adaptations are in turn the product of science, economics, invention, and the refinement of the people's own experience.

The reorganization of farms and better individual management alone could not restore the economy of the semi-arid portions of the country. Needed was a broad scale and thorough reassessment of the entire problem area and also a practical land utilization strategy. Prolonged drought and depression had greatly accentuated a situation of maladjustment which existed from the days when the new settlers had rushed into an unknown environment.

On September 17, 1936, President Roosevelt appointed the Great Plains Committee to draw up a "long term program for the efficient utilization of the resources of the Great Plains." Its report went beyond the management of the individual unit and included suggestions for a broad, land use type of approach.

The President, in transmitting the report to Congress on February 10, 1937, urged that "a new economy must be developed—which represents generally a more rational adjustment . . . to natural conditions." He emphasized the need for cooperation between Federal and State governments, and individual citizens of the region.

He concluded: "A policy should be determined, a long-run program formulated, and execution begun without undue delay."

The development of a sustained land use pattern for the Great Plains required a thoroughgoing assessment of factors which caused development of the maladjusted situation.

It was fortunate that some members of the scientific, administrative, and economic communities had been studying the situation for a decade before the drought, political unrest, and depression struck in full force in the early thirties. They were convinced that if a successful congenial habitat was to be built to survive, it was necessary to ask questions everywhere and of everyone and then look ahead to see what could be done. What they had learned formed a background for the long-term program such as the President had asked of the Committee.

The facts had to be made available to as many people as possible. Most of all, it was necessary that the people accept the hard fact that the Plains country lay in a critical climatic zone and had to be handled accordingly.

To effectively implement a redevelopment program, it was obvious that special care should be taken to correlate the efforts of the citizenry and the Government agencies. The President's Committee suggested a local coordinating effort where the Federal and State agencies would join in shaping programs to the needs of the situation.

During the months following the President's message to Congress on February 10, 1937, arrangements were worked out in the Plains States whereby the local people would analyze their own situation and work out the means for improvement.

As soon as a general consensus had been attained, the Under Secretary of Agriculture, M. L. Wilson, met with representatives of the Land Grant Colleges to formalize the understanding. Shortly thereafter, he assigned a representative of his office to each section of what came to be known as the Great Plains Agricultural Council.

The work program as set out by the group was correlated with the suggestions as outlined by the President's Committee, among these being:

• A problem-oriented research schedule for the next 9 years carried forward by the Federal and State research agencies.

• A policy and a program to shift lands to their most effective use, like moving marginal lands to grazing.

• An outline of policy affecting land and water use, systematic land management, restoration of tax delinquent land to systematic management, and steps for conserving resources.

• Encouragement to the individual manager to bring his operations into harmony with climatic realities, to create feed balances, and to adopt all feasible soil and moisture conservation practices.

It was a program designed to bring about adaptations which would enable citizens of the area to evolve a lasting and satisfactory environment in which to learn, earn, and live.

It may well be that it was because of common goals that the Great Plains community became an outstanding example of development. It is a case where the people took hold of an ineffective and declining economy and drew on the ingenuity of experience, used science, absorbed automation, reorganized resource usage, and revised public service in order to make a more viable and more congenial environment.

With the limited information at hand the people within each locality did the very best they could. They mobilized their resources, made decisions, shaped plans, and entered into an effort to put productivity and well-being on a higher plane.

The Great Plains became a laboratory in which the many elements of adjustment were measured and where development principles were tested. The adjustments were not without great cost to the people involved. Out of the wreckage of the depression, the drought, and maladjustment, a fairly strong economy and a reasonably good place to live has been rebuilt.

Even though not everything was as

effective as it was hoped and even though the cost to the people was great, local planning and concerted effort have brought a higher standard of well-being to America's semi-arid zone than exists in any similar climatic area in the world.

It is a significant note in the history of the world that arid and semi-arid agriculture have given major support to the growth of civilization. Our recorded history shows this in more detail for the eastern Mediterranean areas than it does for Mexico and other parts of the world. The ancient sources of food supply have remained in a more or less traditional status over the centuries while areas of more abundant rainfall became the major suppliers of food and fiber.

An altogether new impetus was given to semi-arid agriculture through a revised system of management which was developed during the second quarter of the twentieth century.

A very distinct set of cultural prac-

Trees planted as windbreaks in Grand Forks County, N. Dak.

tices has been added to the world of agricultural production. The discoveries in science and in economics, as well as the products of engineering, have had a worldwide influence.

Use of the agricultural resources of the Great Plains has been improved very markedly. There is much less likelihood of serious soil erosion since millions of acres of sensitive land have been returned to permanent grass cover, and a large percentage of the cultivated land is being surface cultivated to insure trash cover for wind protection.

Some areas of the wheat producing country are being protected by strip cropping. The techniques of production and the quality of the varieties of wheat have been improved. Yields have increased to the point where one of the States has almost doubled its predrought volume of cereal production.

The skills and the facilities for productive use of the scarce water resources are now such that millions of acre-feet are being beneficially retained. Part of it is in ground storage through the practice of summer fallow. Part is in very small reservoir and diversion installations. Part is in more than a million stockwater reservoirs distributed quite densely over the Plains.

Also, the water available to irrigated land is much more efficiently used because of land preparation and farm layout. Striking laborsaving has been introduced into irrigation farming as a result of research work done on a group of pilot projects established in 1937.

Uncertainty of income and variability in production have been reduced through techniques of tillage, cropping sequence, and timeliness of operation. Security of tenure has been practically assured by adaptations in financing. Volume of production per farm or ranch unit has been made more adequate through increased productivity per capita, as a result of labor distribution, mechanization, and specialization of production.

Newly established waterway in Codington County, S. Dak., fall seeded with rye and bromegrass.

Fifteen to 20 percent more livestock is being carried on the grasslands because of improvements made in the range itself by management practices such as seeding selected grass varieties and rotated grazing. The 1,000,000 stockwater reservoirs have also improved grazing efficiency.

The semi-arid Plains now enjoy reasonable stability in sustained production capacity instead of being a serious problem area.

This stability was made possible by a number of interrelated factors, not the least of which are U.S. Department of Agriculture programs. Long-term credit, cost sharing to install needed conservation practices, and related agency programs teamed up with economic and agricultural research to help make needed changes.

A unique program of long-term cost sharing, through contractual arrangements with farmers and ranchers, was authorized by Congress in 1956. These contracts, based on conservation plans for entire operating units, help bring about needed stability through the planning and application of desirable land use changes, needed changes in cropping and grazing systems, and the installation of conservation practices.

The Great Plains Conservation Program has thus far contracted for complete conservation treatment on more than 36,000 farms and ranches covering nearly 65 million acres.

The quality of living has been raised in many respects and is no longer that of an impoverished community. Housing has been decidedly improved because the economy has been reorganized to bring a better income. The Rural Electrification Administration has brought electricity and telephones even to the sparsely-located farmsteads, reducing drudgery and enhancing livability. Roads have been improved selectively and maintenance of unneeded roads has been discontinued.

However, some aspects of well-being have not yet been brought up to the highest American standard. Creative or even suitable criteria have not been found for providing adequate health facilities or school systems. Recreational and community activities suffer from lack of innovations. The trade and commercial structures have not been revamped to give as much service as would be expected in a genuinely modernized era.

The purpose of improved efficiency and stabilized organization must surely be that of an optimum environment and adequate opportunity for personal growth and expression. Now, since drudgery, isolation, and poverty have been reduced, there can be a commensurate enhancement of the means which allow for the optimum usefulness and enjoyment of a span of life.

COMPETITION FOR LAND RESOURCES

MR. AVERAGE AMERICAN needs less land for his food, less land to provide materials for his clothing and shelter, and less land for his residence and related services; but the number of Americans is increasing.

At present, the more efficient use of our land is counterbalancing the population increase. While there is competition for some resources and unwise use of others, no major shortages of land for the various uses now exist.

But one might ask about future prospects.

An example of competing use of land is the drainage of wetlands for agricultural use, thereby destroying refuges for wildlife. Strip mining denudes the landscape, thereby affecting scenic beauty. Another example is the destruction of homes for innercity throughways. Congested urban build-up uses compete with open-space uses. Prime agricultural land is used for urban purposes in instances where less productive land would suffice.

Compatible uses of land might involve use of agricultural land for hunting. Agricultural use can be complementary to wildlife use.

Some farmers manage parts of their land for various recreation pursuits of urban people, without losing it for cropping or the raising of livestock. Some farmers provide cabins or room and board for vacations with a rural atmosphere. Riding stables, hunting privileges, and management of farm ponds for fishing are other compatible uses of farmland.

Farmers gain supplemental income from these pursuits, and the recreational activities can often be scheduled for periods of the year when farmwork is light.

As the population increases, larger portions of land must be set aside for the benefit of the general population, to uses such as recreation, open space, parks, highway systems, and other nonagricultural uses. As these land use needs are met, we can expect increasing competition for land in some areas.

The United States contains a vast expanse of land. The 48 contiguous States contain 1.9 billion acres of land. Our two newest States, Hawaii and Alaska, push this total to 2.3 billion.

About two-fifths of our land in the 50 States is in Federal ownership or trusteeship. Most of Alaska is in public ownership.

Our land resources consist of many different kinds of terrain, soil, and climate. Because of these different

✦

AUTHOR MELVIN L. COTNER is Director, Natural Resource Economics Division, Economic Research Service.

COAUTHOR LOUISE N. SAMUEL is on the Staff of the Natural Resource Economics Division.

Fishing at Hungry Horse Reservoir, Flathead National Forest, Mont. Reservoirs provide recreation as well as water storage and flood control. The national forests, of course, offer a broad range of recreational and other uses.

characteristics, development and use of the land vary considerably from one part of the country to another.

Historically, too, the use of land changes. The most important changes in recent years have been the decrease in land used for agricultural purposes, and the much smaller but significant shifting of land into urban development, transportation, recreation areas, and similar uses.

For many decades, over half the land in the 48 contiguous States has been used as agricultural cropland, grassland pasture, and range.

In 1900, total cropland acreage accounted for little more than a fifth of the country's area. As the population grew, cropland area also increased. By 1920 it occupied about a fourth of the land.

During the 1930's, there was a slight decrease in cropland. Severe drought and subsequent wind erosion of the soil in the Great Plains brought about the abandonment of many farms in the so-called Dust Bowl.

Some other farmers left their land or gave up farming because of low prices they received for their crops and livestock during the depression years.

World War II brought increased demands for food and fiber for domestic use and export. To meet these needs, land used for crops again increased. By 1950, much of the abandoned land had come back into production. Currently, total cropland accounts for only 23 percent of our land resources.

From 1950 to 1970, there was an estimated net reduction of 37 million acres of total cropland in the 48 States, or 1.9 million acres a year, on the average.

Nationwide, the amount of land used for crops is decreasing. The change in cropland varies by region, however. In some areas, cropland has remained stable or has increased, while other areas have released cropland for other uses. During the 1944 to 1964 period, a total of 54 million acres shifted to noncrop uses. At the

205

same time, 27 million acres of new land in other areas were brought into crop use.

Shifts of land to noncrop uses have been most prominent in the Southern Plains and in the States south and east of the Corn Belt—that is, in the Northeastern, Appalachian, and Southeastern States. Low productivity of the soil, and fields that were too small, too rough, or too isolated for cultivation with large modern farm machinery, were mainly the reasons for abandonment in the Southeast and the Appalachian area. On the eastern seaboard, considerable acreages of land going out of agricultural use have been converted to residential development, recreation use, transportation facilities, and similar uses.

There has been a continuing, long-time downward trend in total cropland in the Southern Plains (Oklahoma and Texas). In some parts of the area, soil moisture is inadequate even for dryland farming. The loss of land has been partly offset by newly irrigated land in the west Texas High Plains.

The cropland acreage overall has changed little in the Mountain and Pacific regions in recent years. Irrigation projects have improved productivity on existing cropland, and have brought new land into use.

The appearance of new cropland in southern Florida is associated with clearing and irrigation projects, in the Mississippi Delta with clearing and draining, and in the Texas High Plains, California, and Washington with expanded irrigation facilities. Expansion is associated with dryland farming techniques in northern Montana, and with various techniques such as drainage, clearing, leveling, and contouring throughout the Corn Belt.

MAJOR LAND USES, 48 CONTIGUOUS STATES, 1950–1980

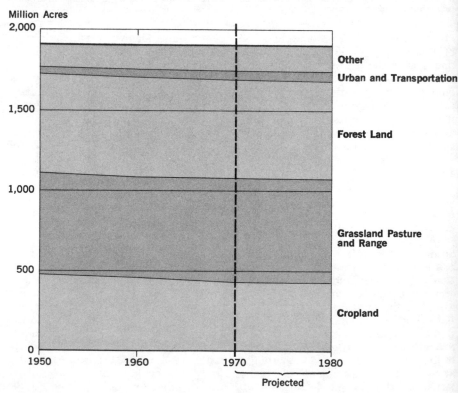

Development and improvement of land resources have added to our stock of cropland in some regions, even though the overall cropland acreage has been downward. In effect, there has been an appreciable cropland shift to areas not only more productive but better adapted to modern farming technology.

Several factors have contributed to our increased agricultural productive

the area in the 48 States, and this share will probably continue, at least through 1980.

Pasture acreage has not changed significantly in recent years. Range and pasture management practices, including brush and tree clearing, have increased forage production significantly.

Americans are eating increasing amounts of meat, especially beef. As long as personal incomes keep rising

Cattle being moved across good rangeland of native grass in Washington State.

capacity. Among them are heavier use of commercial fertilizer, expansion of irrigation facilities, increased mechanization, shifts of high-value crops to better soils, greater use of pesticides, and development of improved varieties of crops.

Land is being released from cropland use in some areas where competition for the land is keen, especially in the large metropolitan regions in the East. This makes more land available for recreation and associated uses. Much of this land reverts to permanent vegetative cover, which increases the amount of wildlife habitat.

At the present time, grassland and pasture ranges occupy about a third of

and population continues to grow, this trend will continue. Although livestock numbers have been increasing to meet demand, the use of feed concentrates has reduced the pressure on our grazing land.

Increasing numbers of cattle are being finished in feedlots, and the feedlots are growing in size. For example, the number of feedlots in the Great Plains actually decreased about 15 percent from 1962 to 1968, but the number of cattle marketed from feedlots almost doubled. The expansion of irrigation and improvement in other management practices have increased the output of feed grains and forage per acre, to take

207

Agriculture and hunting are compatible uses of this land near San Francisco Bay. Oat stubble, left standing after harvest of the grain, provides good cover for pheasants and good shooting for hunters from a private club.

care of more animals on less land per head.

Forest land use has increased slightly over recent decades, but the regional shifts have been more pronounced. In recent years, substantial areas of noncommercial forest in the West and the Southwest have been cleared or reclassified to other uses. Commercial forest acreage in the South and East has increased.

There may be some gains of forest land in localized areas through reforestation of cropland and pastures. This may be offset in part by diversion of forest land to other uses, such as residential areas, highways, reservoirs, and transmission lines.

Forest and woodland occupied a little over 30 percent of the area of the 48 States in 1970. This share is projected to increase only slightly by 1980.

The shift of land into intensive urban uses has been increasing gradually over the years to meet the demand of our growing population. Currently, about 3 percent of our land is devoted to intensive urban and transportation uses.

Our population is highly concentrated. Seventy percent of the people reside in urban areas that comprise around 1 percent of our geographic area. Population pressure for residential and industrial locations is expected to mount in the coming decades. More and more land will go into urban development and transportation uses.

Given that the U.S. population is expected to increase about 15 percent during the decade of the seventies, land used for urban purposes probably will reach 65 million acres by 1980. Currently, about 58 million acres are classified as being in intensive urban and transportation use.

More land is being used for less intensive special uses such as parks, related recreation areas, wildlife refuges, and public facilities. By 1980 these uses are expected to total 92 million acres, about 7 million acres more than is currently used.

As the population expands and as the workweek shortens and more leisure time becomes available, additional park and recreation space will be needed. And hunting enthusiasts will desire more space for preserves, refuges, and wilderness areas.

Land requirements for new public facilities probably will not be large.

Two patterns of urbanization are typical of all parts of the country. One is suburban or fringe development adjacent to the older urban areas. The second type is noncontiguous or "leapfrog" development, which takes place in scattered areas and regions ranging in size from small groups of houses to larger and relatively independent communities.

Development along fringe areas does not follow a single pattern. In some areas, development takes place along the periphery of the older city. In other areas, development may take place along major highways, stretching out from the city's edge into the countryside.

A recent study on urbanization of land, based on interpretations of airphotos of 48 counties in eight Western States, is indicative of changes taking place in metropolitan areas throughout the United States.

Of some 465,000 acres of land converted to urban use in the study counties from about 1950 to 1960, about 71 percent went into dense residential use such as apartments, row houses, and small house lots. Another 13 percent went into open residential use—one house or less per acre.

Of the remaining area, industry took 6 percent; institutions such as schools and hospitals, 4 percent; commercial developments (such as shopping centers), 3 percent; recreational use, 2 percent; and airports, nearly 1 percent.

About three-fourths of the land that was urbanized was previously in crops, usually high-value irrigated crops. The share in crops ranged from over 90 percent to 10 percent for various counties. Grassland also contributed land for urbanization. Only 2 percent of the land had been idle prior to its conversion to urban use. Significant quantities of land around Seattle and Portland were previously in forest.

In California, Los Angeles, Orange, Riverside, and Santa Clara Counties used cropland for over 90 percent of their expansion. An average of 14,000

acres per year in these four counties were taken for urban expansion during a period of about 11 years.

Phoenix (Maricopa County) used 80 percent cropland for its urban expansion. The shift to urban land averaged over 3,000 acres per year. At the other end of the scale, only about 10 percent of the land that was urbanized in the Seattle area came from cropland.

As an area becomes more populous, land is used more intensively and less of the area is left as open space. In the Western study there were recognizable patterns of urbanization related to the size of the parent community. The larger metropolitan areas had 60 percent of the total increase in population during the 1950–60 period, but took only 40 percent of the area that was urbanized.

The gain in areas for the larger metropolitan communities was .05 acre per new inhabitant for the population gained, compared with .13 acre in the smaller communities. The average for all counties was .07 acre per capita.

The relationship of land urbanized and population increase varied greatly within the study area, however. In Monterey County, only .02 acre per new person was urbanized. In two counties in the Portland vicinity, the area averaged .24 acre. San Bernardino County, Calif., was at the other extreme, with .43 acre per capita population gained.

Many factors affect the urbanization of land. The size of lots is often regulated by zoning laws or the specifications for a particular subdivision.

Topography, and to a less extent soils, also have a significant influence. Some areas are easily developed for intensive residential use; other areas develop into housing patterns involving large lots.

Although residential development is not directly related to development of commercial and other nonresidential uses, there is some correlation between them. Business and industry locate where they will find customers and labor, or else they come first and the people move in afterwards. Intensive

recreational facilities such as golf courses and drive-in movies are generally developed in populated areas.

Recent trends in land use and the prospect for the decade of the seventies suggest that the competition for land will not be severe. From a quantitative standpoint, this may be true. Even with modest increases in our exports, our food and fiber productive capacity appears adequate to 1980 and beyond, with land to spare. Likewise, with proper management, our grazing land and forest land acreage should prove to be adequate. Urban and industrial land uses could increase severalfold

before major conflicts in use come about from a total area standpoint.

The price of land continues to climb. Land prices increased from $116 to $194 per acre during the decade of the sixties.

Agricultural land, as well as land for urban uses, has increased in sales value. A number of factors are related to the rise in land values. Urban and industrial developers will be able to outbid

Above, farmland near Idaho Falls, Idaho, in 1951. Opposite page, urban development that had taken place by 1966.

210

griculture for their land requirements.
'rice levels for urban lands will in-
luence the location and extent of
iousing development. High land prices
vill discourage extensive agricultural
ises, such as forestry and grazing, in
ome areas.

The emerging problem concerns *how*
ve use our land resources. Questions
iow center on the *quality* of the service
,nd products coming from our land
esources.

While our land resources appear
o be adequate, are we using them
visely? Are we using them in a man-
ier consistent with environmental

quality objectives? The health and
welfare of our population will be
greatly affected by where new urbanization takes place. New towns must
be judiciously located within our
boundaries to accommodate some of
the 100 million additional people in
prospect by the year 2000. Migration
patterns will need modification. The
alternative is to crowd the existing
urban areas.

Air and water pollution within
existing urban areas recommends
against further concentration of economic activity. New urban centers
need to be planned and developed to

minimize environmental problems. Such developments will displace some agriculture and other extensive resource uses. Such adjustments in land use are justified when personal health and welfare are benefited. Living conditions in rural areas can be improved through changes in land use and improvements in housing and public services.

Thus, an emerging issue is distribution of our population and change in land use patterns to be consistent with desired living standards.

At the same time, land resource use should complement programs to provide job opportunities and foster economic growth. Creation of new urban centers by themselves are not solutions unless job opportunities exist or are created.

Land provides unique locations (harbors, rivers, lakes, rail centers) or the primary raw materials for industrial activity and employment. Not all new urban areas need to depend heavily on raw materials for job creation. Raw materials can be transported and many urban communities, of course, can focus on service industries. But plans for future growth must take into account the location of land resources and job opportunities.

Multiple use of land resources can be increased to improve not only the economic uses of the land but the environmental uses as well. Private lands can be used to provide wildlife habitat and recreation opportunities. Agricultural use of land can be compatible with programs to provide open space in some instances. Some strip mines can be used for land fills or for recreation development.

On the other hand, not all uses of land are compatible. Rules may be required, for instance, concerning the location of livestock feeding operations in relation to cities or water courses. Land that is limited in supply and uniquely suited to a particular agricultural use (for instance, cranberry bogs) should be conserved for that purpose, even if more profitable alternatives exist.

Certain land use practices involving the use of pesticides and fertilizers may also require regulations on their extent and location. Laws, regulations, and systems for compensation and taxation will be necessary to handle resource uses causing damages.

Conservation of the soil goes hand in hand with the use of the land. Traditionally, farmers have been concerned with this problem. But as more land shifts from rural to urban uses some of the responsibility for conservation also shifts from the shoulders of farmers to those of urban residents, developers, and industrialists. Urban users of the land are faced with problems of ground stability, sedimentation, flood control, sewage disposal runoff, and other land management practices that farmers have generally recognized since the start of soil conservation programs in the 1930's.

The emerging land use problems will require new policy and program approaches. New towns, and different growth and migration patterns, will come about slowly through existing arrangements; perhaps too slowly.

An effective system of land use will require a coordinated effort of private interests with the local, State, and National Governments. Moreover, organizational arrangements are needed to represent the various private and public interests, and to manage and finance land resource programs.

Planning for future growth and population locations will be essential. Where conflicts occur between competing land uses, the losses and gains must be carefully weighed to determine the best use of the land. In some instances, careful planning may permit compatible uses of the same areas. In other instances, a choice must be made between purposes or uses to provide the kinds and the qualities of services needed from our land resources.

Yes, we have sufficient land resources for the foreseeable multiple uses, but the emerging question concerns the quality of our existence in the use of our land. In this sense, there is a keen competition for land resources

SERVING MAN'S NEEDS—OUR RURAL ENVIRONMENT

MORE THAN 97 PERCENT of our environment is *rural* environment! No wonder the songs of our youth and of our country say—

And to my listening ears,
All nature sings; or

O beautiful for spacious skies,
For amber waves of grain,
For purple mountain majesties
above the fruited plain

What of this rural environment—the hill and dale, the mountain and the plain, the pond and the lake, the brook and the river?

Of what is it made?

There are crops, animals, fish, fowl, trees, shrubs, microbes, soil, water, and the atmosphere, including energy from the sun.

Taken together, they comprise most of the complex system that yields our food, fiber, and materials for shelter and, considering only soil, water, and air, the media for our transportation systems and much of our power production.

There are bugs and worms, some with gloriously colored wings and some too small to see with the naked eye.

There are many kinds of wild plants, and the wildlife that live among or in them.

Consider, too, minerals for energy and our devices and constructions.

There are our neighbors and our fellow countrymen—the people of the land and the small community. With them go buildings—houses, barns, steepled churches, general stores, water towers, and with increasing frequency, the low spreading buildings of relocated or newly established industries.

Surely, the other key components of the rural environment are the parts to which our senses and our psyches react—open spaces, wildflowers in bloom, birds in flight and in song, leaves in fall color, untrammeled wilderness areas, scenic vistas, water-based recreation areas, hiking trails, and clear lowland and mountain streams.

Have we exhausted the list? Not by a good deal. And we won't in this short article.

We must consider the rural environment, the countryside, in terms of the way it serves our needs, from the most functional biological and physical ones to those of esthetic, and psychological, social, and spiritual natures.

What of this "quality of the environment?" What are our needs, what are our goals?

Foremost among our needs from the countryside, I submit, is a healthy base from which to continue to obtain or produce adequate supplies of good quality, economical food and fiber and of water.

Other needs, some referred to in the paragraphs above, are—clean, healthful waters; bright, open skies; uncluttered, unspoiled, and attractive roadsides, fields, and woodlands; relatively uncrowded surroundings for our day to day living; an extensive transportation system connecting the centers of commerce and affording us mobility to move ourselves and our products about freely; sources of materials for our devices and constructions and power for our machines.

Still others are organized areas and the open countryside for participatory or relaxed recreation; habitat for wild things; and wilderness and natural areas for solitude with the things of

✦

AUTHOR DAVID J. WARD is Executive Director of the USDA Environmental Quality Executive Committee.

213

nature and for better understanding of natural processes.

These needs, and others not mentioned, are often interrelated; they often involve the same piece of geography and similar resources.

Our goal, then, for a quality rural environment is for a spacious, functioning, healthy interwoven biological and physical system in the countryside that will effectively serve the needs of man in the immediate future and for the centuries to come.

If we are to best serve ourselves and future generations, a whole series of rural environment "we musts" comes to mind. We must succeed in our efforts to:

Prevent soil erosion and protect and enhance the productivity of croplands.

Guard against despoiling the earth and the organisms that live in it.

Effectively harvest, conserve, use, and control precipitation and the early stages of surface water movement.

Adequately distribute and efficiently use water from streams, rivers, and lakes.

Protect and enhance water quality and beneficial aquatic organisms.

Maintain clean air.

Set aside undisrupted wildlands and natural areas.

Manage and protect wildlife and fish and their habitats.

Maintain and improve the condition and appearance of buildings and other construction.

Practice localized and grand scale landscaping to maintain and create pleasant immediate surroundings and scenic vistas.

Control economic and nuisance pests, including those affecting human health.

Prevent and control wildfires and use controlled burning judiciously.

Provide the economic, educational, social, recreational, psychological, and spiritual essentials for making the countryside an attractive, inviting place for living, working, and relaxing.

How do we stand; are we going to Hades in a hand basket? Certainly not

Do we have big, widespread problems; must we do better? Yes, indeed

Is there hope for dealing with our problems? Absolutely!

Producing food, fiber, and material for shelter always has involved managing most of the rural environment—manipulating and modifying it on an enormous scale. And it always will. Let there be no room for doubt or misunderstanding about this.

The generations to come will manage and protect the rural environment even more intensively and completely than those in the past.

Producing our essential food and fiber involves using, protecting, and perpetuating basic and vital biological and physical processes—such as reproduction; absorption and conversion of the sun's energy by plants; cycling of water, nitrogen, and other compounds and gases; absorption or consumption of nutrients and feeds to release growth-supporting energy; synthesis or conversion of simple chemicals to complex ones in plants, animals, and fish we harvest; and the rotting and final decomposition of leaves, straw, branches, and other unused organic materials.

Food and fiber production requires practices that result in diverse and efficient germ plasm; productive and safe soil, held in place; adequate supplies of safe and desirable water and clean air. Furthermore, it requires controlling insects, parasites, and other pests of crop plants, livestock, and trees; it involves the prevention and control of wildfires.

Agriculture, forestry, and other technologies relating to the country side (all involving biology and a hundred other scientific disciplines) are applied for the good of man and have resulted in safe, nutritious economic food in our bellies; durable and practicable clothes on our backs; functional and comfortable shelter

214

A PHOTO
PORTFOLIO

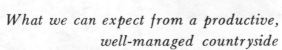

What we can expect from a productive,
well-managed countryside

*Food and fiber
for sustenance
and shelter*

216

*Pure water for man
and wildlife*

Space for industry,
recreation, living

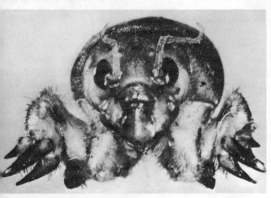

*To do this, we need
better housing,
safe pest control,
lagoons and other ways
to prevent livestock
pollution.*

219

Patterns of good land use—food for our families,
contours for conservation, woodland for timber and wildlife.

healthful, ample supplies of drinking water; restful and attractive local surroundings; plentiful wildlife and game fish for viewing and sport; inviting, developed outdoor recreation areas; and accessible natural and cultivated areas for scenic vistas, solitude, and communing with nature.

A fact of great importance is that the success of our modern agriculture has made possible the release of great acreages of land for nonagricultural uses.

Assess, please, the significance of a drop in harvested cropland from 339 million acres in 1954 to an estimated 291 million acres in 1969, while at the same time our food supplies were ample and our population was increasing steadily. Further acreage reductions are anticipated in the years immediately ahead.

Consider further the implications of 75.5 million acres set aside for recreation and wildlife areas by 1964 compared to 61.5 million acres in 1959.

What do statistics about cropland and recreation tell us about the quality of the rural environment? They highlight, emphatically, that we have vast land areas available for living in less crowded surroundings, for recreational and esthetic purposes near our centers of population, for complex transportation systems, and for wildlife habitat.

Examples of other successes and progress are legion.

Today, more than 3,000 Soil and Water Conservation Districts embrace more than 3.7 million farms, ranches, and other land holdings. They cover more than 1.7 billion acres, most of which are in private land holdings.

Conservation practices on farm, forest, and range lands involving grasses, trees, and other vegetation assist the land in absorbing and storing water. They contribute to maintaining adequate streamflows and to limiting sediment-releasing erosion and flood potentials. They also help beautify the conserved lands, roadsides, riverbanks, and other areas as well as hold the soil in place. They provide forage, food, and shelter for wildlife and enhance recreation areas.

Our countrywide interstate highway system—graded, seeded, and landscaped—is progressing toward completion, expediting, extending, and beautifying our travel. Many, many new vistas have been opened.

Nearly 10 million acres of the countryside are included in the National Wilderness Preservation System—all but 3,750 of them consisting of National Forest lands.

A National System of Wild and Scenic Rivers and a National Trails System were created by Congress in 1968.

Several river basin studies are underway and others will follow. Comprehensive plans are being prepared for developing water and related land resources.

Adequate soil surveys for technically sound conservation plans and other uses now cover more than 731 million acres.

Our National Forests are managed on a multiple-use basis for sustained yield of timber and wood products, water, recreation, wildlife habitat, and grazing livestock.

Successful pest control has played a major part in affording us an increasing amount of many kinds of food of superior quality. It has also protected us against numerous insect-borne diseases and enabled us to make a more pleasant use of the environment.

Fishing in some lakes and streams has been rejuvenated by judicious use of chemicals to clear them of trash fish and stunted fish, excessive weeds, and other aquatic life.

Toxic chemicals with great chemical stability in the soil around and under buildings have effectively controlled termite damage.

Populations of deer and quail are higher now than at any time in the history of our country.

Not all of our problems are solved. Sometimes our achievements have led to new problems.

Erosion still leads to enormous soil losses. Agriculture and wooded lands supply the greatest amount of sediment to the total sediment load of our streams. Erosion is also heavy from alongside rural roads and highways—particularly during the building period; from other construction projects; and from stream and river banks.

The total amount of sediment moving into streams, rivers, channels, reservoirs, and lakes each year approximates 4 billion tons. Knowledgeable people have said that sediment is the number one water pollutant. Certainly, no water pollutant exceeds it in quantity.

Our new roads are not entirely blessings. In addition to the erosion problem, highway construction often finds itself competing with other priorities for resource use. This is true in relation to wildlands, wildlife habitat, and existing or potential recreational areas.

Some object to the appearance of massive ribbons of concrete, asphalt, and steel. We litter our streets, roads, and highways with a remarkable range of waste products tossed from cars.

Most National Wilderness areas are far removed from centers of population. Thus we are often frustrated in our attempts to build understanding of the ways and wonders of nature.

Pressures for economical supplies of raw products challenge our multiple-use concepts and procedures. From long experience, we have perfected value systems for raw products. This is not so for scenery or a deer or a chipmunk in his natural habitat. We have yet to learn how to best determine the uses to be made of our resources.

Individual farm units are fewer in number and larger in size than in the past. This is in response to advances in mechanization and other production practices as well as to reductions in the availability of labor. Old fence lines and the associated undergrowth are much less plentiful or gone; so

went much of the wildlife habitat in the great farming belts.

Progress is being made in purposefully establishing vegetation for wildlife or leaving standing stalks and other crop residues in certain areas of farms. Much remains to be accomplished.

Pesticides that contribute to our bounty and our health are introduced directly or indirectly into the many corners of the countryside. Some pesticides are carried with eroded soil particles into water. Inadvertent and intentional applications to streams or ponds reach lands, water, or wildlife not intended to be treated.

Probably significant amounts of pesticides are transported in air from their place of application as a result of drift and volatilization.

Varying levels of pesticides have been found in wildlife. Accumulations of pesticides over time have been demonstrated and some harmful physiological effects have been found.

Certain forms of aquatic life assimilate almost infinitesimal amounts of some kinds of pesticides in water. Fish living in waters containing parts per trillion (ppt) levels of pesticides have been found to contain parts per million (ppm) of those chemicals in their fat.

For a given species, there is evidence that the pesticide level in the whole fish increases directly in proportion to the size of the fish.

The worldwide distribution of certain pesticides is well established. Much more needs to be known about their long-term ecological effects.

New and improved methods of pest control minimizing the amount and frequency of pesticide use and achieving greater specificity for the target pest are sought in Federal, State, and industry research programs. Though pesticides will be essential for a long time to come, we must find ways to eliminate or minimize their unwanted effects on the environment.

Another growing problem is that of solid wastes. The most common method of disposing of them is an open dump in the countryside. Increasingly the wastes we generate consist of packaging materials that degrade slowly.

We have a heritage of land disposal sites, thousands of them, that are very unsightly sources of soil and water pollution and potential health hazards. At a per capita rate of solid waste production exceeding 5 pounds per day, and increasing, our problems will get worse before they get better.

Many small rural communities have declined in population and in economic vigor. As with marginal farm enterprises, buildings have fallen into disrepair and lack paint.

Though not characterized by the dense smog associated with cities, the countryside sometimes has its own air pollution problems. Cement plants, alfalfa dehydrators, and cotton gins have had some of the most conspicuous "plumes." Gases from some kinds of industrial plants have debilitated vegetation for miles downwind.

Fortunately, the dust storms of the 1930's are no longer with us, but certain combinations of weather conditions and farming practices still result in occasional darkened skies. Smoke from controlled burning of enormous quantities of excess forest and crop residues has led to unsightly air pollution in some areas.

Automation and centralization of meat, milk, and egg production has led to more and more concentration of animal wastes at specific locations, a number of which are near urban areas. A single very large poultry operation may produce more than 5 tons of waste each day.

More than 1.7 billion tons of animal wastes are produced annually. As much as half of this is associated with concentrated production systems.

Pollution problems relate to animal wastes (materials handling, fly breeding, disposal, utilization), water (plant nutrients, infectious agents, minerals), and air (odors, dusts). Also, many people are offended by the unsightliness of huge manure piles.

The land continues to be the best medium for use and disposal of animal wastes, but in some instances rates of application have already been so high as to cause agricultural production problems.

Fertilizer use has increased dramatically over the past few decades. This use will climb to even higher levels in the years ahead. Advanced methods for improving control of surface runoff and of leaching to groundwater must accompany practices involving the intensified use of fertilizer.

Our concerns about runoff and leaching relate to unwanted growth of aquatic plants in streams, ponds, and lakes; public health aspects of water quality; and, in some instances, soil contamination.

Our streams, rivers, and lakes are increasingly burdened with many kinds of pollutants. These materials make them unattractive, significantly reduce their biological vitality, and limit their utility for human consumption, use by industry, and recreation.

Wastes enter our surface waters from land, barnyards, and feedlots, community sewage disposal plants, dumps, mines, and industrial plants.

Waters may receive sediment, which is both a pollutant per se and a major carrier of other pollutants; organic materials and plant nutrients from fields, animal wastes, and sewage; organic material and chemicals from food and fiber processing plants; and acids from mines and industry.

I've tried to provide some illustrative examples of the good and the bad of our countryside.

Though no constant traveler, I've been to most of the corners of this beautiful land. I believe that the good in our environment far outweighs the bad. I believe, also, that a well kept, wooded farmstead with fertile acres of crops around it, with perhaps a few steers grazing the pasture, and a meandering brook in the lowlands, is a thing of beauty to challenge the best of undisturbed nature. I love them both, the cultivated and the natural—each in its own place, each in its own way.

We have many long-time environmental management programs such as those for conserving soil and water, managing forests, and operating public parks; and we have numerous new ones such as those for setting standards for air and water pollution. All of them, the old and the new, are based on the will of the people as expressed in laws, public programs, private enterprise, and individual initiative.

"Pollution" has become a heavily used word since passage in the 1960's of specific Federal legislation dealing with air and water pollution and solid wastes.

We are in an era of new awareness of the environment and its meaning to people. This is as it should be.

We must know more about the planet on which we live. We must use our knowledge to draw upon and use its resources in ways that will not unnecessarily or irretrievably damage its underlying systems and functions.

WAYS TO REGULATE THE ESTHETICS OF OUR RURAL ENVIRONMENT

NATIONAL PUBLIC CONCERN for our environment is now a matter of record. As the population becomes more mobile, our interest in esthetics expands beyond the vicinity where we live and work. Consequently we now commonly speak of the national demand for such things as natural beauty, open space, and outdoor recreation. The esthetics of our rural areas is a significant national asset. Public action

is necessary to preserve this asset on private as well as public land.

Traditionally the contribution of agriculture to society has been assessed mainly from the standpoint of production of food and fiber, and land has been considered simply as a factor of production. While the conservation movement and, more recently, concern for the environment have expanded the perspective, policymakers still have felt compelled to justify programs along traditional lines.

The role of agriculture as custodian of three-fifths of the Nation's landscape has received relatively little attention. The rural-urban distinction has perhaps fostered this neglect. However, we have tangible evidence that the distinction is breaking down. Legislation is being considered or has been passed in many of our most urban States to support the preservation of agriculture as a land use.

This support does not appear to be based simply on the future demand for land to produce food and fiber. At least one factor in explaining the response is a desire by many people for retaining agriculture as an amenity.

In many situations agriculture is compatible with demands for open space. In some situations it is a positive factor. For instance, along highways any single land use at some point becomes monotonous. Even forestry has been criticized where it has been used extensively, and a preference has been expressed for some variety including agriculture as a part of the pastoral setting.

While agriculture is generally esthetic and is compatible with certain open space objectives, we must recognize that there are conflicts. The qualities that have been attributed to agriculture in the past may change with time. At least two factors must be considered.

First, technological change has influenced agricultural practices so that

✦

AUTHOR WILLIAM DYER ANDERSON is an Attorney, Natural Resource Economics Division, Economic Research Service.

many criticisms that were levied at other industries in an earlier era are now being directed at agriculture. Pollution is a good example. Concentrations of livestock tend to accentuate the problems of both air and water pollution.

The increasing use of pesticides and fertilizers to insure efficient crop production is also becoming more offensive to those concerned with the environment. Modern farm equipment and certain types of buildings do not have the same esthetic appeal that was associated with earlier farm-

ment including esthetics is simply an extension of the trend which began as population pressures grew on our fixed land base. Over the years this has resulted in evolutionary redefinition of rights and duties with respect to private land use. The public interest in the way private land is used has become greater. Concurrently, there has also been a shift from almost exclusively local interest to more regional and national interest.

Government programs are designed to give expression to the public interest and are implemented through

pen space in Maryland countryside. Pond adds beauty to setting, and serves practical purpose of conserving and storing water for farm use.

ing practices. Traffic and noise are also identified with the technology of modern farming. Future changes in technology may further aggravate the problem.

Second, esthetics are based on individual tastes and values. In the past the population consisted of many individuals who were raised on farms. With this background they would naturally have tastes that are different from the population of today, which is largely of nonfarm origin. Will present and subsequent generations be as willing to accept what in many instances are necessary adverse effects of farming operations? Population mobility further increases the potential for these types of conflicts.

Present concern for our environ-

the powers of taxing and spending, eminent domain, and regulating land use. The focus of this chapter is on land use regulation and the implication of regulation for agriculture.

Since the Federal Government generally does not have the power to regulate land use directly, this device has not been tried to any significant degree in national programs affecting rural land utilization including agriculture. This may change, however, particularly as programs involve other levels of government in pursuing national objectives.

Recent legislation by Congress affecting certain areas administered by the Department of the Interior offers a good example. The areas include the Cape Cod National Sea-

225

Strip mining in Washington State, as in many other parts of U.S., has left ugly scar on countryside. Some abandoned mines are being adapted to landfill use and recreation.

shore, Fire Island National Seashore, Whiskeytown National Recreation Area, Indiana Dunes National Lakeshore, and certain rivers and adjacent lands that have been designated as part of the National Wild and Scenic River System.

The legislation provides that local zoning, a land use regulatory measure, which conforms to standards set by the Secretary of the Interior, may be applied in lieu of condemnation in order to achieve the desired national objectives. Since the land covered by acceptable zoning does not have to be purchased by the Government, costs of achieving the objectives in these areas is reduced. This approach may also be more desirable from the standpoint of individual landowners because the land remains in private ownership.

Looking to the future, we can anticipate an increase in national programs designed to preserve and protect the scenic and recreational values of our rural countryside. A variety of tools

will be employed including land use regulations. We can expect that the regulations may apply to agricultural as well as non-agricultural rural land utilization.

Hawaii is the only State that has extensive land use regulation at the State level. The State Land Use Commission in Hawaii is charged with classifying all land in the State into four major land use districts: urban, rural, agricultural, and conservation.

Lands having the highest capacity for cultivation are, to the extent possible, placed in the agricultural district. Counties are responsible for administering regulations of the State Land Use Commission in agriculturally zoned areas. To give support to the regulatory approach, land may be "dedicated" by the owner to an agricultural use; an act which entitles the owner to have the land assessed at value solely based on that use.

The 1969 session of the Oregon legislature passed an act which gives the Governor the authority to plan and zone all lands in the State not subject to a comprehensive land use plan and zoning ordinance by the end of 1971.

While authority to regulate land use generally rests with State government in our system, the authority has traditionally been delegated by States to local governments. The delegation is typically made by enabling acts for zoning and subdivision control. The decision to exercise the authority under the legislation is almost always at the option of the local government.

In every State there is some legislative authority for regulating land use in unincorporated or rural areas. The unit of government authorized to regulate and the scope of authority vary significantly from State to State.

Early zoning enabling legislation was typically designed for municipalities and attempted to deal with urban problems such as excessively high population density. As legislative changes have been made to permit regulation of land use in rural areas, stated objectives of such legislation have tended to change.

Illustrations of these changed objectives include preservation of historic and scenic attractions, conservation of natural resources, and fostering of agriculture and industry. The enabling legislation in 21 States expressly provides for establishment of agricultural zoning districts by local governments in rural areas.

Emphasis in exclusive agricultural districts is on the prohibition of uses that are incompatible with agriculture. By eliminating nonfarm uses the potential for land use conflicts is minimized and there is less need for regulating the permitted agricultural and agriculturally related uses. In addition such districts can provide large tracts of contiguous land as open space.

The agricultural zoning district most widely used by local governments is the cumulative rather than the exclusive type. Almost any land use is permitted in cumulative agricultural zoning districts. The cumulative agricultural zone actually is a residual zone, and is relatively ineffective in dealing with many land use problems.

In over 20 States agriculture is currently exempt from zoning regulations. For some States the exemption applies only to agriculture on tracts above a certain minimum lot size.

While a variety of objectives are set forth in zoning enabling legislation, it is apparent that the effect of many types of zoning regulations is visual. Since the origin of zoning, courts have been increasingly tolerant of land use restrictions which may, to a great degree, have been directed at improving the appearance of communities. However, general court acceptance of regulations which are designed only for esthetics remains doubtful.

In many cases where esthetics is an issue the courts will strive to find a legitimate reason other than esthetics to uphold a zoning ordinance. In such cases esthetics may be justified as a secondary purpose. Frequently the courts will find a relationship between esthetics and preservation of property values, the latter being a frequently specified objective in zoning enabling acts.

In determining whether a land use regulation is reasonable, and therefore constitutional, the courts generally attempt to balance the public interest against the private interest. During the balancing process, esthetics will often be weighed along with other factors.

There are limits on how far we can go in placing burdens on individuals under the regulatory power for the benefit of society as a whole. Beyond the point of reasonable regulation our system dictates that society must pay for the benefit.

Issues that have developed regarding land use regulation and esthetics, generally, are relevant to the regulation of agricultural land utilization. In most land use regulations, including those that apply to agriculture, esthetic considerations enter through other stated objectives such as promoting orderly land development and exercising control over incompatible land uses. Greater restriction is placed on uses that are offensive to adjacent property owners.

How far the regulatory power could or should be used in controlling agricultural land utilization to improve esthetics is difficult to answer. At least two settings should be considered separately.

RURAL-URBAN FRINGE

The first setting is the rural-urban fringe. A desire to preserve agricultural land on the rural-urban fringe, as was suggested earlier, is not based generally on the need for land to produce food and fiber except where certain agricultural land is a unique resource. The public interest in this setting is generally in preserving open space and avoiding urban sprawl.

Purchase of land by a local government for open space in rural-urban fringe areas is extremely expensive. Agriculture is one of the few uses of privately owned land which can provide both a return to the owner and benefit the public as open space.

Since the public is receiving a benefit it is reasonable to expect that certain burdens must also be accepted. It would be senseless as well as illegal to zone land for agriculture on the one hand and at the same time place such restrictions on land use that the owner could not profitably operate. It would be just as unreasonable to expect that the public should suffer the adverse effects of all possible agricultural practices.

Land use conflicts in rural-urban fringe areas should be anticipated, and corrective measures taken to minimize the conflicts through the design of local zoning ordinances. Various types of agriculture should be considered from the standpoint of positive and negative effects on the community interest. The effect of changing technology should be appraised.

In selecting the agricultural use to be permitted, attention must be given to the effect that any restriction on use will have upon the owner. Exclusive agricultural districts should be considered as a way of minimizing

conflicts in areas where agriculture i to be retained.

A failure to realistically consider these various factors prior to adopting the ordinance will lead to difficultie. later on if the ordinance is challenged in court. While certain adverse effect: of agricultural land use can clearly be regulated under a number of enabling acts, there are limits. This would be particularly true if regulations tended to be directed primarily at esthetic: and were at the same time especially burdensome to the landowner.

The second setting is in rural areas A suggestion that private land use in rural areas should be regulated to preserve esthetic values primarily for urban people calls for a somewhat different analysis.

Since zoning has been used almost exclusively as a tool of local land use planning, the rationale for it has developed in that context. Courts have usually looked more favorably upon regulations that benefit land at the same time its use is being restricted. In many instances the arguments are related to the objective of preserving local property values.

Effective planning in this developing area can preserve open spaces for improved environment.

Should the restrictions be designed primarily to benefit those outside the locality, the traditional framework for analysis is more difficult to apply. As a practical matter, such a hypothetical situation would not likely exist so long as the zoning authority remains with county and municipal governments.

If, however, zoning authority was to be exercised by some higher unit of government, new issues might arise. It seems reasonable to expect that certain minimum standards should be met with all land use. Land use regulations for control of billboards and junkyards are examples of esthetic regulations that have received fairly wide support.

As restrictions tend to become more burdensome on the individual owner and at the same time are directed more toward providing a public benefit, they are less likely to be considered reasonable. For instance, architectural controls, which are becoming increasingly important in urban land use regulation, would be difficult to justify if they were being applied in rural areas primarily to benefit a non-resident urban public.

To supplement the regulatory approach, such devices as tax incentives, grants, purchase of easements, purchase and lease-back, and compensative regulation could be used to improve the esthetics of rural areas.

To sum up, today there is genuine concern by both the rural and urban public about environmental quality including esthetics. As the population increases, the Nation becomes more concerned about open space, natural beauty, and outdoor recreation. As the population becomes more mobile the community of interest in how land is used expands across the boundaries of towns and counties to the States and to the Nation. Agriculture is generally considered by urban as well as rural people to contribute positively to the Nation's landscape.

With increased social interaction and changing technology, the potential for land use conflicts increases. Governmental programs must be designed to minimize the conflicts and give positive expression to the public interest in how private land is used.

The power to regulate land use has a role in implementing programs by all levels of government. But since we are a nation which cherishes private ownership in land, there are limits to what can be achieved with this approach.

Regulation of land use for esthetics involves one of the major issues of our time—establishing a proper division between the public interest and private property rights. The problem is one of balancing the benefits and burdens in establishing reasonable regulations.

We can anticipate that courts will be increasingly tolerant of regulations that are related to esthetics. At the same time there may be a need to develop supplemental programs to provide compensation through devices like tax incentives, grants, easements, user fees, and compensative regulation in situations where the objective sought goes beyond the scope of reasonable regulation.

LIVING HISTORIC FARMS TELL IT LIKE IT WAS

ALL OVER AMERICA remnants of our agricultural past survive, unused and largely unappreciated, but potentially of great educational value. Although most Americans no longer farm, they still retain an interest in agriculture. Farmers and nonfarmers alike seem eager to learn about our agrarian past.

Few educational methods can show the amazing progress in the pro-

Thresher operating with power from tractor through a belt, probably in mid-1920's.

ductivity and living standards of the American farmer better than the contrast between farms of yesterday and today. Almost by definition, progress becomes apparent only when men know where they have been, and by what route they have travelled.

Knowledge of this past can be transmitted in a multitude of ways: by the traditional lectures and books, by motion pictures, and even by museums. Although agricultural museums identify objects, they leave the impression that farmers give their primary attention to tools, implements, and machines. Actually, farmers deal mostly with living things. They carry on a complicated business in which they center their attention on land, plants, animals, and the weather.

Basically farmers intentionally produce commodities by controlling biological activity as best they can. They raise food (wheat, meat), industrial materials (cotton, hides), and amelioratives (tobacco).

The farmer, in regulating and managing biological activity, uses tools, implements, and machines, of course, but these things of themselves only vaguely hint at the more essen-

✦

AUTHOR JOHN T. SCHLEBECKER is Curator, Division of Agriculture and Mining, Smithsonian Institution, Washington, D.C.

tial biological processes. In almost every sort of farming, for example, the number of important genetic-biochemical discoveries equal in importance the number of mechanical advances. Unfortunately, a jar of herbicide or a sack of fertilizer shows even less about life than a six-blade cheese curd knife, or a four-finger grain cradle.

Furthermore, the machines and devices rarely explain themselves, and printed labels do not help much. Static displays of farm machinery simply do not tell enough about farming, to say nothing about farm life. In addition, such exhibits seldom show any stream of development in man's progress from child of nature to manager of living things. Much can be learned about farming from books and motion pictures, of course, but more could be learned by watching farmers at work in the field and barn.

The actual use of historical implements and machines in an historically restored or re-created farm setting would better allow people to understand how our forefathers lived. Not only Americans, but people from around the world could also see how the American farmer came to be the food producer he is. The lesson might be that what men have done once they can do again. Living historical farms, using the appropriate plants, animals, ools, implements, and methods could show better than any museum just what farming was, and is, all about.

Everywhere in the country people have found a "pioneer" farm or house which they want to preserve. Should the general program of restoration and re-creation go in the direction of preservation of a pioneer past, however, the country could be swamped with a vast sameness. Contrary to popular lore, pioneer farms varied little across the country.

Pioneer farms seem to attract the most attention primarily because of local pride in frontier ancestors. Accidental survival of a few ruins of uncertain and uncertified age tend to center attention on the pioneer stage. Pride and accident, however, seem inadequate justification for setting up a living historical farm.

Seen from a larger view, the farming of the past which led most directly to the present seems most worth saving or re-creating. In short, the historical sources or origins of commercial farming ought to have priority of development. The farms of great men, or pioneers, cannot be excluded, of course, but memory should recall something more than just a series of local heroes. Ordinary farmers in the mainstream of history also deserve to be remembered.

And the materials for such farms also survive, often in better condition than the earlier subsistence farms. Much could be learned from visiting a few farms of the commercial era, remembering that from the beginning Americans have also been commercial farmers.

Even so, we should also remember that the Indians farmed before the white man came, and that the first Europeans in our New World struggled painfully to create a civilization in the wilderness. We could appreciate again the heroism of our forefathers.

Above all, Americans could rediscover how important farmers were in the history of the Nation. Until the present century, most Presidents were raised on farms, and even in this century, several spent their boyhood helping on the family farm.

Any living historical farm could be instructive in itself, but a visit to several could well create a better appreciation of our heritage. Americans could see how other Americans once lived and handed on our common traditions. The farms, to do this, should be scattered across the country, and should cover every area, every time period, and every type of agriculture.

Farms should depict the maize culture of the Iroquois, the subsistence farming of the Pilgrims, the tobacco and rice plantations of the Old South, the later cotton plantations, and the modern farms of the New South.

Americans should be able to visit pioneer farms of the Old Northwest, the Prairies, and the cattle ranches of the Open Range. Duplicates of the orchards and vineyards of the Great Lakes and the Pacific Coast could alike reappear, as well as dairy farms of every time and region.

On such living historical farms people could see the authentic clothing, animals, crops, and methods used in the past. In both field and barn, work would go on as it once did. Men would throw grain cradles instead of driving combines, and cows would be milked by hand instead of by machine.

It seems particularly desirable to have such farms because ours is no longer an agrarian society. At the time of the American Revolution, an estimated 90 percent of the American people lived on farms. In 1969 the farm labor force came to less than 3 percent of our total population, and less than 6 percent of our countrymen lived on farms. Only tremendous increases in the efficiency of farmers now make it possible to sustain such a high proportion of nonfarm population.

Obviously, living historical farms would help portray a way of life that is already outside the experience of most Americans. Farmers themselves might achieve a new pride in their vocation by discovering the many

231

Tobacco field at Colonial Williamsburg, Va., an historic restoration.

changes which have transformed their lives, and even altered American civilization.

Tools, plants, livestock, and methods would all have to be historically accurate, of course. In no case could complete authenticity be achieved, primarily because the farm would be open to visitors. Farming in the presence of even moderate numbers of people automatically becomes non-authentic farming. Furthermore, the implements, machines, and buildings would generally have to be re-creations because genuine museum pieces would not stand up under regular use. The problems stemming from these circumstances would have to be solved, and in fact, have been in several places.

When people are told they are looking at an 1850 dairy farm, the farm should be as much like an 1850 dairy farm as possible. Modern Holstein cows and milk tanks should not be in evidence. Determining the condition and appearance of an 1850 dairy farm requires considerable historical research, and that is not as simple as it may seem. Also, the

amount of research needed depends to some extent on whether the farm is typical of a region, or is a reconstruction of a famous farm.

Daniel Webster and Henry Clay had the newest animals and implements and used the most advanced methods of their time. A typical farmer of the same period, however, did things rather differently because of his inability to afford the best. The typical farm, if re-created, could be more freely reconstructed, but not carelessly so. Obviously, difficulties arise in trying to discover just what a typical farmer had at some time in the past.

It might seem that the re-creation of some specific farm would be easier, but in fact two problems peculiar to this type of farm emerge almost at once. In the first place, the farm of a prominent man will be typical in most ways. Thus, in order to re-create much of it, the restorer must know how the typical farmer of that time and place farmed.

No matter how much a man may innovate, no matter how unusual his farm or his methods, he still invariably follows the ordinary patterns of his time and place. No man can pursue any other course, because no man can constantly innovate and still do his ordinary tasks.

In most of their affairs, even great men behave much like their neighbors. Thus the history of men round about invariably tells much about the special farm, and indeed, such knowledge in general may be essential. The apparent short-cut in historical research when a certain farm is to be re-created thus disappears at once.

Abe Lincoln's boyhood home illustrates the problem. Scholars do not know just exactly what Tom Lincoln raised and exactly where he raised it. Farmers in the area typically grew a small amount of tobacco, so probably Tom did too. And so on through a long catalogue of commodities, methods, and implements. The actual grain cradle that Tom Lincoln used has long since disappeared, so a copy would have to be made, based on those commonly used by farmers in southern Indiana in 1825.

The second problem involves historical accuracy. In the case of the Lincoln Homestead, historians know approximately where the barns and the pigpens had been, but a railroad now crosses part of the farm, and a highway runs too close to where the pigs had once been kept. Perfect authenticity would require abandonment of the railroad and relocation of the highway. Obviously, compromises will have to be made.

Furthermore, historical accuracy cannot always be merged with the best current practices in fertility preservation and soil conservation. Authenticity must also be adjusted to the best methods of plant and animal husbandry. In raising both plants and animals, protecting the health and safety of people requires considerable technical skill.

Past methods of handling crops and livestock cannot always be copied, and compromises with history will have to be made. Still, the compromises should not do excessive violence to the truth. Tell it like it was. But then again—

Although everyone knows that farming has changed across the centuries, the substantial nature of the change sometimes escapes notice. Livestock and plant diseases, for example, present some perplexing technical problems. A dairy farmer of the 1850's would have done little to control brucellosis, yet precautions against this disease would be necessary on a modern farm. A cattle ranch of the 1870's would not have had tick vats, but nowadays cattle would surely have to be sprayed.

Soil depletion and erosion often progressed rapidly in the past, but steps would have to be taken to prevent this. Strip cropping and contour plowing would be inappropriate, but fertilizers might be added in large enough quantities to promote a natural cover and control erosion. Possibly several fields could be used to illustrate the farming. Then in any given year only one field would be open to erosion, while the others would be in a cover crop and farmed by the best methods.

Diseases and insects present special problems. The boll weevil did not enter the United States until 1892. On a re-created plantation of 1850, controls would now be required even though the planter of 1850 had no trouble with the weevil. The European corn borer has entered the country in this century. It would have to be controlled even though it might not have existed in the United States at the time of the re-created farms.

The living historical farms would have to regulate and control these and other pests even if the loss of the crop would not matter. Farmers in the surrounding country would hardly delight in having a pest-infested neighbor. Then too, screw-worms and grasshopper plagues cannot be brought back just to make farming more realistic.

Hazards to human health will have to be avoided or overcome. Hemp, for example, should probably be eliminated as a possible crop because it can also be marijuana. Animal dis-

233

McCormick reaping and mowing machine of 1857 at work in the field.

eases would have to be controlled, especially if they also infect man. These controls would be required even though the precautions might not have been used in the period being reconstructed. Then too, the livestock should be protected against diseases carried in by visitors, or the animals should be replaced when infected.

Visitors present other difficulties. Few farmers constructed their barns to stand up under both the ordinary wear and tear of farming, and the treading of 100,000 visitors a year. Hidden additions to structural strength may be required, but no steel beams should be seen, even though they may be present. In short, the blending of the past into the present requires patience and some skill. Even after research has shown what the old farm should be, the farm still has to be re-created to meet the needs of a modern society.

Through much of our history a large amount of the processing of farm products took place right on the farm. Farmers husked and shelled corn by hand, threshed and winnowed their wheat, churned butter, pressed cheese, slaughtered hogs, and smoked their own ham and bacon. Farmers usually performed these tasks fairly promptly,

albeit sometimes infrequently, as the opportunity arose.

The husking bee, so well known in American life, finished the job quickly for most farmers. Even now, a husking bee could be arranged for a living historical farm. The next week, however, visitors would be complaining about missing the event, and would want another staged for them.

Should the processing be done as it was, all at once or nearly so, or should the threshing and such be extended unrealistically across time? Each farm must solve this problem, but historical accuracy appears to be the best solution. After all, no reasonable visitor to a farm should expect to see a crop planted, cultivated, harvested, and threshed on the same day. On farms, as in nature, events should happen in their season. But if visitors must be accommodated, a motion picture showing the yearly cycle on the farm might serve.

Not only methods, but plants and animals have changed markedly across the years. The tobacco of today bears only a slight resemblance to the tobacco grown in the 17th and 18th centuries. Turkey Red—the hardy wheat of the Plains, introduced in the 1870's by Mennonites from Russia— has nearly disappeared as a commer-

234

cial crop, and the situation continues through a long list of plants and animals.

Farmers of other years raised rather small horses, cattle, and hogs. Not all of the animal smallness resulted from inadequate attention and poor food; our ancestors often bred for small size for various reasons. That is, securing the proper size animals does not call for mistreatment, nor would it produce the proper results. The exact breeds must be found.

Finding the proper animals and plants requires time and knowledge, although the breeding stock can usually be found or, sometimes, developed.

The historical research needed to find all the various elements of the historical farm takes time, and costs money when done professionally. Nevertheless, amateur historians trying to start a farm for some era can discover a great deal if they work patiently and carefully. Many general studies give detailed information on farming in certain places, but the novice may encounter difficulty in finding sources.

The easiest place to start is with *A Bibliography of Books and Pamphlets on the History of Agriculture in the United States* (Santa Barbara: American Bibliographic Center, 1969). This will introduce the beginner to the vast literature on agricultural history. The bibliography is indexed to facilitate pinpointing for specifically needed information.

For newspapers and magazines, which can be marvelously revealing, the *Union List of Serials* should be consulted, although not every library has the list and it may take a bit of effort to figure out how to use the reference work. Still, it should be possible to come up with a good list of local newspapers for the relevant period. The Union List will give some idea of where these can be found if, as often happens, no local collection exists any longer.

In the case of certain crops and commodities, and in certain areas as well, it would be helpful to do research in special farm magazines. These have been helpfully listed in Stephen Conrad Stuntz, *List of the Agricultural Periodicals of the United States and Canada—1810–1910* (Washington: U.S. Department of Agriculture, Miscellaneous Publication 398).

For those working in the period since 1850 the United States Census Reports will give more information than may at first be supposed. For one thing, the census will show what crops the farmers grew in any time or place, and will give some general idea of the relative importance of the several crops.

As early as 1850, the material appears for any county. The amount and variety of printed census infor-

Combined harvester and thresher drawn by horses and mules, in Umatilla County, Oreg., wheat field in 1925.

mation increases until comparatively recent times. But even the most distant census tells things which may run counter to, or be unremembered, in the folklore of a region.

The census schedules, the printed forms on which the enumerators put down the information, have been opened to the public up to the census of 1880, inclusive. These have been mostly deposited in the several States, but can be found and often reveal more than the printed summaries.

Those interested in the years from 1837 to about 1855 should check the *Annual Reports of the Commissioner of Patents*. These reports were the predecessor to the *Yearbooks of the Department of Agriculture*, and for the years mentioned, contain detailed reports from many sections of the country on actual farming methods and conditions. Generally, the reports have been indexed by State; the researcher has to know and find the appropriate counties.

Manuscripts, such as diaries, account books, and the like prove very helpful when they can be found. If they don't turn up readily, courthouse probate records of wills, and sometimes inventories of estates, give important tips on farming methods and equipment. In the more anciently settled parts of the country, these records may run back to the 18th century.

In more recent periods, advertisements in farm magazines and manufacturers catalogues give illustrations and descriptions of machines employed. Farm journals also carry pictures of the more common kinds of farm animals and plants. Of course, sources given in the footnotes and bibliographies of the general agricultural histories should be checked. All may use what other scholars have used, and these sources may prove helpful, especially if looked at from a fresh viewpoint. Bit by bit information can be built up on every aspect of a proposed farm.

All of those who have an interest in an historical farm could unquestionably learn a great deal from one another. Unfortunately, no general organization exists, nor is there, properly speaking, a clearing house for information. Even so, help in locating those interested in historical farms can be had from the Agricultural History Branch, Economic Research Service, U.S. Department of Agriculture, Washington, D.C. 20250, or from the Living Historical Farms Project, Smithsonian Institution, Washington, D.C. 20560.

The few living historical farms operating in 1970 have visitors swarming through them. These visitors show more interest in the farming aspects than in most of the other events and exhibits which can be seen at these open air museums.

Throughout the country, people are flocking into all types of museums at an astounding rate. Museum visitation has risen between 5 percent and 15 percent each year since 1956. Any activity in a museum draws crowds, and farming is mainly activity. The combined increase in visitors, and the activity of agriculture, assures popular support for living historical farms, which if properly done, will tell it like it was.

WHO SHOULD PAY FOR CONSERVATION?

CONSERVATION, like some other well advertised products, doesn't cost—it pays. Yet the benefits may be so delayed and so dispersed that the man who pays the cost is not the chief beneficiary. This is a conservation dilemma: How do you pay for work that is on private land yet essential to survival of the race?

The Nation must look to the owners and managers of private agricultural land for most of its conservation work.

236

Conservation on farmland contributes to urban benefits from San Antonio River—a major tourist attraction as well as a source of water for city of San Antonio and nearby Texas towns. Practices that slow runoff of water aid in recharging underground reservoir that feeds river.

Private land produces virtually all of our food and most of our fiber. It catches most of the rainfall that feeds our streams, lakes, and reservoirs. It incubates and protects wildlife and provides most of our outdoor recreation.

Nearly three-fifths of the Nation's land area is privately owned rural land. A high percentage of this land is in crops, pasture, range, or other non-forest agriculture. Thus the watersheds that sustain municipal and industrial uses are largely agricultural. And even the most highly urban populations, whether they realize it or not, must look to farmers and ranchers for protection of their basic resources.

The Columbia River is an urban resource. It feeds Northwestern cities with hydroelectric power exceeding the entire load for New York City. And it has a potential for more than double that capacity. Yet much of the Columbia drainage area is agricultural, and the very life of the river is affected by land use decisions as far

✦

AUTHOR J. DON LOOPER is Director, Foreign Market Information Division, Foreign Agricultural Service. He was formerly Deputy Director, Conservation and Land Use Policy Staff, Agricultural Stabilization and Conservation Service.

away as the Palouse wheat country 300 miles from the sea.

Three million people live on the shores of San Francisco Bay, a magnificent estuary now threatened by pollution and filling. This is an urban problem. Yet the land drained by the Sacramento and San Joaquin Rivers, which contribute so much to the ecology of the whole Bay area, is 90 percent in private farms and ranches.

Cities bordering the Connecticut River are no less affected by the quality of the river than are the farmers in upstream watersheds. Yet the Connecticut Valley, which includes the high population areas of Hartford, Conn., and Springfield and Holyoke, Mass., is still four-fifths agricultural in land area.

There are 27,000 farms in the Nashville Basin of central Tennessee— less than one-seventh of the State. The thousands of land use decisions made by these farmers, individually and independently, bear directly on the viability of two highly developed river systems—the Tennessee and the Cumberland. These decisions affect Tennessee Valley Authority (TVA) power, navigation at Memphis, and siltation as far away as Pilottown in the Mississippi mouth.

So the urban dweller must look far beyond the city limits if he is to appreciate the range of problems affecting his own environment. And while the environment failures of rural America do not burn the eyes and offend the nose, as urban failures do, the fact remains that we are making too little progress in the countryside just as we are in the city.

Based on an evaluation of the National Conservation Needs Inventory of 1958–60, the U.S. Department of Agriculture estimated a "conservation need" for the investment of $2.4 billion a year on agricultural lands. This was the amount required to do the conservation job that needed to be done.

We have not invested anything like that amount of money over the past decade; the actual expenditure was about a third that much. In 1962, USDA estimated our total conservation investment by individuals and the public (but not including forest conservation by the timber industry) to be about $750 million a year. Our investment has increased very little since that time, particularly when measured against the rising costs of conservation services and materials.

This deficiency is borne out by the new conservation needs inventory, now being completed. A comparison with the old inventory of a decade ago indicates that accomplishments in those years have provided only a reasonably effective holding action. In some areas, we have actually lost ground.

The results are plain:

• Almost two-thirds of our present cropland still needs conservation treatment.

• Almost two-thirds of our privately owned pasture and rangeland needs conservation treatment.

• More than three-fifths of our private forest and woodland needs conservation treatment.

Pollution of our waters is so common that we take for granted the "unsafe" signs that mark once-wholesome swimming waters. Formerly clean streams are loaded with sediment from rural and urban lands, if not actually poisoned with sewage or chemicals.

Why are we failing? The answer boils down to the non-esthetics of money: How to get it, who provides it, how you spend it, and what you give up in order to make these funds available.

We have the technical know-how to do the farm conservation job. This knowledge is in the hands of conservationists in every farm county of America. Generally speaking, the farmer no longer neglects the land because he cannot get needed technical help. Today it's mostly a question of economics.

Who pays for conservation?

Who pays for work that may add to a farmer's long-run income, but also preserves the Nation's ability to produce?

Who pays for practices that do nothing for a farmer's income, yet add beauty to the countryside?

Who pays for measures that send clean water into city reservoirs?

Who pays to insure the propagation of wildlife in a nation that continues to value the "free hunting and fishing" ethic of its frontier days?

It can be argued that somebody pays for conservation whether it is done or not. If the work is not done, society pays through rising costs for water purification, the rehabilitation of reservoirs, the dredging of rivers and harbors, and the building of higher levees. Society pays in possible future crop shortages, higher food costs, a degraded environment, dying lakes and estuaries, the loss of wildlife and any number of esthetic values.

Conservation work that *is* done is paid for predominantly by the owners and operators of farm and ranch land. Of the current annual conservation investment of possibly $1 billion, about one-third is Federal. The other two-thirds is non-Federal, and most of this investment is by owners of the land.

Many people still reflect a traditional view that the landowner should pay the entire cost of work done on his land. But even if you accept this as a philosophical argument, you still

238

have to answer the practical question whether the conservation needs of the Nation can be met by this means. Can and will farmers and ranchers sharply increase their investment in land and water conservation?

If farmers and ranchers are to do this, the increased investment must come out of their income and predominantly out of their net income. In 1969, realized net income per farm averaged a record $5,401, but per capita income was still only three-fourths the level of American nonfarmers.

These averages do not, of course, reflect the wide range of net income received by individual farmers. It is nevertheless true that most farmers realize incomes well below the average urban family's income.

In 1968, two million of America's three million farms produced a *gross* income of less than $10,000. Another half million farms realized less than $20,000 in gross income.

The remaining half million larger farms (those grossing $20,000 or above) do, of course, control a large land area—between 40 and 50 percent of our total farmland. But even these farmers must contend with the high cost and uncertainty that prevail in agriculture. And they must produce in a highly cost-competitive economy where conservation work may produce less immediate return than other capital investment.

Experience shows us that landowners assign a low priority to conservation investment in relation to some of the other immediate operating costs. This is understandable, and there is no reason to believe it will change.

If the conservation work implicit in the conservation needs inventory were to be applied over a 20-year period, the cost would be about 20 percent of current net income from farming. Instead, farmers and ranchers are now investing about 4 to 6 percent of their net farm income in soil, water, pasture, and forest conserving measures, with about 60 percent of these measures accompanied by Federal cost-sharing.

Based on this percentage of income going into conservation work, a billion dollar increase in net farm income would likely yield at most a $60 million increase in conservation investment. It would therefore seem that increased income alone cannot be relied upon to achieve an annual conservation investment comparable to what is needed.

So the point is this: While the conservation of our agricultural resources must be carried out through the farm family, the farm family does not generally have the financial means to do conservation work on the scale we now consider necessary. The average farmer cannot be expected to carry alone the total burden of conservation that needs to be done.

The man on the land realizes that conservation is desirable—socially, esthetically, and economically—yet he has a prior responsibility: to feed his family and provide its members with other essentials of modern living, including a nonagricultural education for those young people who increasingly must turn away from the land as they mature.

The farmer knows most conservation will, in the long run, boost income. Or, more accurately perhaps, the failure to conserve will reduce income. Nevertheless, a man's family must be fed and clothed and his taxes paid—for the short run as well. And it is only after these items are taken care of that he can move on to the longer term economic and social considerations that include conservation.

At the same time, there is wisdom, as well as economy, in looking to landowners for a reasonable share of the cost. Farmers are generally willing (and to some degree able) to share the investment. In fact, experience shows that the landholder who does put a personal investment into conservation practices will usually do a better job of maintaining them.

The public, then, must be realistic in assessing its own environmental needs and its own obligation to help meet these needs into the indefinite future. There can be no question that public and private demands on natural resources will continue to grow rapidly—a growth related to the rise in population, the growth of industry and urbanization, rising levels of living, and expanded leisure time.

By the year 2000 we can expect the addition of at least 100 million people. This implies a need for at least 50 percent more food, at least 50 percent more housing, twice as much water, and three times the demand for outdoor recreation. There may be a tripling of the amount of land used for homes, schools, and factories, and more than a doubling of land for transportation.

Faced with this kind of pressure, public agencies and programs over the years have reflected some basic changes in the old philosophy that the landowner was entirely responsible for all work needed on his land.

In 1928 Congress appropriated the first funds for soil erosion research— the Buchanan Amendment to the USDA Appropriation Act.

In 1933 a new land use policy began to emerge in connection with cropland programs of the Agricultural Adjustment Act of May 12, 1933. Land diverted from crops in over-abundant supply had to comply with the terms of rental-benefit contracts for conserving uses such as ". . . planting additional permanent pasture; for soil-improving and erosion-preventing crops not to be harvested; for resting or fallowing the land; for weed eradication; or for planting farm wood lots."

Federal support for technical assistance was provided when Congress created the Soil Conservation Service under the Soil Erosion Act of 1935.

The Soil Conservation and Domestic Allotment Act of February 29, 1936, added conservation practice cost-sharing assistance under the Agricultural Conservation Program, the Naval Stores Conservation Program, and the Range Conservation Program. Mean-

while, the Tennessee Valley Authority, established in 1933, began to provide test-demonstration materials and technical services through the Cooperative Extension Services to farmers in the seven valley States, for conservation treatment.

Beginning in 1944, the Agricultural Conservation Program (ACP) was limited to conservation cost-sharing only. Since that time, Federal cost-sharing funds provided annually under the program (exclusive of administrative costs) have ranged from $270 million to as low as $125 million. These funds were matched by farmers, usually on a 50–50 basis.

State governments have also helped. They have provided to farmers participating in the ACP various conservation services or materials such as soil testing and tree seedlings.

New Mexico has been contributing a share of the cost of rehabilitating ancient Spanish irrigation systems (acequias) as a water conservation and erosion control measure. The governments of Puerto Rico and the Virgin Islands have provided substantial funds along with the ACP funds for sharing costs of conservation practices with farmers under "unified conservation programs."

The principle of public-private sharing of costs for "works of improvement" in small watershed projects was added under the Watershed Protection and Flood Prevention Act (PL 83–566) of 1954. Congress adopted this as a general principle after it had been applied to a limited extent in the 11 flood prevention watersheds authorized by the Flood Control Act of 1944 and to more than 50 "pilot" small watersheds authorized in the USDA appropriation act of 1953.

Later, Congress introduced the principle of long term cost-sharing contracts for conservation work, in the Great Plains Conservation Program authorized by an amendment to the Soil Conservation and Domestic Allotment Act on August 7, 1956.

This program is aimed at long term conservation planning and financial assistance in selected counties of 10 Plains States. It authorizes complete conservation planning for up to 10 years, with Federal cost-sharing obligated in advance so that the farm or ranch operator knows when he starts out that his conservation plan can be made to come true.

Earlier in the same year (1956), the Soil Bank Act had linked acreage diversion payments and conservation practice cost-sharing under 3- to 10-year contracts. Similar arrangements were continued under the Cropland Conversion Program authorized by the Food and Agriculture Act of 1962 and the Cropland Adjustment Program authorized by the Food and Agriculture Act of 1965.

Federally assisted conservation work has also made a contribution through the regional development programs authorized by Congress in 1965. Section 203 of the Appalachian Regional Development Act (PL 89–4) specifically authorized the Secretary of Agriculture to enter into agreements of not more than 10 years with landholders to help them perform approved practices.

Funds are transferred by the Appalachian Regional Commission to the Department of Agriculture for technical and cost-sharing assistance for these landholders through the Appalachian Land Stabilization and Conservation Program.

The Public Works and Economic Development Act of 1965 (PL 89–136) authorized economic development regions to be established by the Secretary of Commerce upon petition of the State Governors in a region. Five regional programs are now in existence under this authority—for New England, the Ozarks, the Upper Great Lakes, the Four Corners area of the Southwest, and the Coastal Plain area of the Southeast. This act has resulted in only a little direct conservation assistance to farmers, but is regarded as a promising venture in Federal-State development with potential for additional aid for conservation work in those areas.

In the 1960's, cost-sharing under the Agricultural Conservation Program was broadened to include wildlife conservation as primary benefits, and beautification-conservation practices. In 1970, the program included practices primarily for pollution abatement for the first time—authorized by new language in the 1970 USDA Appropriation Act.

Congress has, in a number of acts, recognized the farmer's unique ability to provide recreation to city families. Acreage diversion programs have encouraged recreational uses through adjustment and cost-sharing payments to farmers and through special incentives to owners and operators who permit free public access to their diverted acreage.

USDA credit and technical assistance programs and other cost-sharing programs have also encouraged recreational development.

The Nation is experiencing a sharp growth in concern about the natural environment. It would be good to report that this sudden enlightenment was entirely the result of educational work by conservationists over the years. The fact is, however, that this concern also grows out of the increasing seriousness of the problem, which is now so acute it is hard to ignore.

It took a 5-year drought in the Northeast to alert New York City residents to the fact that the water they drink and wash their cars with comes from somewhere. There is new awareness that someplace back of the tap the rain must fall—and that land treatment in the Hudson and Delaware Valleys is of life-giving importance to Manhattan.

The Sioux City stockyards flood of 1952—which washed pens, cattle, and railway cars into the Missouri River—was the impetus for watershed conservation on the tributary Floyd River. This is the story in many watersheds; there is nothing like a flood to create interest in upstream land treatment.

The Nation's Capital was appalled a few years ago when a water skiing exhibition was canceled at the last

241

minute because the Potomac was not even safe for skiers, let alone swimmers. Today, water quality standards being adopted by the basin States will permit swimming again in some parts of the Potomac.

Still, the most prevalent water pollutant by far is silt. The sediment being washed from our lands, road and stream banks, and urban developments is at least 700 times the mass of the sewage discharge. Moreover, advances in the recycling of sewage and industrial wastes raise the possibility that the "pollution gap" between farm and nonfarm sources may widen.

A stir was created in a Midwest State by the prediction of a responsible official that soil conservation, as well as other types of pollution control on farms, might some day be mandatory under State regulation. Rural zoning, land purchases, easements—all are being used or considered as ways an urban society might protect its interest in the use of rural land.

Practical, moral, and legal problems aside, any program that introduced a higher degree of public control over agricultural land use would still have to meet the question of the cost of conservation measures. The fact would remain that agriculture is not returning enough net income to its families to support a vastly higher level of conservation spending.

Agriculture is, of course, changing rapidly. It is hard to predict what advances in technology, financing, and organization might bring in terms of improved income to agriculture. It may be that, over time, most of America's farmland will be in "stronger hands" which could be expected to invest the needed amounts in land treatment.

Still, these funds would have to come from somewhere—whether they originate as a part of the food dollar or as a part of a Federal or State or local budget, or a combination of these. The larger society should not expect to be spared a concern and a financial responsibility for its own survival and well being. Nor will it be so spared.

America's New Role in World Agriculture

INTERRELATIONS IN OUR POLICIES FOR AGRICULTURE, TRADE, AND AID

U.S. AGRICULTURE really does have a new role in the world, a role that has been slowly evolving for three decades and one that we have been slow to fully comprehend. We have been guilty of underestimating the importance of what we do. But in the last few years there has been a change in our approach to several of our agricultural, trade, and aid policies. This change has reflected our understanding that our policies are important to the rest of the world, not in a peripheral way but in a way that matters to farmers and consumers almost everywhere.

For more than three decades the United States has been the leader in the free world's effort to achieve a reduction in barriers to international trade. A great deal has been achieved through reciprocal trade agreements and multilateral trade negotiations since the passage of the Trade Agreements Act in 1934. But much less has been achieved for agricultural trade than for trade in industrial products.

While agricultural trade has been increased significantly since World War II, most of the increase has been due to economic growth rather than the reduction of trade barriers. The Kennedy Round of Negotiations (1964–67) was a success for industrial products, but relatively small reductions were achieved in trade barriers to farm products.

One reason we have not had more success in reducing trade barriers against farm products has been the nature of various farm programs around the world.

The source of the conflict has been the efforts of many countries, including the United States, to increase farm incomes by increasing farm prices, while at the same time technology was bringing new increases in productivity.

Increasing the prices of most farm products cannot be achieved without interfering with either exports or imports or sometimes both. Export subsidies have been required to achieve higher prices for export products, and import quotas for products that would be imported because of the higher domestic prices.

Recognizing these facts, drafters of agricultural legislation of the 1930's in the United States included provision for both export subsidies and import quotas. Our use of these devices has probably made it more difficult to negotiate with other nations for reductions in barriers to trade.

One of the major goals of a liberal trade policy is to eliminate the use of quantitative restrictions on imports, another is to prevent an unfair expansion of exports by payment of subsidies. However, when the General Agreement on Tariffs and Trade in 1947 was negotiated, exceptions were made to the general principles for the conduct of trade to permit the use of both export subsidies and import quotas for agricultural products.

Since 1951 each of our trade agreement acts has stated that no international agreement, old or new, could interfere with the application of import quotas under Section 22 of the Agricultural Adjustment Act, which permits us to restrict imports of certain farm commodities.

While Section 22 has been administered with considerable restraint and, where possible, with a concern for the interests of other nations, the fact that

✦

AUTHOR D. GALE JOHNSON is Professor of Economics at The University of Chicago. He is author of *Trade and Agriculture: A Study of Inconsistent Policies*, and *The Struggle Against World Hunger*.

on occasion we have resorted to import quotas to reduce the governmental costs of domestic farm programs has made it more difficult to convince others of the wisdom of reducing barriers to trade in farm products.

Recent years have seen important changes in U.S. domestic programs, especially price supports, that have reduced tensions between these programs and a freer trade policy. When farm price supports were above world market levels, export subsidies were necessary.

Since export markets were essential for several price-supported commodities—especially cotton, wheat, and feed grains—U.S. price supports were set at or below world market prices in the latter half of the sixties and direct payments were used to maintain farm incomes at politically acceptable levels. Markets allocated farm products between the domestic and foreign buyers, and farm exports increased as a result.

The elimination of most, though not all, export subsidies has gone a considerable distance toward removing important inconsistencies between farm programs and trade policies of the United States.

However, many countries still have commodity programs that interfere with free trade. In the United States, the programs for many dairy products, sugar, peanuts, and long staple cotton still depend on import quotas. But many countries have such conflicts between farm programs and freer trade. The European Economic Community provides a striking example.

The EEC's trade policy for most agricultural products is a direct extension of internal agricultural programs. For the variable levy commodities, including wheat, feed grains, meats, and poultry, the domestic target price is met by limiting imports until the price rises to the target level. If the EEC is still an importer when the market price equals or exceed the target price, the farm policy is the trade policy.

In some few cases, such as wheat, the EEC has a surplus of certain types of wheat and disposes of the excess in world markets through the use of an export subsidy.

From the viewpoint of supporters of a freer trade policy, the clash between freer trade and domestic farm policies is all too often won by the latter.

If a nation wishes to export, it must import. Exports and imports are generally in approximate balance, though exports can exceed imports if a nation makes loans or gifts to other nations.

It is sometimes hoped that our agricultural exports can be paid for by the importation of industrial goods. And to some degree, when the value of our commercial or dollar exports of farm products exceeds the value of agricultural imports, this occurs. But many nations with whom we trade have little to export except farm products.

Thus our trade with such nations, in South America, Africa, and Asia depends upon their ability to find a foreign outlet for agricultural products. And as the richest nation in the world, the United States must provide a significant part of that market.

Trade permits the countries of the world to specialize in those products that their particular resources permit them to produce most cheaply relative to the rest of the world. Interference with trade, through tariffs or import quotas, induces production of products at higher costs than the cost of importing the same product.

Trade is one of the means by which nations can increase the level of living of their citizens. A way that trade increases the level of living is by making available certain products which cannot be produced at all in the importing country or can only be produced at extremely high cost. Examples are coffee, bananas, tea, and cocoa. However, the same basic principles apply even if a product can be produced domestically, but at a cost above its import value.

Trade is important to the developed countries; it is critical for the economic well-being of the developing countries. The developing countries that do not have petroleum or minerals to export depend upon agricultural exports for foreign exchange earnings.

Foreign exchange earnings are necessary to purchase the machinery, equipment, fertilizer, and services needed for investment to increase national production. Without such earnings, the prospects of rapid economic growth in most developing countries would be dim indeed.

Because of the importance of agricultural exports for developing countries, the agricultural policies of the developed nations are of critical significance. When developed countries encourage uneconomic production of farm commodities through high prices and subsidies, the foreign markets of the developing countries are seriously and adversely affected. The developing countries simply do not have the resources to subsidize their own agriculture; it is only a rich country that can afford to do so.

U.S. agriculture had an important role in the Nation's efforts to assist many nations to rebuild after World War II and to help the developing nations.

The full productive capacity of our agriculture was brought into focus in the years from 1945 through 1950 and the outpouring of food was an important factor in preventing starvation or hardship in war-ravaged areas. With the economic recovery, including the recovery of agriculture, in Europe, food and other agricultural products were available to meet the needs of developing countries.

Our reasons for providing such aid were mixed ones—to find outlets for certain key products, to meet emergency conditions, and to assist countries in meeting their food needs while industrializing.

We supplied significant amounts of resources to the developing nations. But Public Law 480 resulted in objections from our trading partners on the grounds that we were reducing the available commercial markets in the developing countries. By the mid-sixties it was feared that some developing nations were becoming dependent upon our agricultural surpluses and were failing to give high priority to raising their own farm output.

The shift in emphasis in food aid from surplus disposal to concern for the effect of the aid upon the recipient country was a mature and highly principled action. The Food for Peace Act of 1966 recognized that while the United States and other developed countries can assist the developing countries to meet their food needs, the primary contributions must come from within each country.

U.S. agriculture has more than farm products to offer the developing world. The United States has the world's most developed agricultural research and educational system. Since the enunciation of the Point IV program by President Harry S. Truman in 1948, we have tried to make our scientific and technological knowledge available to developing countries. Thousands have come to our land-grant colleges and universities for advanced training in biology, the physical and social sciences, and all aspects of agriculture.

Efforts to extend American methods of farming to developing areas have seldom been as successful as had been hoped. A technique or a crop that is highly productive in the United States frequently has not been of significant benefit under different climatic, soil, and biological conditions in the developing countries. But in the past decade we have learned a great deal about how our scientific knowledge can be applied for the benefit of developing countries.

New varieties of grains have been created that outyield native varieties up to four times, and cultural practices suited to particular areas have been discovered by research carried out under local conditions.

To a very considerable degree the cautious optimism concerning the ability of the developing world to provide better diets for their growing populations has been due to the applied research made possible by our basic scientific knowledge.

A SINGLE CHARIOT WITH 2 HORSES: THE POPULATION AND FOOD RACE

THE GROWTH OF WORLD POPULATION and world food supply has been described as a "race." At times, some observers thought they saw world population pulling ahead, and several even became so discouraged they tore up their parimutuel tickets and left the stands, telling bystanders the race was all over. More recently other spectators thought they saw the green colors of food production moving ahead, and some of them also decided the race was all over and moved toward the parimutuel windows to collect their bets.

To the extent that the metaphor is apt, my money is on food production. If you can find a bookie willing to take your money at this point, I think food production is a very good bet indeed.

However, to me it really doesn't look like a race at all. Let me lend you my binoculars. I think if you will look carefully, you will see there are not two horses running independently toward the goal. Rather the two horses are hitched together by an intricate harness so that it is impossible for one to get very far ahead or behind. The horses are not being ridden by two separate jockeys, but are hitched to a single chariot with a driver, who sometimes shouts at one or the other, and sometimes applies his whip to one or the other, and sometimes hauls back on one or the other.

The driver is humanity, and while I don't have a very good name for the chariot he is riding in, we could call it "modernization," or "economic de-velopment." Economists have a short-hand name for the harness that holds the horses together; it's called "supply and demand."

This metaphor has weaknesses, but I think it is much more realistic than the notion of a race. And my conclusions about the eventual outcome are profoundly different from those of excited observers who have seen at times a coming radical deterioration in the world food situation, or at other times a quick solution to the problems.

My view is that, barring great catastrophes, and especially broad political upheavals and widespread wars, a serious deterioration of the world food situation is unlikely. However, a rapid approach to the condition where everyone in the world will be well fed and well nourished at all times also is not very likely. For a long time ahead there will continue to be many very poor people in the world who are not well fed. Some of these, such as pregnant women and children, will have great need for special feeding programs to meet crucial nutritional requirements.

For the long pull, I think the food horse is much the stronger. He did stumble several years ago when he stepped into a big weather-made pot-hole. But now he's straining hard against the harness. On the other hand, the population horse shows some signs of weakening.

A shortcoming of my harness metaphor is that a real harness doesn't stretch very much as time goes by, but this harness does. As indicated above, at a given time, within a short period, there is little likelihood of world food production moving very far ahead of world population, or falling very far behind. However, as time goes on it is very likely that world food production will move further and further ahead of world population. The harness binding the two together will be lengthened by rising incomes, which will

✦

AUTHOR JOSEPH W. WILLETT is Acting Director, Foreign Regional Analysis Division, Economic Research Service.

give consumers the economic power to demand more food, and by technological developments, which will bring down the cost of increased supplies per capita.

Let me make clear that I am not counseling complacency about the world food situation. These horses are both spirited and erratic. They are not very well matched nor very well trained. The driver will have to work hard and he'd better not lay down either his whip or his reins if he wants to get wherever he's going in one piece.

The track is rough. Wars, social upheavals, political pressures, and technological developments provide a lot of bumps. Government policies for agriculture, population, foreign trade, and aid will be important in determining the trends as well as in determining how well the bumps are smoothed out.

Weather makes potholes that the food horse is inclined to stumble over. There will be droughts, floods, insects, and disease problems, but the effects of these in one country tend to be offset by good conditions in other countries. The world's production of food in any year seldom deviates from the upward trend line by more than 2 percent.

When there is a bad year, or a series of bad years, in a country there is usually some room for adjustment by drawing down food stocks, feeding less to livestock, slaughtering livestock, or importing food.

Let's take a look at an instant rerun of the progress of this team. What has actually been happening? Keep in mind that for the world as a whole—and for most countries—trends in food production are about the same as trends in total agricultural production, which includes cotton, wool, tobacco, and other farm products not used as food. In most countries, and for the world as a whole, food makes up by far the greater share of total agricultural production.

From the late 1930's to the late 1960's world food production increased at an average rate of about 2 percent per year. Population increased somewhat more slowly so that by the end of the period, per capita food production was about 8 percent higher than it was at the end of the 1930's.

Food production increased at about the same rate in the poor or "underdeveloped" countries as it did in the rich or "developed" countries. However, because of the more rapid growth of population in the poor countries, per capita food production in those countries has increased only slightly.

The point which needs emphasis is that for the world as a whole, and even for the poor countries as a group, not only has there been no deterioration in the average availability of food, but there has been some improvement over the long run.

If we look at shorter periods, and individual countries, we see there has been a substantial variation in the rate of growth of per capita food output. Looking at the recent past, we see that in the poor countries there was a decline in per capita production in 1966, but a big recovery in 1967. In 1968 per capita production increased in the rich countries but remained about level in the poor countries. Preliminary estimates indicate there was another expansion of world agricultural output in 1969.

There was an imbalance in food production between the rich countries and the poor countries during the last two decades or so. As indicated above, per capita food production increased much faster in the rich countries, and large shipments of food—much of it as aid from the United States—went from the rich countries to the poor. Agriculture had been neglected in development programs in poor countries and there were lags in making use of improved seed, fertilizer, and other modern inputs. Meanwhile, agriculture had been over-expanded in the rich countries.

The imbalance would have been much greater if the United States had not held millions of acres out of production during most of those years to bring output down more in line with

248

demand and to cut down surplus stocks. The United States now uses about 335 million acres of land for crop production, with about 55 to 60 million held out under conserving uses of farm programs. The United States has been the only country to deliberately hold back much acreage. However, programs to take wheat land out of production are being implemented in Canada and Australia.

In recent years agricultural production has been increasing much faster in the group of other developed countries than it has in the United States. As a result, stocks of grain are at record levels in Canada, the European Community, Australia, and Japan. In France the production of grain has increased very sharply and exports are heavily subsidized.

Huge surpluses of dairy products, especially butter, have built up in the USSR and the European Community. In the latter, programs to take acreage out of production and reduce dairy herds are being discussed.

There have been great differences in the rate of growth of agricultural production among the less-developed countries. Some have made outstanding progress. In a study by the Economic Research Service a few years ago, it was found that in 21 of 26 less-developed countries examined, the rate of increase in crop output exceeded population growth during a 15-year period.

In 12 of the countries crop output increased more than 4 percent per year. This growth rate surpassed the rates ever achieved by the more developed countries, including the United States, during a comparable period of time. In seven of these countries—Israel, Sudan, Mexico, Costa Rica, the Philippines, Tanganyika, and Yugoslavia—crop production increased more than 5 percent per year.

The so-called "Green Revolution" has had important effects on agricultural production in some poor countries. In the last 3 years, highly productive new varieties of rice and wheat have spread very rapidly in several countries in Asia. These new varieties of grain, along with better weather, more and cheaper fertilizer, higher prices to farmers, and other factors, have helped to bring about dramatic increases in grain production in India, Pakistan, and the Philippines.

The new wheat was developed in the late 1950's in Mexico. The rice varieties were developed in the early 1960's at the International Rice Research Institute in the Philippines. Under suitable conditions, both types of grains produce much higher yields than traditional varieties.

These new grains have some disadvantages, including not being very palatable to consumers, so their future spread and production is somewhat uncertain. Their spread and continued use will depend on prices of grain and fertilizer, extension and improvement of irrigation systems, damage from pests, and other factors.

There have been countries in which the food situation has not improved, or has even deteriorated. In the Caribbean countries per capita food production in 1968 had fallen to only 70 percent of the 1957–59 level. In several South American countries production has not been keeping up with population. In a substantial proportion of the countries of Africa and the Near East also, production of food has not kept up.

Increases in agricultural production come about mainly because of changes in the overall economic and agricultural situations in each country. The whole system of changes which, over time, increases a country's ability to produce economic goods, including farm products, are referred to as "economic development." Increased production may arise from increased inputs of land, labor, and capital, or changes in combinations of inputs that use new technology.

For U.S. agriculture as a whole, the total amount of inputs, that is, land, labor, and capital, have changed very little in the last 15 years and the main developments have been the downtrend in the use of labor and the increase in capital inputs.

Substitution of machinery, and especially large-scale machinery, for labor is perhaps the most significant characteristic of agriculture at the stage of development reached in the United States. This kind of change, combined with the increases in yields, allows one farmworker in the United States to produce enough farm products for more than 43 people.

The increasing use of improved seed, chemicals, and machinery not only has been the main factor in increasing agricultural output in the rich countries, but has necessarily led to a greater commercialization of farming, since more and more of the inputs come from outside agriculture and require money outlays. The family farms in the United States have grown larger and larger, with little change in the amount of labor but with rapid increases in the amount of capital used per farm.

In most of Western Europe the use of fertilizers, mixed feeds, fuel, and chemicals is also increasing rapidly. Investments in buildings and machinery also have increased at a rapid rate. However, in a number of countries in Western Europe the average size of a farm is small. And until a substantial segment of the agricultural labor force retires or moves to other occupations, agriculture cannot be organized into efficient large-scale modern units.

Before economic development starts to proceed rapidly in a particular country, agricultural methods change only very slowly. Agricultural production increases mainly through expansion onto additional land and by use of traditional methods. Most developing countries have been able to expand their cultivated area by putting crops on land formerly unused or occupied by pasture or forests.

In the last two decades the area in crops in the poor countries has increased by nearly a third, but yields per acre increased only about a tenth.

Good, unused land is becoming less readily available throughout the poor countries, and especially in a number of countries in Asia and Central America.

In much of Africa south of the Sahara and in South America, the man land ratio is less stringent and the average farm is larger. However, even in those areas average farm size is declining. And to make use of much of the large reserves of land not cultivated now would require large expenditure for clearing jungles, establishing soil conservation programs, building irrigation systems, controlling malaria and tsetse flies, and building new settlements for colonizers.

For these and other reasons, the moving of large numbers of people to remote new areas is difficult and has not been very successful lately. Thus it is likely that in Africa south of the Sahara and in South America, as well as in most of Asia, Central America and the Near East, increasing dependence will have to be put upon the more intensive forms of agriculture using modern technology to raise output per acre.

What is happening in a number of less developed countries, and has already proceeded quite far in the developed countries, is that the connections between land and other kinds of farm inputs are being changed greatly by the process of economic growth. Fertilizer, insecticides, herbicides, and improved seed are, in a real sense, substitutes for land. Although, of course they must be applied to land, they make the land so much more productive that less land is needed or the shortage of land becomes a much less restricting element on agricultural production.

Increased yields have already made important contributions to rising output in some poor countries. As mentioned above, the "Green Revolution" is already increasing productivity per acre in a number of countries. Because these improvements give large returns they have been able to get quick acceptance from farmers and have been able thus to add substantially to overall production. However

250

as the new varieties spread to less suitable land, or as problems of diseases or pests develop, additional gains from their use may slow down.

There will need to be further developments and changes in technology, the marketing situation, availability of credit, and other aspects of agriculture. Research should continue to develop still better varieties of grain and will also have to be focused especially on improved varieties of other crops.

Farm machinery is in a sense a substitute for land in that it helps to increase production from land by making it possible to do a better job of plowing, cultivating, and harvesting. Farm machinery is also especially important as a substitute for farm labor.

For some years ahead it seems that technological developments which save labor will not be very important in the poor countries. In fact, the problem may tend to be in the other direction. Because of the rapid increase of population in the rural areas in many of these countries, the farm labor force will grow at a very fast rate for a good many years. Thus the problem will tend to be more in the direction of finding productive work on the farm or in farm-related activities rather than in supplanting farmers with machinery.

The agricultural system of the poor countries will remain far different from that in the United States for a long time. Much can be done to modernize and make it more productive, but different combinations of capital and labor must be used, reflecting their availability and costs, which are unlike those in the United States.

Some of the research which has developed the highly productive agriculture of the United States is adaptable to the farm problems of the less developed countries. However, it must be adapted, taking into account the fact that labor is much cheaper, and far more readily available, while capital is relatively dearer and much scarcer than here.

Markets for exports will have to be found for some of the increased farm production of the poor countries, or their economic growth will be slowed. Here their aspirations may conflict with the desires of rich countries to protect markets for their own farmers. On the other hand economic growth will make the poor countries better markets for some imports.

WORLD TRENDS IN THE USE OF FARM PRODUCTS

FOOD CONSUMPTION per capita during the past 20 years has been increasing at a slightly higher rate than production per capita in the less developed countries. Grain imports from the developed world—partly in the form of food aid—have filled much of this gap between production and consumption.

Population growth, the trend toward urbanization, and increased incomes are major factors accounting for the relatively sharp increases in food consumption.

A major feature of the world food problem has been the fact that population growth rates have tended to be the highest in the less developed countries where production of food is low.

Much of the rapid increase in population in the last two decades has been due to a decrease in the death rate in Africa, Asia, and Latin America as a result of improved health measures. Accompanying the population growth has been a trend toward urbanization.

This sharp increase in the nonfarm population confronts developing countries with a whole new set of problems in setting up an effective food distribution system. Farmers have to be given incentive to produce in excess of their own needs. Facilities must then be provided to transport, store, process, and distribute the produce for the expanding urban areas.

The urbanization process frequently is accompanied by a change in consumption patterns—for example, a shift from starchy root or coarse grain crops to wheat or rice. Part of this change in the consumption patterns with urbanization is associated with changes in income levels.

Rising incomes are a major factor influencing the demand for food, but the effect of income changes depends on the stage of development of a country.

At the low income levels characteristic of developing countries, a high proportion of a family's total expenditure is for food, and a large part of any increase in income will also go for food. With subsequent growth in income, less of the increase is spent on food, and there may also be some shift to higher priced, so-called "quality" foods.

In countries like the United States, however, a rising share of consumer expenditures on food has gone to food processors and handlers in payment for more services such as packaging and precooking. These higher payments for services tend to mask the decline in the proportion of income spent on the basic food products themselves as incomes grow.

In the higher income range, the calories supplied by cereals and starchy roots and tubers decrease not only in relation to total calories but also in absolute terms. In developed, high-income countries like Canada, Oceania, and the United States there is relatively high consumption of protein-rich animal products and vegetables and fruits high in vitamin and mineral content.

✦

AUTHOR WILLIAM R. GASSER is Chief, Western Hemisphere Branch, Economic Research Service.

In high-income countries animal products provide a large share of the protein intake in the average diet. But in developing countries much of the protein intake is of plant origin, and may or may not be adequate depending on the source of the protein. Pulses (dry beans and peas, lentils, chick-peas) and such grains as wheat, millet, and sorghums are relatively good sources of protein.

A recent study by the Food and Agriculture Organization of the United Nations notes that in eastern Africa and in the Savannah zone of western Africa, where income levels are very low, the protein/calories ratio is high and compares well with that of diets of industrialized countries. The reason for this good protein score is the high protein content of the millet, sorghum, and pulses which form an important part of the diet in this part of Africa.

By contrast, in equatorial Africa and in northeast Brazil starchy foods such as yams, cassava, and plantains are the primary source of calories, but these foods are very low in proteins and hence diets are not well balanced in relation to calories and proteins.

FAO concludes that protein inequalities among groups of countries are much more significant then the differences in their caloric intakes.

Grain is a major food item in diets throughout the world. In developed countries direct food use of grains per capita has shown a declining trend as incomes rise. At the same time, however, use of grain for livestock feed has increased substantially, so that the developed countries show the largest gain in total grain consumption.

In developing countries, total and per capita consumption of grains has continued to increase, primarily from direct use as food, with some shift to higher quality grains like wheat and rice.

More rice is consumed than any other food. It is the basic item in the diet of half the world's population, and more than 90 percent is consumed in Asia. The developed countries of the

Bringing in sheaves of wheat, harvested with sickles, in India.

Although rice is the staple food of about half of the world population, only about 3 to 4 percent of world production moves in international trade.

In the past two decades many of the major rice consuming countries have lost their self-sufficiency in rice and become net importers.

In 1967–68 the United States became the leading rice exporter, shipping about 1.8 million tons each year. In 1967 Thailand was second and Mainland China, third, but in 1968 Thailand and Mainland China each exported about 1 million tons. In Japan, record rice harvests in 1967 and 1968, coupled with declining rice consumption, have led to a burdensome stocks situation.

Wheat is another of the world's most important foods and is, by far, the most widely traded internationally.

Wheat provides directly about a fifth of the total food calories of the world's population and is the national food staple in countries accounting for about a third of the world's people.

In Southern and Eastern Europe, the Soviet Union, Argentina, and West Asia, over 30 percent of the calories come from wheat. In East and West Africa and East Asia it is less than 5 percent. In most developing regions, however, as per capita incomes rise, the relatively low level consumption of wheat increases.

About a fifth of the wheat produced enters international trade. World levels and patterns of wheat trade have changed substantially in the past two decades.

World wheat exports totaled about 62 million tons in the peak year 1965–66 (July–June)—more than double the level 10 years earlier. In the last several years, however, exports have dropped sharply—to about 47 million tons in 1968–69, the lowest level in 6 years.

Two factors account for much of the drop in the late 1960's—first, Soviet Union recovery from the poor crops of 1963 and 1965 and a resultant sharp decline in imports and second, de-

world as a group have the lowest per capita utilization of rice, ranging from less than 2 kilograms per capita per year in some countries in western Europe and Australia to some 120 kilograms in rice-eating Japan.

For the developed countries as a group, utilization of rice usually exceeded production up to the mid-1950's, but in most recent years production has exceeded utilization.

Within the various regions comprising the developing world, the per capita utilization of rice, while universally high as contrasted with developed countries other than Japan, varies greatly between countries—from over 200 kilograms per capita in Southeast Asia to around 12 kilograms in North Africa.

Since 1950, the most rapid gain in per capita utilization has occurred in West Asia with an estimated annual growth of 2.6 percent. Latin America, South Asia, Southeast Asia, and all regions of Africa showed increases, reflecting rising incomes and the trend toward urbanization. Both these factors bring about a dietary shift from coarse grains, cassava, and other root crops to rice or wheat.

creased import needs in India and Pakistan following several very good food grain crops. But even with this decline the average level of imports in the period 1966–68 was about 50 percent above the level a decade earlier.

U.S. wheat exports peaked in 1965–66 at more than 23 million tons, but the 1968–69 level of less than 15 million tons was the lowest in 9 years.

Besides changes in the level of world wheat trade, there have been significant shifts in the pattern of trade. For example, Mainland China began importing wheat in 1961, and in the past 8 years Chinese imports have averaged nearly 5 million tons annually.

Canada and Australia have increased production and trade to supply the wheat import demands of Mainland China and the USSR. But with the decline in Soviet imports, Canadian stocks have reached a record level—higher than the U.S. carryover during the last 3 years.

Coarse grains (corn, barley, oats, rye, millet, sorghum, and mixed grains) account for almost half the world's output of grain.

Developing countries use much of their coarse grains—perhaps up to two-thirds of the total—directly for food. But, as indicated above, direct consumption of these grains has some tendency to decline in favor of rice, wheat, and animal products, as incomes rise and urbanization proceeds.

In developed countries direct consumption of coarse grains is very low, but feed use has trended upward with corn showing the largest increase.

International trade in coarse grains rose by about two-thirds in the period 1960–61 to 1965–66 but since that year trade has leveled off at about 42 million tons. Increased shipments of U.S. corn and sorghum accounted for much of the expansion, although several other countries—including Argentina, France, and the Republic of South Africa—also have boosted their coarse grain exports.

Although coffee is not one of the world's major agricultural crops, the proportion of world production enter-

ing international trade is one of the highest of all agricultural commodities.

The United States, Canada, and Europe account for more than 90 percent of world imports of coffee, with the United States importing almost 45 percent of the total. The U.S. share, however, has been decreasing, due both to increased consumption in other countries and a decline in U.S. per capita consumption.

U.S. coffee imports in 1968 were the largest in 20 years and almost a fifth more than in 1967; imports had peaked in 1962 and had been on a downward trend through 1967. The rise in imports in 1968 was due largely to a buildup of inventories in anticipation of the dock strike which began in December 1968.

Brazil is the largest producer and exporter of coffee, although her share in the world export market has dropped from about 50 percent in 1950 to some 35 percent in 1967. Africa's share of the export market, on the other hand, has increased sharply,

Pearl millet variety developed by Indian breeders.

from less than 15 percent in the early 1950's to about 30 percent in 1967.

Among the world's major nonfood commodities, cotton holds a special position as the most important plant fiber for clothing use. It is a major crop and export earner in many developing areas of the world.

World consumption of cotton has shown less growth than for total fibers and much less than for manmade fibers. During the decade 1957–67, per capita use of cotton remained unchanged as contrasted with an average annual increase of over 6 percent for manmade fibers. In this period cotton's share of total fiber consumption dropped from 69 to 59 percent.

Cotton's share of fiber use is generally highest in the developing countries and lowest in the developed regions, ranging from about 90 percent in Communist Asia and South Asia to less than 50 percent in Japan and Western Europe.

Absolute levels of per capita consumption average higher in the developed regions than in the less developed countries—ranging from about 10 kilograms in the United States to about 1 kilogram in parts of Africa and Asia. During the period from the mid-1950's to the mid-1960's the highest increases in per capita cotton use occurred in Japan, East Europe, and the USSR. There were slight decreases in per capita use in the United States, Canada, Communist Asia, East South America, and East Africa.

The United States is the world's major exporter of raw cotton, with the USSR in second place. In the 10-year period, 1955–57 to 1965–67, U.S. exports dropped nearly a fourth, while Soviet exports increased more than three-fifths.

Japan is the single major importing country for raw cotton but is also the leading exporter of cotton textiles. Western Europe is the major importing region both for raw cotton and for cotton textiles, with the United States the second largest importer of textiles.

U.S. FOREIGN TRADE IS VITAL TO OUR FARMERS AND TO OUR ECONOMY

SINCE THE UNITED STATES is the world's largest exporter of agricultural products and the second largest importer of farm products, foreign agricultural trade is very important to the American economy. The foreign market contributes about a sixth of our total farm income. It takes the output of one out of every 5 harvested acres in the United States.

Nearly three-fifths of the rice produced in this country is sold in the foreign market; two-fifths of the hides and skins, tobacco, tallow, and soybeans; and about a third of the wheat.

The value of the two movements of agricultural trade exceeds $10 billion a year. This trade extends the market for U.S. farmers to over 150 countries. It creates jobs for workers in financing, processing, storing, shipping, and trading. It results in higher living standards here and abroad and helps in developing a strong world economy.

Our exports of farm products reached a record $6.8 billion in 1966–67. However, they declined a billion dollars by 1968–69, mainly because of increased production of grains in many of the principal import markets as well as in the major exporting countries. Wide acceptance of synthetic products in the foreign market, also, has hindered or limited

✦

AUTHOR DEWAIN H. RAHE is Assistant Branch Chief of the Trade Statistics and Analysis Branch, Foreign Development and Trade Division, Economic Research Service.

the growth in exports of farm products such as cotton and wool.

The United States accounts for nearly a fifth of the world's agricultural exports. But the U.S. share of the world market has declined for commodities like cotton, wheat, feed grains, and meats since 1960.

There are two principal methods by which agricultural products may be exported. First, they may move through regular commercial channels. The exporter has to find the buyer and make arrangements to complete the transaction. The other method to move our farm products to the foreign market is the Food for Peace program.

Commercial sales today account for over four-fifths of all U.S. agricultural exports. These sales have accounted for most of the gain in U.S. exports of farm products s nce the mid-1950's. In fiscal year 1969 (July 1968 through June 1969), commercial sales for dollars totaled $4.7 billion, down 15 percent from the record $5.5 billion exported in fiscal year 1967.

From 1955 to the record in fiscal year 1967, commercial exports advanced an average of 7½ percent per year. In this period a number of favorable conditions helped to expand the level of commercial agricultural exports. First and probably most important was the rapid economic growth in Western Europe and Japan. For example, industrial growth in Japan averaged 14 percent a year. The growth in Western Europe was also substantial but less spectacular than Japan's.

The United States has had large supplies of many agricultural products available for export at competitive prices. However, for some of the price-supported commodities, the Government provided export-payment assistance to make U.S. prices competitive in world trade.

These price-supported commodities have domestic prices higher than world prices. In order for the exporter to compete, payment assistance bridges the gap between the world price and the domestic price and enables him to offer the commodity in foreign trade at the lower export market price.

Major commodities to receive export payment assistance in fiscal year 1969 were wheat products, tobacco, and rice. Exports of wheat grain received no net export payments in 1968–69 as export certificate costs collected from exporters exceeded export payments made to them. Other commodities were peanuts, relatively small amounts of cottonseed meal, nonfat dry milk, poultry, and lard. Export-payment assistance was provided for $0.6 billion of the $5.7 billion of U.S. agricultural exports. In 1967–68, assistance was provided for $1.4 billion of $6.3 billion worth of exports.

The export-payment assistance to the exporter, not included in the value of our exports, amounted to slightly over $60 million in fiscal year 1969, down from $107 million in 1967–68.

Barter for overseas procurement for U.S. agencies is now considered as a commercial export. These supply-type transactions are essentially equivalent to dollar sales since they offset dollar expenditures which would otherwise impair the U.S. balance of payments. In fiscal year 1969, about 6 percent of U.S. commercial sales were barter.

Barter for strategic materials—still considered a Government program—amounted to only $1 million in 1969.

Less than a fifth of U.S. agricultural exports are shipped under Food for Peace programs (Public Law 480) to developing countries. In fiscal 1969, they totaled $1 billion, down from the $1.3 billion in 1968.

Under our Food for Peace program, food is shipped to needy countries by three methods: Sales for foreign currency, long-term credit sales for dollars or convertible local currency, and donations to provide disaster relief and promote economic development.

A general rise in the level of protectionism of agricultural commodities has been a major factor in reducing the level of U.S. agricultural exports. For example, the increased protectionism n the European Community is ssociated with a substantial rise in roduction of many agricultural products by EC nations. Milk production has increased 13 percent; wheat, 40 percent; coarse grains, 41 percent; nd meat, 16 percent.

The United Kingdom has been promoting increased self-sufficiency in griculture as a way to improve its balance-of-payments position. The British have used a minimum import price scheme for grains since 1964 to increase domestic production and reduce the level of imports.

Japan has a high degree of protection for many of its agricultural products by tariffs, licensing, exchange controls, and Government monopoly. Rice, for example, is supported at $421 per metric ton and imports are regulated through the Government Food Monopoly.

The most important commodities in U.S. agricultural exports have traditionally been cotton, wheat, feed grains, and tobacco. But these commodities now represent less than half of our total farm exports.

Since 1960, U.S. exports of soybeans, soybean products, and rice increased substantially. In addition, many minor export products have become more important, such as variety meats, hides and skins, tallow, poultry meat, and meats.

Except for fiscal 1969, U.S. exports of wheat and flour have totaled over $1 billion since 1960. About half of the wheat and flour exports were under the Food for Peace program. The United States accounted for nearly a third of the world wheat trade in fiscal year 1969, down from two-fifths in 1963–64.

Shipments of wheat to the developed countries, primarily Western Europe, are mainly high protein wheat needed for blending with indigenous wheat to obtain the desirable baking qualities. Nearly two-fifths of the exports to Japan is Pacific Northwest white soft wheat used for making noodles and other products. Japan is now the largest commercial market for U.S. wheat,

taking around 80 million bushels annually.

In the last few years, developing countries made considerable progress in increasing grain production by adopting new high yield varieties, and by increasing fertilization and improving cultivation practices. At the same time, developed countries are expanding production of wheat in response to high support prices and policies designed to spur self-sufficiency.

Overall, the gain in production, well distributed between importers and exporters, sharply reduced the level of world wheat trade in 1968–69.

Rice exports totaling 38.6 million bags, three-fifths of U.S. rice production, in 1968–69 were more than double the level 10 years ago. Nearly half of the rice exports were commercial sales for dollars. The sharp increase in production in many of the developing countries as the result of adoption of the high yielding varieties may limit future expansion in U.S. exports.

U.S. feed grain exports increased tenfold since World War II. Rapid economic growth in Western Europe and Japan boosted the demand for meat and other animal products. This, in turn, raised requirements for imported grain for the production of livestock in these economically advanced countries.

U.S. feed grain exports reached a high of $1.3 billion in 1965–66, then dropped to $774 million in 1968–69. About half of U.S. feed grains moved to Western Europe and over a fourth to Japan. Overall, the United States had about two-fifths of the world export market for feed grains.

Nearly all U.S. feed grain exports were commercial sales for dollars except in 1967 when large quantities of grain sorghums were exported to India because of famine conditions there. Being an efficient and low-cost producer, the United States was able to export feed grains through most of the post World War II period without the aid of export payments.

Since 1966, soybeans and soybean products have been the Nation's top

Sculptured in American lard, little pigs above went to market at London food show to stimulate U.S. lard exports. Below, soy sauce plant near Tokyo. Japan imported 95 million bushels of soy beans in 1969, with U.S. supplying 81 million bushels.

dollar earner for agricultural exports, totaling over $1 billion annually. Prior to 1950, U.S. exports of these commodities were less than $50 million. The increased demand for soybeans, as with feed grains, reflected expanding demand for meats and animal products in industrially advanced countries.

In 1968, about one-half of protein meal, including meal equivalent of oilseeds, imported into the European Community (EC) originated from U.S. soybeans or oil cake and meal. In the last 5 years, about two-fifths of U.S. soybean production was marketed overseas. The United States accounted for over 90 percent of world soybean exports. The high prices of grains in the EC placed U.S. soybean meal in a favorable competitive position and thus stimulated use of soybean meal in animal rations.

Exports of most animal products have experienced sharp rates of growth. These products are used in most industrial countries as raw materials or to supplement local products such as cattle hides, poultry meat, and variety meats. However, the downward trend in exports of dairy products and lard because of worldwide surpluses has limited overall growth of this group. Exports of animal products totaled about $760 million in 1968–69.

Exports of fruits and vegetables, totaling $461 million in 1968–69, held relatively stable since 1960. High wages for producing and handling fresh products in the United States, and other rising production costs, hampered the expansion of production for export. While technology is improving the speed and efficiency of harvesting and packaging fruits and vegetables, increased mechanization is still relatively expensive.

Canada, the largest market for U.S. fruits and vegetables, takes over half of our export total.

Over a fourth of world tobacco exports are U.S. leaf. The United States produces high-quality tobacco, with a taste and aroma desired by smokers throughout the world. The United Nations trade sanctions against Rhodesia reduced tobacco exports from this major competitor of the United States.

Tobacco exports totaled over a half billion dollars in fiscal 1969, and represented nearly two-fifths of U.S. tobacco production.

The United Kingdom, consistently the major overseas tobacco market, received one-fourth of the total in 1968–69. Other important markets include West Germany, Japan, the Netherlands, Belgium-Luxembourg, Thailand, Taiwan, and Switzerland.

Before World War II, cotton exports accounted for over half of U.S. agricultural exports, but since 1966, cotton made up less than 10 percent of the total value.

Two major factors contributed to the decline. First, cotton production increased substantially in the foreign free world in the past two decades to an estimated 25.6 million bales in 1968, from 12.2 million in 1950. Developing countries expanded cotton production and export sales so as to purchase goods from industrial countries for economic development projects. Second, the production of manmade fibers in the foreign free world advanced sharply. Consumption in 1968 was equivalent to 27.4 million bales of cotton.

We imported $4.9 billion worth of agricultural products in fiscal year 1969. This is the highest level since the record $5.1 billion in 1951 when imports rose sharply because of the Korean War. Imports were equivalent to slightly over a tenth of our cash receipts from farm marketings—$44.1 billion.

Agricultural imports accounted for only about a seventh of imports of all commodities ($34.2 billion) in 1968–69. In 1960–65 they accounted for about a fourth of total imports, and in 1955–59 about a third. Since 1960, imports of nonfarm products have increased at an annual rate of 11 percent while farm products increased only 2 percent annually.

Generally, the United States has a

liberal policy towards imports of agricultural products. The American farmer receives less protection from imports than do the farmers of most other countries. About half of our agricultural imports—principally noncompetitive products—enter free of duties. For the rest, the duties average about 10 percent.

The United States has been reducing tariffs on agricultural products since passage of the Trade Agreement Act in 1934. This act permitted us to negotiate with other countries to reduce our tariffs if they reduced theirs. We have cut the average duty rate on dutiable farm products to around 10 percent in 1968 from the 85 percent level in 1934.

Since 1948, the General Agreement on Tariffs and Trade (GATT) has provided a framework for conducting trade among many industrialized countries. The most recent GATT (Kennedy Round) negotiations were concluded in 1967.

Imports of some agricultural commodities may be restricted through non-tariff measures. The President is authorized under Section 22 of the Agricultural Adjustment Act to impose a quota or a fee, in addition to an import duty, when imports of a product tend to impair agricultural price-support programs. Commodities controlled by Section 22 in 1968 were wheat and flour, cotton, certain dairy products, and peanuts. Sugar is regulated by the Sugar Act.

Under certain conditions, the President is authorized to regulate imports of fresh, frozen, or chilled meats of cattle, goats, and sheep (except lamb), by means of quotas. Since the principal supplying countries have voluntarily limited their shipments, it has not been necessary to use quotas under this act.

Our imports of the supplementary or partially competitive agricultural products increased by over $1 billion since 1960. They accounted for 62 percent of the agricultural imports in 1968–69, compared with slightly over two-fifths of the total in 1955–59.

About half of this gain was increased imports of animals and animal products—primarily meats. The other principal advances occurred for sugar, tobacco, fruits, vegetables, oil-bearing materials, edible nuts, and wines.

Meat imports increased rapidly since 1960. Most of the gain occurred for boneless beef and veal which is used for making hamburger, luncheon meats, frankfurters, and other prepared meat products. Demand for prepared meats expanded sharply as people desired more leisure time. U.S. production of comparable meat remained relatively stable.

Expanded dairy product imports are related to the sharp increase in world dairy production, widespread protectionism in other major markets, and the resultant surpluses competing for a market in the United States. Imports of $100 million in 1968–69 were more than double the level in 1955–59. The imposition of quotas on

Garlic imported from Mexico is unloaded at Laredo, Tex.

260

products not previously covered will limit growth in the future.

Large increases have taken place over the past decade for several fruits and vegetables such as strawberries, melons, tomatoes, cucumbers, mushrooms, garlic, and onions. Restrictions on the number of migrant foreign workers, poor growing conditions in many regions, and competition for farmworkers from other sectors of the economy contributed to the large growth. However, imports of fruits and vegetables accounted for only around 9 percent and 7 percent, respectively, of the consumption of these commodities.

Expanding U.S. affluence associated with the sharp rise in disposable personal income stimulated imports of wines, edible nuts, and other specialty products. Wines and nuts each totaled over $100 million in 1968–69. They have grown at an annual rate of 12 percent and 10 percent, respectively, since 1960.

Sugar imports totaled a record $629 million in 1968–69. Imports were about half of U.S. consumption. A steady or declining output in Hawaii and Puerto Rico resulted in a shift to foreign sources.

Increased use of oriental tobacco and especially the use of bottom leaves in producing filter cigarettes encouraged larger imports of tobacco. Manufacturers tended to substitute imported tobacco for the higher priced U.S. leaf. Imports in 1968 made up about 16 percent of the tobacco in cigarettes, compared with less than a tenth in 1955–59.

Imports of other supplementary products have been relatively stable. Cotton and wheat are regulated for the most part under Section 22. Apparel wool imports trended downward because of increased use of synthetic products and imports of manufactured textiles.

In contrast to the sharp increase in competitive imports, complementary (noncompetitive) products have been relatively stable since 1960. In fact, complementary products totaling $1.9 billion in 1968–69 were down more than $1 billion from the peak of $2.9 billion in 1950–51. The volume, measured by the quantity index, rose a fourth between 1955 and 1969.

A substantial increase in world production of many of these commodities resulted in an oversupply and sharply lower prices. The principal complementary items include coffee, rubber, bananas, cocoa beans, tea, crude drugs, spices, and carpet wool.

The volume of coffee imports increased to some 3 billion pounds in 1968–69, from about a 2.7 billion average in 1950–54. This rise reflected the gain in population, as per capita consumption of coffee has declined slightly since 1955. But the value of imports fell with the lower prices for Brazilian and Colombian types as production and competition increased from African and Asian producers.

Cocoa bean imports and prices fluctuate sharply because production is very sensitive to weather and growth conditions. However, long-run trends have been moving downward for value and price while moving upward for volume.

A shift to the use of synthetic rubber brought about lower prices for imports of crude natural rubber. Synthetic products also reduced imports of carpet wool, raw silk, and hard fibers. Upward trends for complementary imports were evident for bananas and spices.

Traditionally, the United States has had a favorable merchandise trade balance (an excess of exports over imports). Agriculture contributed significantly to this trade surplus, offsetting the deficits in other balance-of-payments accounts like foreign aid, military cost abroad, tourist spending, and foreign investment.

The U.S. agricultural trade surplus was $2.3 billion in 1964, and reached a peak of $2.4 billion in 1966. However, it declined to $1.0 billion in 1969 as a result of a 4-percent drop in exports. Agriculture accounted for a third of the total U.S. trade surplus in

261

EXPORTS PROVIDE BIG OUTLET FOR MANY FARM PRODUCTS
Fiscal Year 1969

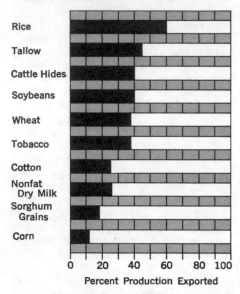

Rice
Tallow
Cattle Hides
Soybeans
Wheat
Tobacco
Cotton
Nonfat Dry Milk
Sorghum Grains
Corn

0 20 40 60 80 100

Percent Production Exported

WHAT WE EXPORT
Fiscal Year 1969

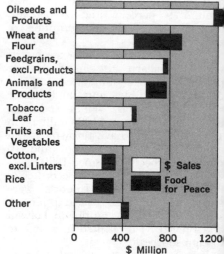

Oilseeds and Products
Wheat and Flour
Feedgrains, excl. Products
Animals and Products
Tobacco Leaf
Fruits and Vegetables
Cotton, excl. Linters
Rice
Other

□ $ Sales
■ Food for Peace

0 400 800 1200

$ Million

12 LEADING SUPPLIERS OF OUR AGRICULTURAL IMPORTS
Fiscal Year 1969

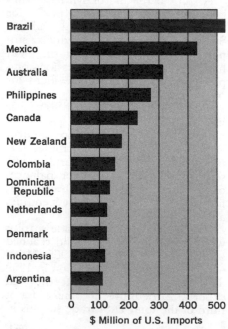

Brazil
Mexico
Australia
Philippines
Canada
New Zealand
Colombia
Dominican Republic
Netherlands
Denmark
Indonesia
Argentina

0 100 200 300 400 500

$ Million of U.S. Imports

OUR FOREIGN AGRICULTURAL TRADE SINCE THE FIFTIES
Fiscal Years

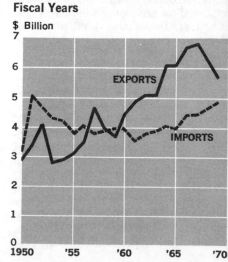

$ Billion
7
6
5
4
3
2
1
0

EXPORTS

IMPORTS

1950 '55 '60 '65 '70

262

1964, three-fifths in 1966, and all in 1969.

Our commercial agricultural trade surplus, which excludes exports under Government-financed programs, reached a peak of $1 billion in 1966. In 1960, this balance was a deficit of $436 million. Because of the decrease in exports and the sharp gain in imports, the commercial balance declined to a surplus of $605 million in 1967 and to a deficit of $129 million in 1969.

Besides the commercial trade, the United States obtains certain benefits from agricultural exports under the Food for Peace program.

These benefits include the foreign currencies that are used to defray U.S. Government expenses abroad and repayment made with interest on long-term dollar credit sales of our farm products.

The dollar returns and savings on noncommercial exports amounted to $360 million in 1969, up slightly from the $314 million in 1968, but up substantially from the $184 million in 1966.

Overall contribution of agricultural exports to the balance of payments (commercial exports and the dollar returns and savings on noncommercial exports) was $5.2 billion in 1969. After deducting agricultural imports, the net contribution was $231 million in 1969. Agriculture's net contribution reached a peak of $1.2 billion in 1966.

The future of world agricultural trade depends upon active cooperation among the major producing and consuming countries.

For our part, we must be willing to import in greater volume than in the past those commodities that can be produced more cheaply abroad. At the same time, we must be permitted access to the major world markets and the opportunity to expand our exports of products such as grains, soybeans, and animal products for which we have a high comparative advantage. Such unrestricted trade would add long-run growth to trading nations.

SPECIAL TRADE ARRANGEMENTS

DESPITE SUBSTANTIAL PROGRESS toward trade liberalization in a series of tariff negotiations since World War II, many policies have been adopted by nations, both individually and in groups, that interfere with the flow of trade among the countries of the world. Trade in agricultural products has been especially susceptible to interference from protectionist policies.

The basic idea of free trade is that every individual area or nation should specialize in what it can produce most efficiently and trade with others for products that can be produced more efficiently elsewhere. In this way, everyone will have more goods and services than if each tries to produce a little of everything.

Recognition of the mutual benefits from freer trade has motivated countries of the free world to hold several multilateral conferences to negotiate reductions in trade barriers. These have taken place under rules of the General Agreement on Tariffs and Trade (GATT), an international agreement that came into force on Jan. 1, 1948.

Six major conferences have been held. The latest and most comprehensive was the Kennedy Round concluded in 1967. In the Kennedy Round, the need for expanding trade opportunities for agriculture was given considerable emphasis. However, the problems encountered led to delay of substantive negotiating sessions in agriculture until near the end of the talks

✦

AUTHOR CARMEN O. NOHRE is Deputy Director, Foreign Development and Trade Division, Economic Research Service.

and no fundamental changes in access to markets or in the national farm policies were achieved. As a result, there was only modest progress toward liberalizing trade in farm products.

Efforts to remove trade restrictions and encourage trade expansion have been more successful for industrial than for agricultural products. Most countries provide some measure of income protection for agriculture through systems of price supports. These are frequently reinforced by extensive export subsidies and special import restrictions such as minimum import price schemes, variable levies, quotas, and other nontariff barriers that have been difficult to modify through international bargaining.

One development that has had an important impact on world trade and trade patterns for both industrial and agricultural products has been the emergence of regional economic organizations.

The most highly developed example of a cooperative effort among countries in economic matters is the European Economic Community (EEC). It was established through a treaty signed in Rome on March 25, 1957 by West Germany, France, Italy, the Netherlands, Belgium, and Luxembourg, and entered into force on Jan. 1, 1958.

The six countries agreed to create a customs union through progressive elimination of trade barriers between members, with concurrent adjustments in national duty rates to achieve a common tariff schedule for the whole EEC on all goods imported from non-member countries.

Besides the free movement of goods, the Rome Treaty provides for the unrestricted movement of labor and capital from one country to another and a harmonization of economic policies to permit the whole Community to function as an economic unit.

To EEC industry, integration of the six national markets offered increased opportunities to develop mass production and improve international competitiveness. Problems encountered

in merging the agricultural markets of the six differed greatly from those in merging their industrial markets.

Each of the member states had developed comprehensive national policies for agricultural support designed to expand domestic production and maintain incomes to family size farms. The differences in national policies and the wide variation in agricultural prices between the countries required that more extensive measures be adopted for integrating this sector.

The method chosen was to develop a Common Agricultural Policy (CAP) spelled out in a series of commodity regulations governing support measures and trade rules. A prominent role is assigned to import measures which are reinforced by internal support programs where they are considered necessary and workable.

Regulations covering individual commodity or commodity groups differ from one another as dictated by conditions of production and marketing, but most have certain common characteristics. The most pervasive characteristic is reliance on a minimum import price, and some form of variable levy to raise the price of imports to this minimum and thus completely insulate the domestic market from lower world prices. The regulations provide for export subsidies to permit sales at competitive prices in world markets.

The result is a separation of the internal market, where trade is relatively unrestricted, from the world market with a linkage provided by variable import levies and export subsidies.

The precise nature of the variable levy varies among commodities. There are differences in frequency of adjustment and in procedures used for calculation. For some products the levies are the sole import measure, while for others they supplement duties prescribed by the common tariff schedule. In all cases arbitrary computations are involved that provide opportunities for padding the levies and increasing the degree of protectionism.

264

Internal support measures consist mainly of government purchases at intervention prices set at levels to prevent market prices from falling substantially below the established price objectives.

Grains, dairy products, and sugar have accounted for the bulk of the purchases by intervention agencies. Beef, pork, rice, fruits, and vegetables are also eligible for intervention or support purchases. Producer subsidies or deficiency payments are important for vegetable fats and oils, and are also used to support durum wheat prices.

The European Agricultural Guidance and Guarantee Fund was set up by the Community to provide for common financing of programs supporting agriculture.

Import protection and the production incentive of high prices without production controls have reduced Community imports for many commodities. Increases in output have led in recent years to a larger part of their food consumption requirements being produced domestically.

Some commodities, especially dairy products and soft wheat, are now in surplus and the Community has been exporting large quantities of them with the use of export subsidies. These subsidies affect the position of other exporting nations, who react by expanding their own subsidy systems.

Importing countries having some home production of their own are under pressure to increase the level of import protection in their markets.

Due to the elimination of barriers to trade between members, the level of intra-Community trade in agricultural products has grown at a faster rate than that of trade with third countries. Imports from Community sources in 1968 were over 200 percent above the average for 1958–60 while imports from outside the area increased by 41 percent.

The European Community is the largest foreign market for U.S. farm products and for several years has accounted for nearly a fourth of total U.S. agricultural exports. After 1958, our agricultural exports to the EEC increased annually, almost without interruption, to a peak of $1.6 billion in 1966. Much of the growth was due to heavy demand for feed grains and oilseeds to support expanding livestock production.

Since 1966 EEC grain production has been substantially above previous levels, and grain imports have been correspondingly reduced. Sales of U.S. farm products declined to $1.3 billion in 1969, some 19 percent below the peak and the lowest level since 1963.

The European Free Trade Association (EFTA) came into being on May 3, 1960. Original members were

Combines harvesting a bumper wheat crop in France.

the United Kingdom, Denmark, Sweden, Norway, Austria, Switzerland, and Portugal. Finland became an associate member in 1961 and Iceland a full member in 1970.

Although its purpose, like that of the EEC, is to facilitate trade and promote closer economic cooperation among members, the institutional machinery in EFTA is much simpler and common rules are fewer and less elaborate.

To achieve a free trade area, each member has progressively eliminated its duties and quotas on industrial products of other member countries, while retaining its own tariff levels against outside countries. There are no provisions for progressive harmonization of national economic policies, although measures to improve coordination may be developed in the future.

Tariff reductions on most industrial goods began in July 1960 for the seven full members; these tariffs were eliminated on Dec. 31, 1966. Most agricultural products are excluded.

However, the Association does seek to expand trade in agricultural products so as to provide reasonable reciprocity to those member states whose economies are heavily dependent on agricultural exports, particularly Denmark and Portugal.

The most common method of promoting agricultural trade is through bilateral agreements under which specific farm exports of one member enjoy duty-free entry or other special treatment in another EFTA country. Both Denmark and Portugal have a number of such agreements with the United Kingdom and other EFTA partners. The most important of these in terms of volume of trade is the United Kingdom-Denmark agreement eliminating U.K. tariffs on Danish bacon, canned pork, and blue cheese.

Agricultural imports into the EFTA countries have increased moderately since 1961. A substantial portion of the increase is accounted for by an expansion of trade among the members. Imports from the United States have fluctuated considerably but have generally been above the level of 1961. In 1968, however, they dropped to the lowest level since 1959 and declined again in 1969.

The Latin American Free Trade Association (LAFTA) was established by the Montevideo Treaty signed on Feb. 18, 1960. Present members are Argentina, Bolivia, Brazil, Chile, Colombia, Ecuador, Mexico, Paraguay, Peru, Uruguay, and Venezuela.

As in other regional trade groups, members of LAFTA seek to develop one large market in the area to replace smaller isolated country markets. This is to be accomplished by gradually removing trade restrictions among the countries. The expanded market is expected to encourage building of larger plants that can produce goods more economically and thus make them available to consumers at lower cost. Each country maintains its own trade policies toward countries outside LAFTA.

The Montevideo Treaty provides for removal of all trade restrictions among LAFTA members by 1973. However, unlike procedures in the EEC and EFTA, no automatic or across-the-board reductions are scheduled.

There is a schedule for the general levels of liberalization to be achieved at specified intervals, but the products included and the extent of the reductions for each product are determined in a series of negotiations among members.

Negotiations in LAFTA are handled through two different concessions lists—the National List and the Common List. Each member has its National List, which is expanded by annual negotiations. It shows the concessions given by that country to all its partners.

A single Common List, applicable to all members, contains the products that are to move freely among the member countries at the end of the transition period. It was to have been developed through four successive rounds of multilateral negotiations at 3-year intervals. Agreement was reached on the first stage in 1964 but the second round, scheduled to be negotiated in 1967, has not been completed.

In late 1969, LAFTA members agreed to postpone the end of the transition period from 1973 to 1980, reduce the rate of annual reductions on the National Lists and postpone indefinitely further additions to and applications of the Common List.

In developing these concessions lists, no distinction is made between the methods of handling agricultural and industrial items. However, LAFTA has considered establishing norms regulating agricultural trade after the transition period. As proposed, these would provide for exceptions to be made with respect to agricultural products and would allow members to continue a number of restrictive policies to protect domestic agriculture beyond the date at which the free trade area was scheduled to be fully implemented.

Intra-LAFTA trade has increased more rapidly since 1961 than trade with countries outside the area. However, member countries still get about half their agricultural imports from non-LAFTA suppliers. The United States ranks first among these suppliers.

About half of the U.S. agricultural exports to LAFTA has moved under P.L. 480 programs. Although trade preferences have adversely affected exports of some farm commodities, total agricultural exports to the area have increased substantially since the formation of LAFTA. In 1969, the total value was nearly $360 million, about 6 percent of our total agricultural exports.

The Central American Common Market (CACM) consists of five members—Costa Rica, El Salvador, Guatemala, Honduras, and Nicaragua. Established in 1961 by the General Treaty on Central American Economic Integration, it has had its present membership since 1962.

Central American countries had previously negotiated numerous bilateral and mutilateral agreements which were consolidated in the Treaty. In addition, the Treaty established fixed schedules for moving toward a common external tariff and the elimination of all duties on products originating within the region except for items on a special list.

As in the Latin American Free Trade Association, internal trade liberalization is intended to promote industrial development by providing enlarged regional markets instead of single country markets while retaining protection against competition from outside the region. With few exceptions, imports from outside the Central American Common Market are now subject to the same duties in all member states, and most domestically produced goods move freely between members.

Regional programs in CACM have mainly been oriented toward stimulating industrial growth. Elements of an agricultural policy have been emerging which provide for stabilization and coordination rather than a centrally directed common policy.

The Protocol of Basic Grains covering corn, rice, sorghum, and beans is the major agreement affecting agriculture. It provides rules for regulating intraregional and international trade of basic grains. National programs of production and supply are formulated by member countries. These programs are to be coordinated according to needs of the region to arrive at a uniform policy regulating trade of the basic grains.

The Protocol provides that all member country surpluses be used before grain is imported from non-CACM countries, and that all member country import requirements be satisfied before grain is exported from the area. Duties are used to maintain import prices at a level at least as high as the importing country's domestic prices.

Trade among members of the Central American Common Market has increased substantially. The greatest expansion has occurred in nonagricultural trade, but intra-CACM movement of farm products has also risen.

U.S. agricultural exports to the CACM increased moderately after 1961, reaching $45 million in 1968, but declined $38 million in 1969.

The four regional groups described have the most ambitious programs for economic integration. This process is continuing. The United Kingdom and several other EFTA countries have applied for membership in the EEC. The LAFTA and CACM countries have agreed to work toward combining both areas into a Latin American Common Market. In addition, other groups of countries in various parts of the world have formed free trade areas or custom unions.

There are also several instances of arrangements that provide for preferential treatment for trade among countries without necessarily involving eventual free trade. The European Economic Community has developed several of these arrangements with countries beyond its borders.

Greece and Turkey are associate members with products from these countries receiving preferential treatment. It is intended that both will ultimately become full members of the Community.

The EEC also has a preferential trading arrangement with 18 African states and Associated Overseas Countries. These countries were former colonies or had other special relationships with France, Belgium, or Italy. With the formation of the EEC, a Convention of Association was devised to replace the former arrangements with individual European countries. A protected market in the EEC for certain commodities and a Community program for providing development funds were established.

In addition, the EEC has granted preferences to several of its trading partners in the Mediterranean area.

Members of the British Commonwealth, along with Ireland and South Africa, have for many years granted each other certain tariff concessions.

These Commonwealth preferences have declined in importance in recent years due to rising prices and the re-sults of GATT negotiations. However, they continue the practice of discriminatory treatment on a large number of agricultural as well as nonagricultural products.

An international commodity agreement is another type of special trade arrangement. This is an undertaking by a group of countries to stabilize trade, supplies, and prices of a commodity. It is usually open to all interested countries. Two major arrangements presently in force are the International Grains Arrangement and the International Coffee Agreement.

The 1967 International Grains Arrangement (IGA) entered into force on July 1, 1968, for a 3-year period. It replaced the International Wheat Agreement (IWA) which had provided rules for world trade in wheat for 18 years. The IGA consists of two parts: a Wheat Trade Convention and a Food Aid Convention.

Minimum and maximum prices for 14 major wheats moving in world trade are set by the Wheat Trade Convention. For U.S. wheats, the minimum prices are generally about 23 cents per bushel higher than the minimum under the IWA. A range of 40 cents per bushel was set to permit prices to fluctuate in response to supply and demand.

The Food Aid Convention contains provisions not found in the IWA. It provides for a coordinated effort by developed countries to supply food aid to less developed countries on a regular and continuing basis.

Members agree to provide a total of 4.5 million metric tons of grain each year. Both exporting and importing countries participate. The U.S. commitment is for nearly 1.9 million tons, or 42 percent of the total. The European Economic Community contributes a million tons, with other members supplying lesser amounts.

Contributions may be in the form of wheat, coarse grains suitable for human consumption, or an equivalent in funds for purchase of these grains.

Liberal supplies of wheat in the world led to problems in complying with the minimum price provisions soon after the Arrangement came into force. Despite numerous efforts to correct the situation, member countries have been unable to hold prices above the minimum levels.

The present International Coffee Agreement went into effect in 1968. Like the preceding 1962 Agreement, its major purpose is to achieve a reasonable long-term balance between supply and demand to avoid excessive price fluctuations. Over 98 percent of world trade in coffee is covered by the Agreement.

Basic export quotas have been determined for each member country to replace those in effect since 1962. An effective world quota is established annually and is prorated among the members in proportion to each country's share of the basic export quota.

Coffee traded in the world markets is differentiated into four different types. Price ranges for each type are set at the beginning of every marketing year. If for any type the price moves above the ceiling or below the floor, quotas for that type are adjusted in an effort to bring prices back within the range.

Several new features were added that were not in the 1962 Agreement. Specific national production goals were established for each exporting member to attempt to insure production adjustments in each country to bring supplies into line with the needs for exports and working stocks by 1973, the last year of application of the 1968 Agreement.

Government export or reexport aid that discriminates in favor of processed (soluble) coffee over green coffee is prohibited. This measure was primarily the result of price competition between exports of Brazilian soluble coffee and unroasted beans.

Another important new feature is a Diversification Fund that provides technical and financial assistance to member countries for production adjustment programs. Producers receive help to convert land from production of coffee to other agricultural products for which there is greater need. The Fund is financed by mandatory payments from exporting countries and voluntary contributions from importing countries.

Sugar has also been subject to some form of international agreement for many years. However, these agreements have covered only about a third of world trade in sugar.

An International Sugar Agreement is now in effect, but the United States is not a member. Approximately two-thirds of the world trade is accounted for by U.S. imports under assigned foreign country quotas, and imports by the United Kingdom at negotiated prices under the Commonwealth Sugar Agreement.

A major objective of regional country groupings is to stimulate economic growth within the regions. Over a long period of time this is expected to increase the demand for commodities and eventually contribute to an expansion of world trade. However, in the early years of their development, regional groups frequently adopt measures that disrupt established trade patterns and interfere with trade liberalization efforts. There is a danger that the restrictions imposed may become so firmly established that the hoped-for benefits to world trade may not materialize.

Of course, individual countries also have protectionist trade policies. In some cases they may be more restrictive than those of the regional associations. Whatever the trading entity, there are several forms of barriers that can be imposed.

Import duties or tariffs probably remain the most common form of trade barrier, particularly for industrial products.

These may be expressed in terms of a given amount per unit of a product, referred to as a specific duty, or in terms of a given percentage of the value of the imported product, or ad valorem duty.

This type of barrier has received the most attention in trade negotiations and the reduction in duties has been the major form of trade liberalization achieved.

Other types of import controls have been much more resistant to reduction or removal by negotiation. They may take many forms. Quantitative restrictions in the form of import quotas or embargoes are very effective in limiting or preventing trade. They are usually implemented by requiring import licenses that are granted only selectively.

Variable levies and gate price systems have become more common in recent years. Instead of providing a uniform and known absolute or percentage margin of protection between world and domestic prices, they are adjusted to bring the price of imports up to established levels. As noted previously, these measures are used extensively by the European Economic Community.

Mixing regulations are established by some countries to assure that all domestic production is utilized. They usually require that a minimum percentage of the ingredients in such products as flour and tobacco products come from domestic sources.

Many countries have government or semi-public agencies that are given the exclusive right to import certain products.

These monopolies may arbitrarily determine when imports are allowed and under what conditions.

Health and sanitary regulations are normally imposed to provide legitimate protection against introduction of products that may be hazardous to human, animal, or plant health in the importing countries. However, in some instances they may be used to limit imports arbitrarily or to discriminate as to source.

These are some of the more common types of measures used by countries to discourage or prevent imports. Countries may also attempt to aggressively expand exports and thereby interfere with normal trade flows. The most common practice is the payment of subsidies on exports.

Export subsidies cause problems for importing countries by abnormally depressing import prices. Their agricultural programs may be jeopardized unless they adopt additional barriers to imports.

Competition among exporters may become competition among national treasuries with little regard to which countries can produce the products most efficiently.

Many of the difficulties encountered in reducing restrictions on trade in agricultural products stem from conflicts between internal agricultural support systems and liberal import regimes.

Programs supporting domestic agricultural prices above world prices exist in most importing countries and also in many exporting countries. Agricultural incomes are usually below those of industrial workers, and the governments attempt to reduce the disparity by supporting agricultural prices.

A rapid rate of technological advance in agriculture is stimulated by the price assurances given through these programs.

New and improved cultural and husbandry practices are adopted more rapidly, increased fertilizer consumption is encouraged, and new crop varieties get widespread acceptance more quickly. As a result, production may increase more rapidly than the domestic requirements and further government action is required to maintain established price levels and to avoid excessive stocks.

For importing countries, this often leads to further restrictions on imports to protect domestic prices from the pressure of foreign supplies.

Both traditional exporting countries and others with surpluses attempt to expand or develop export markets by paying export subsidies.

The basic conflict between domestic agricultural and trade expansion policies has also been a problem in the development of the regional trade groupings discussed. Only the European Economic Community has developed a common agricultural policy with a replacement of many national programs by overall Community programs. Many serious obstacles have had to be overcome. In order to get agreement, the policies adopted have often been as restrictive to trade as the most restrictive existing national policy.

As previously mentioned, the European Free Trade Association has made no attempt to eliminate all restrictions on trade in agricultural products because of the difficulties foreseen in reconciling national policies with free trade.

The Montevideo Treaty provides that agricultural products be included with others in the liberalization process within the Latin American Free Trade Association.

However, the appearance of many problems has led to the consideration of norms for agricultural trade recognizing that exceptions will have to be made for many agricultural products beyond the end of the transition period.

The Central American Common Market has many agricultural products on its special list of products exempted from the liberalization schedule. Coordination of national policies on the basic grains is provided for, but trade is regulated by the price support agencies in each country.

Future expansion of agricultural trade opportunities requires that ways be found to (1) improve access to importing countries, (2) achieve more rational export policies among exporters, and (3) obtain reasonable and more stable world prices.

There is general recognition of the relationship between domestic agricultural policies and trade restrictions. Policies of both regional trade groups and individual countries must be modified.

Careful and lengthy preparations will be required to identify areas where adjustments can be made in domestic policies that will permit easing trade restrictions while retaining measures to support domestic agriculture.

A LOOK INSIDE DEVELOPMENTS IN EAST-WEST FARM TRADE

THE CENTRALLY PLANNED economies— the Soviet Union, Eastern Europe, and Red China—had a major impact on world agricultural markets during the decade of the 1960's which generated considerably more interest in their agricultural trade than previously.

Immediate cause of this interest was the massive movements of these countries into and out of the grain market, especially the wheat market, during 1963–66. China's gross wheat imports rose from 2.6 million tons in 1961 to 4.4 million tons in 1963, and reached 6.4 million tons in 1966. The Soviet Union's gross wheat imports were negligible in 1962, but rose to 3 million tons in 1963, and reached 7.6 million tons in 1966.

Imports by the East European countries did not increase as significantly, but they were shifted to Western markets as the Soviet Union's wheat supplies dwindled.

It would be hard to exaggerate the impact of these purchases on the major world grain exporting countries. Coinciding with large imports of wheat and grain by India and Pakistan, they have virtually transformed the world wheat picture from one of persistent, troublesome surpluses to one of a dangerously rapid drawdown in stocks.

Production was expanded in the

✦

AUTHOR HARRY E. WALTERS is Head, Communist Areas Analysis Group, Economic Research Service.
COAUTHOR ROGER E. NEETZ is an Agricultural Economist, Economic Research Service.

exporting countries only to find that the market had dried up almost as rapidly as it had appeared, because grain production in the USSR and Eastern Europe also rose sharply after 1965. The USSR's gross wheat imports dropped from 7.6 to 1.3 million tons between 1966 and 1968. China's wheat imports dropped from 6.4 to 4.3 million tons in the same years.

Eastern Europe turned again to the USSR for much of its grain, and began to expand its own grain production and exports rapidly so that its net grain imports dropped 4 million tons between 1967 and 1968.

Some of the other large buyers of the 1963–66 period also reduced their purchases—India's cereal imports fell from 10.4 to 5.7 million tons between 1966 and 1968. By 1969 world grain exporting countries found themselves again faced with large stocks, which weakened prices and produced reversals in domestic grain policies.

But grains were not the only internationally traded agricultural commodities affected by trade shifts of the planned economies. During the sixties cotton, sugar, vegetable oils, and oilseeds suffered from sharp and often erratic movements in exports and imports by these countries.

The Soviet Union burst on the world vegetable oil market in the early 1960's as a net exporter, after long being a net importer of oils and seeds. By 1962 its vegetable oil exports grossed 152,000 tons, jumping to 456,000 tons in 1966, and 770,000 tons in 1968. This produced a sharp drop in vegetable oil prices.

Bulgaria and Romania also moved into an export position, sparked by the same expansion of sunflower production which produced the Soviet exports.

Russia's gross exports of refined sugar rose from less than 250,000 tons in 1960 to over 1.3 million tons in 1968, and Russia takes a large part of Cuba's exports of raw sugar. Russia's lint cotton exports moved up from 322,000 tons in 1963 to 554,000 tons in 1968. Soviet exports of flour,

beans, peas, and butter also made sharp gains during 1965–68 in markets where they had not previously been a factor.

These commodity movements generated two questions in the minds of a large number of previously unconcerned persons: first, "How large is the market in the planned economies likely to be?"; and then it quickly shifted to "How strong is the competition likely to be?" Now with some leveling off in these commodity movements, a more sober view is being taken of both export and competition prospects.

This interest is a far cry from the lack of concern of the 1950's, when many of these countries wallowed in the throes of recovery from war, the early stages of collectivization, and autarchic policies which stressed self-sufficiency. Mediocre agricultural performance represented no competitive threat, and tight controls over imports of food, despite shortages and rationing, gave little hope of these countries becoming a market.

The changes in trade of the planned economies during the 1960's demonstrated three things:

• They served notice that these countries had achieved at least some modicum of success in agriculture, and should be considered seriously as potential competitors.

• They underscored the unstable nature of agricultural production in many of these countries, especially the USSR and Southern East Europe, which meant that export surpluses or import requirements could change quickly.

• Most important of all, they showed that these countries would spend hard currency on food imports, if serious shortages developed, and were no longer able or willing to restrict domestic diets too sharply in the face of domestic shortages—this was not the case earlier.

These developments coincided with another change, at least in the USSR and Eastern Europe, which could prove to be of far more long-lasting importance to the future agricultural trade of these countries—the emergence of economic reforms.

Attempts at economic reform in the USSR and Eastern Europe are the result of the gradual realization during the 1960's that the "Command Economy" imposed in the Soviet Union in the late 1920's, and applied to Eastern Europe in the late 1940's, had serious limitations.

The "Command Economy" produced certain kinds of rapid industrial development, especially in countries with considerable underutilized resources, as in Bulgaria and Romania. But it was hard pressed to cope with the problem of more complex economies with large urban sectors and consumers whose incomes were rising, as in Czechoslovakia and East Germany. The goal of self-sufficiency seriously reduced production possibilities of the smaller countries of Eastern Europe that depended on trade.

Sectors which had been neglected and even exploited to advance industrial development during the 1950's—agriculture and consumer goods—logically became the ones most in need of improvement during the early 1960's.

First efforts to correct these deficiencies took the form of improving the relative priority of agriculture in the economies of Eastern Europe and the USSR. Improvements in prices, speeded-up deliveries of machinery and fertilizer, and less rigid planning and production methods helped greatly in the recovery of agricultural production in these countries.

After increasing only about 8 percent from 1958 to 1963, agricultural production in Eastern Europe rose 20 percent between 1964 and 1967. In the USSR agricultural output in 1963 was lower than in 1958, and had only been slightly above the 1958 level in the intervening years. But by 1968 it had risen more than 30 percent above the 1958 level.

The increased effort in the agricultural and consumer goods sectors was of considerable benefit, but it did not change the need for more fundamental economic reform which most of the countries were experimenting with, and some began to put into effect after 1966.

The objective of these reforms is the gradual introduction in the planned economies of what has come to be called "market socialism." Market socialism means essentially that the scope for market forces to reflect relative scarcities and competing demands within a country is broadened, while the economy still retains many elements of planned economic management and direction.

Economic reform has proceeded much further in Yugoslavia than in the other countries, and has made the least progress in the USSR and Romania.

As economic reform develops in these countries, there is a good possibility that production in industry and agriculture will more closely reflect their comparative advantage position (greatest relative efficiency in producing similar products) and efforts to satisfy the demands of consumers.

How fast these reform movements will proceed is difficult to predict. At present, progress has been limited, except in Yugoslavia and Hungary, and the relative position of the consumer and agricultural producer is still clearly subordinate to that of the national planning bodies. Even if the pace of reform is improved, however, there are still many stumbling blocks to rapid shifts in trade patterns.

Foreign trade is the monopoly of the government in each of these countries, and bilateral trade agreements are the dominant method of conducting trade. Limited foreign exchange impedes their imports from western countries, as does a general reluctance to import agricultural products and a high priority for imports of industrial products and technology.

Furthermore, the USSR dominates the agricultural trade of Eastern Europe, and the Soviet has given no indication that it wishes to relinquish its hold. The USSR is also the major country attempting to foster the further development of COMECON, the trading bloc organization for the USSR and Eastern Europe. There are also impediments to trade with these countries by Western governments, including the United States.

Despite these impediments, and without much economic reform, the agricultural trade of these countries (especially Eastern Europe) expanded greatly in the 1960's.

The planned economies are not uniform in their level of economic development or in their agricultural production possibilities. Per capita incomes range from a high of about $1,800 in East Germany and Czechoslovakia to a low of $760 in Yugoslavia, with the USSR, Hungary, Poland, Bulgaria, and Romania ranking in between in that order.

Industrial East Germany and Czechoslovakia have limited production possibilities, use relatively large amounts of productive inputs, such as fertilizer, and are large net importers of agricultural products. Poland, Yugoslavia, Bulgaria, and Romania, on the other hand, are still a long way from being industrialized-urban economies. Bulgaria, Hungary, and Romania are net agricultural exporters, while Poland and Yugoslavia both export and import, with imports having a slight edge for Poland.

Consumption patterns in these countries correspond more closely with their relative standard of living than might be assumed, and do not in most cases differ greatly from Western European countries with comparable standards of living.

Thus, the planned economies comprise a diverse group of countries, some of which are, and will continue to be, large net importers of agricultural commodities, while others will certainly be sources of increasing competition.

The USSR imports about $1.3 billion a year of food products. Russia's food exports amount on the average to about $1 billion. Although grain imports have been the major

interest in recent years, grains are much less important than fruits and vegetables, sugar, alcoholic and non-alcoholic beverages, cotton, and tobacco and tobacco products.

Eastern Europe is an even more important agricultural market, and growth of this market has been rapid. Agricultural imports by the Eastern European countries amounted to $3.5 billion in 1967 and were twice the 1955 level. But agricultural exports were $2.9 billion in 1967, over 3 times the 1955 level, a more than 10 percent annual increase.

Of special note is the rapid growth in agricultural exports of Bulgaria, Romania, Poland, and Yugoslavia. These countries are at present the least developed in Eastern Europe, and have the greatest potential for agricultural growth. The first two are relatively small markets except for certain complementary commodities, but East Germany and Czechoslovakia are each large markets for a wide variety of agricultural products, while Hungary and Poland continue to be sizable markets.

The United States has been relatively unimportant in the agricultural trade of the planned economies. U.S. agricultural exports to the USSR have never been large, except in 1964—the only year the United States shared in the Russian wheat purchases.

U.S. agricultural exports to the USSR declined to a low of $5.3 million in 1968. U.S. agricultural imports from the USSR are even smaller than exports, amounting to only $2.2 million in 1968.

Political considerations on both sides are undoubtedly the important limiting factor in U.S.-USSR trade. There is essentially no commercial U.S. agricultural trade with Mainland China and Cuba for much the same reason.

Of the seven major Eastern European agricultural commodity imports, the United States has had a significant share of only one—grains. The USSR has had the largest share of grains and cotton, while other countries have

274

dominated Eastern Europe's imports of rice, oilseeds, tobacco, and sugar.

In the 1960's, U.S. agricultural exports to Eastern Europe fluctuated between $150 million and $250 million rising from $159 million in 1961 to $266 million in 1964, and then falling to $144 million in 1967.

U.S. food grain exports to the area have declined sharply, but feed grains have held up well, and oil cake and oil meal exports have shown strong growth.

Important trends have been the decline of Poland as the major importer of U.S. agricultural products in the region—it dropped from 78 to 15 percent between 1960 and 1965, but rose to 34 percent in 1967; the continued sizable but shrinking share taken by Yugoslavia— between 35 and 40 percent; and the rise of the other countries as importers of U.S. agricultural products since 1963—from less than 2 to almost 30 percent in 1966 and 1967.

The loss of favorable Public Law 480 (Food for Peace) in 1965 contributed to the decline in U.S. wheat exports to Poland and Yugoslavia. And improved production in Eastern Europe and the USSR after 1965 was the major factor producing the decline in imports by many of the countries in 1967.

Absence of a strong U.S. presence in the Eastern European market is in large part explained by the need for credit, and the wide variety of restrictions on trade.

Credit sales under the Commodity Credit Corporation accounted for 42 percent of all U.S. agricultural sales to Eastern Europe in 1967 (excluding East Germany). This compares with 15 percent in 1966, and only small credit sales to Poland in 1963 and 1964.

Credits can be an effective stimulant to trade in this area of the world, particularly if the credit terms are competitive. Credit was a major factor in maintaining U.S. exports to Poland and Yugoslavia after the withdrawal of Public Law 480 arrangements.

Present restrictions on trade are a major cause for limited U.S. agricultural exports to the area. The cargo preference restriction, for example, which requires that 50 percent of U.S. wheat cargoes destined for Bulgaria, Czechoslovakia, East Germany, and Hungary must be carried by U.S. ships, adds to the cost of U.S. wheat shipments.

Feed grains do not have the same cargo restrictions. But if feed grains are shipped on foreign flag ships, part of the cargo must be destined and first unloaded in a West European or Mediterranean country, including Yugoslavia.

U.S. wheat and feed grain exports to Poland, Romania, and Yugoslavia are not subject to these shipping restrictions. Exports to these countries may move freely on foreign flag ships subject only to the qualification that Poland and Romania may not be considered as the recipient of a "part cargo" of feed grains that is destined to other East European countries. At the present time, Poland is the only country among this group that is importing commercial quantities of grain from the United States.

Validated licenses for shipments of selected agricultural commodities are also required for all countries except Czechoslovakia, Poland, Romania, and Yugoslavia. Applications for licenses are easily obtained and it is rare that a license for the export of agricultural products is refused, but the existence of this small impediment may discourage interest by some firms.

U.S. exporters are also exposed unnecessarily to actual or implied policies to impose trade restrictions on American products by some East European countries. These restrictions currently are not considered impediments, but are a nuisance.

From the East European point of view, the lack of Most Favored Nation treatment (a provision in a commercial treaty that binds all contracting nations to the same favorable trade concessions) for Czechoslovakia, East Germany, Hungary, and Romania places their exports at a competitive disadvantage in the U.S. market, and reduces their potential dollar-earning capacity.

Hungary's current policy gives a preference to countries that extend Most Favored Nation treatment, which in effect places U.S. exporters in a disadvantageous position. Czechoslovakia faces a severe shortage of hard currency and places surcharges on non-priority items, many of which are agricultural.

Poland and Yugoslavia are the only active members of the General Agreement on Tariffs and Trade (GATT). While the special relief features are available to these countries, the imposition of surcharges or flexible import taxes by Yugoslavia affects the sale of U.S. agricultural products to that country.

Probably more important to U.S. traders are the shortcuts Western Europe has to the East European market. For example, the Interzonal Trade Agreements between the two Germanys allows for exchanges that do not follow the true pattern of trade under competitive conditions. The closer West European ties with Eastern Europe add a hidden strength in negotiating commodity exchanges with Eastern Europe.

To meet this competition, an accommodation to the present restrictions now in force is necessary. Granting the Most Favored Nation treatment to all countries may not guarantee additional dollar sales of agricultural products, particularly since trade in planned economies is still a function of administrative decisions rather than a response to effective demand (the desire to buy coupled with ability to pay). But a review of existing constraints to agricultural trade with these countries is certainly in order.

In the final analysis, U.S. agricultural trade with Eastern Europe is contingent on the removal of existing trade impediments by the United States and by the Eastern European countries themselves, on the growth rates and economic diversification within the economies of the area, on the foreign trade policies and possibilities of the USSR, and on the availability of credits and long-term loans.

Future development of trade, however, will probably be much more a function of comparative advantage and competition than was true in the past. But it will be trade in which the planned economies present both a market and a competitor.

SALESMANSHIP HELPS EXPAND OUR MARKETS

BUILDING U.S. agricultural trade abroad is a big job. Competition is tough. But the stakes are high. For the harvest of one acre out of five goes to foreign markets.

Problems of selling abroad are many sided. Just to mention a few, it takes the right price, the right product as seen through the eyes of the foreign consumer, and freedom from barriers that deny access. But even when these items are right, it still requires traditional American salesmanship so as to keep old customers coming back for more and to get new ones to give our products a try.

Uncle Sam's Department of Agriculture has teamed up with industry to provide added salesmanship for our agricultural products around the world. The program is fairly new, stemming from the "Agricultural Trade Development and Assistance Act of 1954," which is popularly known as Public Law 480. A small portion of the foreign currencies generated from the sale of what were originally surplus agricultural commodities under this program were earmarked for the job of pushing foreign sales for dollars.

As we enter the 1970's we are operating in some 75 countries around the world. Some are big, old markets like the United Kingdom, West Germany, and Japan. In these kinds of markets the cooperators carry out sizable programs through field offices. We hold trade fairs—and frequently stage in-store promotions. In three of our older markets we operate Trade Centers. And our agricultural attachés are constantly searching for sales opportunities for U.S. products not currently in these markets.

Some are small markets—just opening up—like the Middle East. Nearly 50 U.S. firms joined with the Department's Foreign Agricultural Service in the fall of 1968 to stage a five-day solo food show in Beirut—economic hub of this area of rising incomes. Some 135 of the 400 products shown were new to the area. And at the close of the show, one of our U.S. exhibitors said, "The response of the Arab buyers has been simply terrific." Sales projections for the 12 months following this one show were placed at $1,110,000.

Total program costs run nearly $30 million annually, for everything. About half of these funds originate from convertible foreign currency under the P.L. 480 law and the other half comes from industry which is helping to stage this big market promotion program.

As to the nature of the program, it divides into two broad areas. One phase of the program is handled on a commodity basis in which government teams up with trade organizations and in which they share the costs.

Initiative for program development is with the trade groups. They make proposals which are assessed by commodity experts in the Department's Foreign Agricultural Service. If the proposal appears good and market research verifies the possibilities for exporting, projects are established covering a 2- to 3-year period. Then detailed promotion programs are submitted annually in marketing plans for government concurrence.

The other major program element is handled on a multi-commodity basis, which is spearheaded by the Foreign Agricultural Service. FAS provides the show window—in which private trade, states, trade groups, cooperators, and others can promote sales of their products. FAS does this through staging of trade fairs, operating trade center programs, and similar activities.

All of this takes place in a highly competitive arena where competing countries frequently outdistance us in their willingness to spend money to promote sales. On an average, our major competitors outspend the United States more than three to one in relation to the value of sales.

For example, the combined agricultural exports of Australia, New Zealand, South Africa, Israel, Denmark, the Netherlands, and Canada total only slightly more than those of the United States. But the 1968 expenditures of these seven countries for government-sponsored promotion in foreign markets ran nearly 1 percent (.86%) of the value of their agricultural exports, as compared with a level of about one-fourth of 1 percent (.26%) for the United States. Private firm expenditures are not included in these percentages.

But let's turn back to the United States program—to the cooperator program particularly. First, who are the cooperators?

The Department has continuing program agreements with nearly 40 trade organizations such as the American Soybean Association, U.S. Feed Grains Council, Rice Council for Market Development, Great Plains and Western Wheat groups, California Cling Peach Advisory Board, and other major U.S. commodity groups interested in pushing sales of their products abroad. And an additional 25 trade groups team up with the Department in occasional joint activities overseas.

+

AUTHOR E. B. WINNER is Director of the Trade Projects Division, Foreign Agricultural Service.

U.S. wheat trade team visits flour mill at Chiba City, Japan.

What do the cooperators do? Trade servicing is a major element in the cooperator program, particularly for bulk commodities such as feed grains and soybeans. To mention just a few, the many activities in this area include market research studies; survey trips to explore U.S. export opportunities; trips to the United States for foreign trade and government groups to acquaint them with the availability, quality, and prices of products and the nature of our trade practices; dissemination of trade information abroad; and providing technical assistance to foreign trade groups on handling, processing, and merchandising U.S. products.

Consumer promotion is another major program element—particularly for cooperators pushing consumer-ready products. Activities are many and varied, including development of public information and educational services; planning and carrying out publicity activities of a "special feature" nature; staging exhibits and demonstrations; production and distribution of recipe and similar materials; holding in-store promotions; and the carrying out of advertising campaigns.

But let's look specifically at some of the programs being carried on abroad. Let's first look at feed grains—one of our top dollar export earners. Strategy of the U.S. Feed Grains Council is to expand the total world demand for their product. Assumption is that as the market is expanded, the United States will be able to get its share. Originally the Council leaned heavily on trade servicing—such as working with government agencies, universities, and researchers in a number of countries to demonstrate the advantage of using a higher percentage of grain in the rations being fed.

But the Council has gone further—notably in countries like Italy and Japan—to give an assist in consumer campaigns to increase the per capita consumption of meat and eggs. For example, when egg production was outrunning demand in Japan in the early sixties the Feed Grains Council put its shoulder to the wheel to mobilize all segments of the Japanese industry that had a stake in the well-being of the poultry industry. Timing was excellent—the Japanese had a sharp interest in improved health and they had the affluence it takes to buy eggs.

The campaign was successful in escalating the rising trend in egg consumption—pushing per capita consumption to 215 eggs in 1968, and requiring an added $55 million of U.S. feed grains for the 5-year period 1963–68 over what would have been needed without the added spurt in egg usage.

Another of our programs has a strictly international flavor. A principal problem for cotton in all the big markets of the world is the continual competitive pressure from man-made fibers. And so several cotton exporting countries—the United States, Mexico, Spain, India, Tanzania, Uganda, and Greece—got together in a common cause, the promotion of cotton.

This international group—known as the International Institute for Cotton—receives its financial support from member countries on the basis of volume of cotton exports to Western Europe and Japan. Contributions from the members are in turn matched or exceeded by cooperating industry groups and firms in the program countries. The idea behind the IIC program is to promote the use of cotton—and assumes that the United States will get its share of the total cotton market if the market can be held or increased.

Major thrust of the program is a teaming up with leading manufacturers in Western Europe and Japan to carry out advertising and merchandising campaigns designed to convince the consumer that cotton is more comfortable, easier to care for, and one of the best materials for clothing, sportswear, rainwear, and household linens.

Here's an example of how the program works. Cotton had lost most of the market for men's dress shirts in Sweden—holding only about 15 percent of the total in 1966. The remainder had gone to synthetics. IIC convinced Melka, largest manufacturer of men's shirts in Sweden, to join hands with the Institute in a major promotion program for the new easy-care cotton shirt which had been developed. Melka and IIC staged promotion campaigns on all-cotton shirts in the springs of 1967, 1968, and 1969. Other manufacturers joined the lead of this principal shirt maker with similar promotions on 100 percent cotton shirts. Result: Sales of 100 percent cotton shirts jumped—standing at 50 percent of the market in mid-1969 and predicted to reach 70 percent by 1970.

Let's look at one additional program in which an industry teamed up with government to sell products abroad. In 1966 Florida citrus producers were suddenly faced with a tremendous production increase—the orange crop jumped from 96 million boxes in 1965 to 140 million boxes in 1966. And what's more, young orange groves in existence practically guaranteed sharply stepped up production in the early seventies.

Florida oranges are largely processed for juice. So a logical step was to find a juice market abroad. The Foreign Agricultural Service and the Florida Citrus Commission entered into a new type of brand promotion in which costs are shared equally by the Commission, FAS, and distributors abroad. From a small start with one foreign distributor in 1966, the program expanded in 4 years to 37 distributors located in the following countries: Austria, Belgium, Denmark, France, Germany, the Netherlands, Norway, Sweden, Switzerland, and the United Kingdom.

This program is different from the other two—and is tailored to meet needs of the Florida citrus industry. Its purpose is to develop a new market for Florida orange juice through establishing a number of brands tied to Florida origin. Once the fledgling program with the country distributors becomes well established, FAS can shift its resources to other supporting activities.

Referring again to the total cooperator program, the task of supervision and program initiation is with the trade groups. Leadership for planning and supervision comes from the headquarters offices in the United States. But the day-to-day and month-to-month job of running a program is frequently handled by country directors who live abroad. Where the program does not justify placing an American abroad, a contract is frequently made with a public relations firm or a merchandising person to handle operation details.

In all cases, programs are carried

279

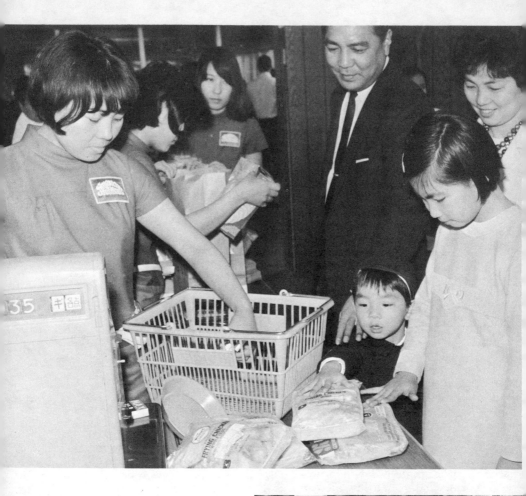

Above, family stocks up on U.S. frozen chickens at 1968 Tokyo food show. Right, Western-style barbecue is served during 1970 U.S. food exhibit in Kuwait. Exhibit displayed over 400 American food items.

out in close liaison with agricultural attachés—the Department's field representatives located at our embassies.

Now let's look at the multi-commodity program in more detail. Trade fairs have been widely used as showcases for American products abroad. We now hold 15 to 20 of these fairs annually. Since 1957 the Foreign Agricultural Service has staged 235 exhibitions in 43 countries. This quick mass exposure of U.S. food and agricultural products includes the display, demonstration, and samp ing of both old and new products for interested consumers and foreign food tradesmen who come to the fair to buy.

Trade fairs come in all colors and sizes. Many U.S. exhibits are part of a larger exhibition in the big cities of the developed world. Occasionally, the Department goes all out with a big solo show. The most recent was the Tokyo show in the spring of 1968. This bright and colorful exhibition covered well over 100,000 square feet, included individual exhibitions by 17 cooperators, featured a Hall of States where products from 12 states were on display, and focused on the products of more than 110 companies that had individual displays.

But the hinterlands are not neglected either. FAS frequently takes part in smaller exhibitions staged away from the major cities in order to reach trade and consumers in the more moderately populated areas.

Furthermore, FAS frequently moves into other areas of the world with a much shorter and simpler show—such as a 2- or 3-day show staged in a public room of a large hotel.

But regardless of size, the trend in exhibitions is more and more toward reaching the trade—the people that deal in large quantities of food products.

Along this line, the exhibition program carried on by FAS in the Trade Centers in London, Tokyo, and Milan are completely trade oriented. These exhibits provide the setting in which American businessmen can display their products with order books in hand. It's really a place where buyer and seller can get together—and do business.

In-store promotions, frequently called American Food Fortnights, are a newer phase of the multi-commodity promotion effort. Such events are staged in most of the major U.S. food importing countries—and provide a means of encouraging millions of shoppers to buy American products. About 25 chains or store groups are included in this program each year, with a total of some 18,000 stores. These are in addition to the thousands of in-stores held individually by cooperators to promote single products.

Both major facets of the program—the single commodity program handled by a trade group and the multi-commodity program spearheaded by FAS—are concentrated in the more developed and affluent countries. That's where the big business is. But both arms of the program reach into developing areas.

An example: Western Wheat Associates opened an office in Taiwan in 1966, as the economy of that country improved and it appeared it could become a good small dollar market for U.S. exports. The National Renderers Association moved in with a soap campaign in 1967, feed grain and raisin groups initiated limited activities in 1968, and the American Soybean Association plans to open an office there in 1970.

Another example: A market profile study of the Southern Caribbean area in 1967 indicated potential for increasing our sales of consumer-ready products in that area too. The three islands of Barbados, Trinidad, and Curaçao were taking about $28 million worth of U.S. foods and other agricultural products. FAS was joined by nearly 50 U.S. firms, five states, and the Institute of American Poultry Industries in staging two-day all trade exhibits on each of the islands in the fall of 1968.

The worldwide market development program now faces the decade of the seventies.

U.S. FOOD AID PROGRAMS

THE UNITED STATES has been carrying on the largest food aid program in the history of the world. This country in the past 15 years has shipped more than $20.5 billion worth of food and fiber to over 100 needy countries. Assistance on this gigantic scale not only has improved the nutritional status of many areas, but it has also helped less developed countries buy some of the time they need for economic growth.

Food aid programs got underway in 1954. At that time the United States was frankly concerned about finding useful outlets for large surpluses of food and fiber that had accumulated following production expansion during and after World War II and the Korean War.

Another cause for our accumulation of surpluses was the drop in foreign sales. Agriculture in many foreign countries had recovered. Also, dollar shortages had appeared in Western Europe, Japan, and other industrialized countries as well as in the less developed countries, where populations press heavily on food supplies. Thus, while there was less willingness or ability to buy our farm products with hard currencies, most foreign countries wanted and needed more farm commodities than they could pay for with dollars.

These circumstances led to enactment of the Agricultural Trade Development and Assistance Act of 1954, commonly known as Public Law 480. The P.L. 480 program, which largely

+

AUTHOR FRANK D. BARLOW, JR., is Assistant to the Director, Foreign Development and Trade Division, Economic Research Service.

supplanted activities under the Mutual Security Acts, was conceived as an instrument to break the foreign exchange bottleneck thwarting the export of farm products to food-short countries that could pay only with their own currencies.

Principal technique for supplying food aid has been sales for foreign currencies, a program under which nearly $12 billion has been shipped over the past 15 years. P.L. 480 grants of commodities to foreign governments and donations through the voluntary relief agencies (such as CARE and the church groups) amounted to another $3.5 billion.

P.L. 480 sales on long-term dollar credit with easy payment provisions amounted to over $1.4 billion. Emphasis shifted to credit sales in 1966 with the idea that this technique would supplant local currency sales as the major vehicle for supplying food aid by 1971.

Food aid shipments under Mutual Security Programs during the 1950's and early 1960's exceeded $2 billion. Barter transactions under the Act, which are more like commercial sales than food aid, totaled $1.7 billion.

Multilateral food aid under the World Food Program (WFP) initiated in 1963 by the United Nations Food and Agriculture Organization has grown in volume, but it is still small compared with P.L. 480. Some $93 million in commodities, cash, and services was disbursed during 1963–65, $188 million was pledged for 1966–68, and $200 million was planned for 1969–70.

Although over 70 countries have made food and cash contributions to the WFP, the United States has provided about half the total. The United States matches commodity contributions (including cash contributions for purchase of commodities) made by other donors until the pledge target is reached. The pledge target for 1971–72 has been set at $300 million. Most multilateral food aid has been used for economic development projects, mainly in the agricultural sector.

Iran farmer with food package distributed after earthquake and flood devastated large area.

Emphasis has been placed on providing assistance to previously underemployed or unemployed people in exchange for work on projects such as land reclamation, development, and settlement. Other projects have included community and rural development, and institutional feeding programs—school lunches, hospitals, and the like.

WFP activities have been concentrated in the Mediterranean area—North Africa and the Near East.

Bilateral food aid from countries other than the United States has been relatively small. Canada is the only country other than the United States that gives food aid on a regular basis.

Canadian food aid increased from about $12 million annually in the early 1960's to commitments of $30 million in fiscal 1966 and about $75 million in 1967. The bulk of this aid was wheat shipped to India and Pakistan.

France and Australia periodically have provided small amounts of food aid, mainly for emergency use.

Several donor countries are providing 4.5 million tons of grain annually as food aid for 3 years under the Food Aid Convention of the International Grains Arrangement of 1967. The United States is contributing 40 percent of the total. Also providing grain under the arrangement are the six European Economic Community countries, Canada, Australia, Argentina, the United Kingdom, Switzerland, the Scandinavian countries, and Japan.

Authorizing legislation for P.L. 480 reveals the changing times and changing attitudes of both donor and recipients alike. Over the past 15 years the act has been amended some 32 times, including seven extensions.

The original act built in safeguards to ensure that food and fiber exports would be in addition to normal commercial trade and that the normal commercial trade channels be utilized as much as possible.

Original motivation on the part of Congress to reduce surpluses began to shift to the constructive use of our agricultural abundance by 1957. This was anticipated in the original act as set forth in its title "Trade Development and Assistance." By 1959, the contribution of food aid to development was clearly recognized and the Food for Peace office was established in the White House.

Food for Peace helped in many ways. Commodities transferred on concessional terms represented additional resources needed for development by the countries which received them.

Local currencies generated through their sale had an important secondary impact in the domestic economy. About two-thirds of the currencies generated were loaned to recipient governments for financing the development of schools, hospitals, improved government services, highways, power, irrigation, and essential heavy industry. Loans were made also to American and foreign businessmen for vital activities in private enterprise.

As the role of food aid in economic development gained recognition during the first decade, the self-help principle began to take hold, especially in connection with the use of food aid to support various enterprise and community development projects. It

283

became official when the self-help principle was written into the Food for Peace Act of 1966.

In general, the emphasis on self-help encourages establishment of national policy objectives placing high priority on agricultural development.

As we move into the 16th year of food aid, we are witnessing increasing emphasis on a new and important dimension—better nutrition. More attention is being given to the relative efficiency of food nutrient sources and the increased use of prepared food products and food mixes for improving nutritional levels in the human diet.

This important facet of food aid is currently backed up by more vigorous action in nutritional education, in the formulation of new food products and processes, and in the nutritional fortification and supplementation of basic food sources with specific amino acids, vitamins, and other additives.

Few people appreciate the magnitude of food aid in relation to the total flow of aid from the developed to the underdeveloped countries. Over the decade 1955–65, food aid accounted for about 42 percent of the total foreign economic assistance supplied by the United States which in turn supplied over half the total assistance from public sources. Thus, food aid represented nearly a fourth of the world's net public economic aid to the developing countries during the decade.

With food aid representing such a significant proportion of development assistance, donor countries have given much attention to coordinating food aid policies and programs with global economic assistance programs. This not only has helped to avoid unwise food aid distribution, but over time it has helped to make food aid an integral part of foreign economic development strategies.

From the beginning it was obvious that food aid could create problems as well as benefits. The original act and subsequent amendments set forth the guidelines to help avoid such problems.

Aid was to be provided in such a way as to: (1) protect normal commercial trade of the United States and avoid disrupting the trade of third country suppliers, (2) avoid possible interference with agricultural development in recipient countries, and (3) utilize local currencies generated through the sale of food aid imports to facilitate market and economic development.

Let's see how food aid has assisted in foreign economic development. Where food shortages occur, they contribute to economic, social, and political instability. By being able to obtain food and fiber on concessional terms to meet essential food requirements, recipient governments have been able to achieve greater stability, which is essential to progress and growth.

The P.L. 480 program aided development by providing a number of countries with greater flexibility in planning the efficient use of agricultural resources. Among these countries were Turkey, Spain, Greece, Israel, Colombia, Taiwan, India, South Korea, Yugoslavia, and Pakistan. It also provided greater opportunity for larger investments in agriculture without augmenting inflationary pressures.

It has been the policy of all recipient governments to stabilize food prices within the framework of overall national policy objectives. In the absence of P.L. 480 imports, many governments—such as Turkey, Israel, Greece, Pakistan, and India—undoubtedly would have relied more on consumer rationing, price controls, and mandatory procurement during periods of scarcity to prevent prices of food from rising to exorbitant levels.

Sales for foreign currencies, accounting for two-thirds of total P.L. 480 shipments from 1955–68, made it possible for recipient countries to conserve scarce foreign exchange reserves and still meet critical food needs without seriously reducing the capital imports needed for overall economic development.

Approximately two-thirds of the foreign currencies collected by the

United States from P.L. 480 sales were loaned or granted to recipient countries. In many cases, these funds were invested in agriculturally related enterprises or facilities that were of either direct or indirect benefit to agricultural development.

Colombia offers an interesting case history in the effective use of P.L. 480 local currency loans and grants. They were used to support fertilizer production, development of storage facilities, livestock improvements, agricultural access roads, water control, electrification, and land development in the Cauca Valley.

Spain is another success story. Feed grain imports assisted in the expansion of poultry and livestock enterprises as well as the feed mixing industry. This in turn increased the domestic market for grains. Local currency loans of $184 million were used to promote agricultural development, particularly projects designed to increase productivity in agriculture—such as irrigation, land consolidation, reforestation, watershed control, and soil conservation.

Pakistan also used food aid imports effectively to achieve stability and stimulate development. These imports provided flexibility in the use of land and funds to make more effective use of agricultural resources. They also helped to stabilize food prices, enabling the government to abolish rigorous controls over wheat prices and marketing. The local currencies were used to help finance development of ground water resources. And they provided a large share of the domestic financing for the Indus Basin works, a large rural works program in Pakistan.

Impact of the food aid program was beneficial to Yugoslavia in many ways. It contributed to greater stability in food supplies, permitting increased per capita consumption and diversification of diets. And it helped to stabilize the structural development of agriculture during the period of decollectivization, especially after 1953. Food aid helped provide greater flexi-bility in forward economic planning and permitted a more liberal Government policy toward the private sector in agriculture.

South Korea's food for work program is an outstanding example of how food aid contributed successfully to both economic and social improvement. Under this program land in the highlands was reclaimed by constructing terraces to prevent erosion. Small farmers who were in dire need of increasing their productive land area were given food in exchange for work. Under the technical supervision of Korean and U.S. experts, thousands of acres were reclaimed and brought into production.

The Korean program was warmly received by both the people and their Government officials because of its economic implications, and because it provided the means of improving social conditions of many small subsistence farmers who had been outside the mainstream of Korean life.

Food aid programs do not appear to have seriously conflicted with efforts of recipient countries to expand domestic agricultural production.

Governments generally controlled the distribution and pricing of aid imports within the framework of national food and pricing policies. Thus domestic producers were insulated from external competition whether the imports were on a commercial or concessional basis.

Besides contributing to more rapid recovery and development, food aid actually helped create and expand commercial markets for the United States. This has meant increased business and income for the U.S. economy.

Japan, an early recipient of Title I commodities during the mid-1950's, is now the United States' best commercial customer for farm products.

Italy, another early recipient, is an important customer for agricultural products.

Increases in per capita income, foreign exchange earnings, and reserves in the rapidly developing

Left, work underway on irrigation project in India. Below, Indians receive food donated by U.S. as partial payment for their labor. Above, child eating rice on Taiwan.

countries—Spain, Israel, Greece, Taiwan, and South Korea—have recently enabled these countries to increase significantly their commercial purchases of U.S. farm products.

In all of these countries showing substantial progress, our commercial exports have increased significantly. Comparing 1966–68 with 1955–59, our cash exports of farm products to Spain increased by 18 times, to Israel 12 times, Greece 7 times, Taiwan 25 times, and Korea 4 times.

The evidence strongly indicates that, in the aggregate, food aid shipments were actually additional to what total trade would have been in recipient countries in the absence of food aid.

An appraisal of our food aid programs leads to the conclusions that P.L. 480 exports were also additional (1) to the total level of international trade, (2) to food consumption in the recipient countries, and (3) to the available resources for economic development.

Major benefits to the United States should not be overlooked. Some of the local currencies generated by P.L. 480 transactions, ranging up to 25 percent in some cases, have been used to cover U.S. overseas expenses. This has had a positive balance of payments benefit to the United States.

In addition, sizable repayments of principal and interest have been received from exports under the credit provisions of P.L. 480. Over the past 5 years these have averaged about $225 million annually.

Finally, a portion of the P.L. 480 generated local currencies plus payments convertible into dollars or other currencies have been used to develop foreign markets and promote exports. These programs cover a wide range of activities from using feed grains to encourage development of livestock enterprises abroad to promotion of cotton exports.

The programs have been important in expanding U.S. agricultural exports from $3 billion in 1954 to $5 billion in 1962 and to the recent 1966–68 year average of $6.5 billion annually.

THE DEVELOPING WORLD: PROBLEMS GO ALONG WITH OPPORTUNITIES

THREE-FOURTHS of the world's 3.5 billion people live in Asia, Africa, and Latin America where incomes are low, food consumption levels inadequate, life expectancy is short, and education facilities are poor for most people.

No sharp line separates the developed from the developing or less developed countries. However, if we compare the industrial or developed countries of Western Europe, the United States, Canada, Australia, New Zealand, Japan, and South Africa with the less developed non-Communist countries of Asia, Africa, and Latin America, wide differences may be observed:

• Gross national product, the value of products and services produced, averages nearly $2,300 per person a year in the developed countries compared with $185 in the less developed.

• Food consumption in calories averages nearly 3,000 per person a day in the developed countries compared with 2,280 in the less developed.

• Life expectancy averages 70 years in the developed countries compared with 49 years in the less developed.

• Nearly all adults in the developed countries are literate compared with only 39 percent in the less developed.

A basic question facing the world today is, how can economic growth in

✦

AUTHOR RAYMOND P. CHRISTENSEN is the Director, Foreign Development and Trade Division, Economic Research Service.

287

the developing countries be accelerated? The poor people in the developing countries know about the high consumption levels enjoyed by a few within their countries and by most people in the developed countries. They want and expect better living conditions in the future.

We in the developed countries are concerned about improvement of liv-

less than 1 percent a year in the early 1900's to 2.6 percent in 1968. High population growth rates have resulted from declining death rates accompanying improved health and disease control methods and continued high birth rates.

Rapid population growth makes it difficult to increase production and income per person. Increased produc-

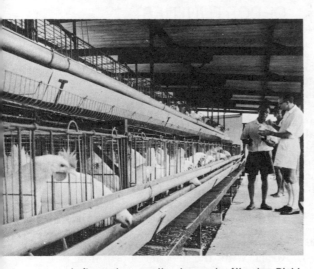

Left, modern poultry house in Nigeria. Right, taking up young rice plants from a seedbed at Central Rice Research Institute in India.

ing conditions in the developing countries for humanitarian reasons. We expect that improvement of living conditions for the poor people of the world will contribute to peace and political stability. Moreover, we know that the developing countries will become better markets and trading partners with economic growth.

Many of the economic problems the developing countries face today result from high population growth. Population growth rates in the developing countries now are twice as high as those ever experienced in Europe or Japan or in the United States, Canada, Australia, and New Zealand except during years of large immigration.

Population growth rates in the developing world have gone up from

tion per worker requires more capital goods per worker. But it is difficult to channel into savings and capital formation a large part of current production for use in future production when population growth is rapid, incomes are low, and people want to improve their consumption levels. Also, it is difficult to provide enough productive employment opportunities when the number of people seeking jobs is increasing rapidly and capital goods are scarce.

Despite the upsurge in population growth, the developing countries are making economic progress. Gross national product went up a little more rapidly in the developing countries than in the developed countries during the 1960's.

288

But because population growth was more rapid in the developing countries, per capita incomes went up less in these countries than in the developed. For example, per capita gross national product increased 2.3 percent a year in the developing countries during the 1960's compared with 3.8 percent in the developed. Per capita income differences between the poor and the rich countries widened.

Per capita income growth in the developing countries depends heavily upon an increased productivity in agriculture and its closely associated industries because agriculture is the dominant economic sector in these countries.

Except in countries rich in mineral or petroleum resources, 50 to 85 percent of the total labor force is employed on farms and farm products account for 30 to 60 percent of the gross national product. In addition, much of the economic activity of the nonagricultural sectors in these countries is concerned with transporting, storing, and processing raw materials from agriculture or with supplying farmers with tools, machines, fertilizer, pesticides, and other materials for use in farm production.

Approximately 70 percent of the manufacturing industries in developing countries are based on raw materials from agriculture or produce materials for use in farm production.

Agricultural production in the developing world has increased 2.7 percent a year since the early 1950's, more than enough to keep pace with population growth. However, the per capita demand for food has increased with rising per capita incomes. Population growth and higher per capita incomes have caused the economic demand for agricultural products to increase 4 percent or more a year in many developing countries.

Failure of production to keep pace with growth in demand for agricultural products has retarded economic growth in many countries. It also has caused the developing countries to increase agricultural imports more than agricultural exports since the early 1950's.

Looking ahead, a major problem facing the developing world is, how can agricultural output be expanded rapidly enough to keep pace with the rising demand for agricultural products? Population can be expected to increase 2.6 percent a year for the next decade. As per capita incomes rise, people will spend a large share of the additional income, 50 to 70 percent, for more and better food. Consequently, if per capita incomes increase 3 to 4 percent a year, food supplies must increase 4 to 5 percent a year to keep pace with growth in demand for food.

There are opportunities for increasing total agricultural production 4 to 5 percent a year in most developing countries, provided the necessary things are done. Mexico, Taiwan, and Israel are examples of countries that have increased agricultural output 4 percent or more a year since 1950. Essentials for achieving high growth rates in agricultural production include:

• Technological advances like new high-yielding varieties of crops, and diffusion of knowledge about these advances among farmers.

• Larger supplies of capital inputs from nonfarm sources such as fertilizer, pesticides, tools, and equipment needed to apply the improved techniques and achieve higher levels of output per acre and per worker.

• Improvement of land and water resources including land clearing, leveling, drainage, irrigation, and flood control facilities which can be carried out largely by human labor with limited use of purchased equipment and machinery.

• Expanding markets for farm products at prices high enough to provide economic incentives for farmers to adopt improved techniques, purchase additional capital inputs, and develop land and water resources.

• Institutional arrangement to improve land tenure, credit, marketing, transportation, and facilities to im-

Indian farmer in South America's Andes with good results he achieved through selected wheat seed and fertilizer.

prove education, health, and other services for rural people.

The Punjab of India, where total crop output increased 5.5 percent a year from 1951 to 1965, illustrates how agricultural productivity can be increased. Conditions have been more favorable for achieving large increases in agricultural production in the Punjab than in most other parts of India.

Crop output increased 90 percent per acre and 80 percent per worker. Improved varieties of wheat, rice, and cotton were introduced. Land area under cultivation increased 11 percent, and more land was irrigated and double cropped.

Purchased capital inputs like fertilizer, pesticides, fuel oil, oil engines, electricity, electric pumps, iron plows, and tractors increased 300 percent. But the increases in purchased capital inputs were small compared with the increase in crop output. In fact, value of crop output increased 13 rupees for each additional rupee of purchased input.

Of course, additional farm-produced capital (bullocks, feed, and other items), expansion in land area under cultivation, and irrigation improvements helped to increase agricultural production. Also, the number of farmworkers increased 17 percent.

After allowing for the additional purchased inputs from nonfarm sources, net value of crop output per worker increased 75 percent when measured in constant prices. The gain in net output per worker was large enough to increase real income per worker 4 percent a year.

The new high-yielding varieties of wheat, rice, and other grains introduced into the Philippines, India, Pakistan, Turkey, and other Asian countries in the last 3 years provide opportunities for doubling output per acre in irrigated areas when sufficient quantities of fertilizer and pesticides are applied and improved cultural practices are followed.

These new production possibilities, called the "Green Revolution," have generated much optimism about the ability of the developing world to meet rapidly expanding food needs. It has been demonstrated that research to discover new superior production technology, combined with larger supplies of fertilizer, pesticides, tools, and equipment from nonfarm sources, can rapidly increase productivity per acre and per worker.

But technological advances do not benefit all farm people equally. For example, the new varieties of wheat and rice introduced into the Asian countries are not well adapted for increasing crop yields in dryland areas which make up 70 to 80 percent of the total cultivated area. Larger supplies of food grains from irrigated areas could depress prices and incomes of farmers in dryland areas, unless market demand increased rapidly enough. Obviously, ways must be found to increase output per acre and per worker in dryland areas.

In many developing countries, some farming areas have benefited from technological advances while others have hardly been touched. In Mexico, for example, total agricultural output has increased 5 percent a year since 1950, but gains in agricultural output per acre and per worker have been limited mainly to irrigated areas.

In India, some states' agricultural output increased twice as rapidly as farm population from 1950 to 1965, but in other states agricultural output did not increase as rapidly as farm population. Consequently, per capita income differences among farm people in different states have widened.

National economic growth depends upon economic progress in the nonagricultural sectors as well as in agriculture. In fact, gains in agricultural productivity cannot proceed very rapidly unless the nonagricultural sectors provide the following: (1) Expanding markets for farm products at incentive prices, (2) larger supplies of capital inputs like fertilizer, pesticides, tools, equipment, and other materials, and (3) employment opportunities for workers not needed in farming.

Earlier it was pointed out that the economic demand for agricultural products in the developing countries can be expected to increase 4 to 5 percent a year if population increases 2.6 percent a year and if per capita incomes increase 3 to 4 percent a year. However, if per capita incomes do not increase, agricultural production increases of 4 to 5 percent a year would depress prices of farm products and discourage the adoption of improved technology and the use of purchased inputs to increase output per acre and per worker.

Colombia is an example of a country where per capita demand for farm products in urban areas has not increased since 1950, because per capita incomes have not increased. Agricultural production has increased at about the same rate as total population, about 3.3 percent a year. Larger increases in agricultural production would have depressed farm product prices.

Of course, it may be possible in some countries to find markets for large increases in agricultural production by expansion of exports or reducing imports of farm products.

The Punjab of India illustrates that large increases in supplies of capital inputs from nonfarm sources are required to achieve gains in agricultural productivity. Improvements in the manufacture and distribution of these inputs which reduce their costs to farmers help to increase their use on farms. Technological advances in the manufacture of nitrogen fertilizer in recent years, for example, have reduced costs of nitrogen fertilizer to farmers and made its use more profitable.

Improvements in marketing which reduce the costs of moving farm products from farmers to consumers also may help to increase demand for farm products. In addition, expansion in supplies of consumer goods at low costs by the nonagricultural sectors help to provide economic incentives for farmers to take advantage of opportunities to increase their incomes.

The demand for food and other agricultural products goes up with per capita income growth, but it does not go up nearly as much as the demand for other products and services. Consequently, national economic growth requires that employment of labor and other resources increase more rapidly in the nonagricultural sectors than in agriculture. If nonfarm employment opportunities are not created rapidly enough, many farm people will need to remain on farms where their productivity and incomes may be very low.

In most developing countries, per capita incomes average only one-fourth to one-half as high for farm people as they do for people in urban areas. These wide differences in per capita incomes have persisted even though there has been a large net migration of farm people to urban areas.

For example, the urban population in Brazil, Colombia, and Mexico has increased over 5 percent a year since 1950 while the agricultural population has increased less than 2 percent a year. However, a large share of the people who have migrated from farms to cities are unemployed much of the time or are employed at very low wages.

A major problem facing the developing world is, how can productive employment be provided for increasing numbers of workers? Even though population growth rates may decline in the future, people who will be in the labor force 15 years from now already have been born. In Latin America, for example, the total labor force is expected to increase 3.1 percent a year from 1965 to 1980 compared with 2.6 percent a year from 1950 to 1965.

If nonagricultural employment opportunities increase 4 percent a year from 1965 to 1980, which is about as much as can be expected, the number of workers dependent upon agriculture for employment will increase 2.3 percent each year. Because agriculture accounts for a large share of total em-

ployment, and growth in the number of people seeking employment will be rapid, people dependent upon farming for employment will continue to increase for the next decade or two in most developing countries.

Agriculture in the developing countries must find ways of increasing output and income per worker at the same time that the total number of workers is increasing. This is not an impossible task. In fact, many countries in the developing world are doing it, although not as rapidly as would be desirable.

Opportunities for accelerating rates of growth in output and income per worker in agriculture in the developing world will increase as rates of population growth decrease, the share of current output devoted to capital formation increases, and technological advances are speeded up by more emphasis on agricultural research and education.

U.S. A PARTNER IN DEVELOPMENT OF THIRD WORLD

IN THE MID-SIXTIES, many experts forecast a collision course between runaway population growth and stagnant agriculture in most of Asia, Africa, and Latin America—the Third World.

Since then we have seen the development, throughout much of Asia and other areas, of new, high-yielding varieties of grain, notably rice and wheat. These are the world's leading food crops.

The new seeds, along with improved weather, better farming methods, irrigation, and pesticides, have resulted in a doubling of yields over traditional varieties and methods in some areas.

This improvement, notably in Southeast Asia, is helping to increase food production in developing countries, buying time to bring population under control. And, equally important, some peasant farmers, until now growing barely enough to feed their families, can sell part of their crop, thereby earning more money for themselves and helping to feed city people.

The United States helped develop the new grain varieties. It has also invested much of its know-how in agricultural development, and can take pride in its efforts to increase food production in the hungry countries.

Agriculture in the United States has been highly productive for several reasons: We had tremendous natural resources such as soil, water, and climate; our farmers were not fettered by centuries of tradition; we encouraged public and private agricultural research; and hard work and individual enterprise were rewarded.

Many of these assets have not been available to the Third World. Hungry countries faced—and still face—such obstacles as debilitating tropical climates, traditional cultures, closed societies, lack of natural resources, and economies that provide little incentive.

Until the mid-1960's, agriculture had a relatively low priority in many developing countries, and farming was a low-status occupation. Investments in agriculture were small. Research was either nonexistent or not related directly to local problems. Fertilizer use was minimal. Credit and food distribution systems were frequently antiquated. Farmers' prices were too low to attract investment in improved technology.

Many governments thought they could quickly industrialize, skipping the agricultural phase of development. Until recent years the United States was sometimes a partner to such policies.

✦

AUTHOR EDWARD KOENIG is special assistant for nutrition improvement in the Office of the Secretary of Agriculture. He was formerly information director for the International Agricultural Development Service.

Foreign aid, from a variety of sources including the United Nations, the Soviet Bloc, the United States, other nations, and private agencies, was often uncoordinated, sometimes competitive, and occasionally misdirected. However, during the fifties much valuable work was done which helped to make possible the so-called "Green Revolution" of the sixties. Roads were built, dams for both electric power and irrigation constructed, education institutions established, and credit institutions strengthened.

From the late 1940's through 1969, the United States trained 40,000 agriculturists from other countries. Each year, over 1,000 came to the United States to study in our schools, on our farms, in private industry, and in government agencies. They ranged from village advisors to Ministers of Agriculture, and 99 percent returned home to put their training to practical use.

Meanwhile, new approaches to agricultural development were being tried. In 1943, the Rockefeller Foundation laid the groundwork for wheat breeding in Mexico, seeking to find high-yielding varieties suitable for local conditions.

During 20 years of experimentation, the small foundation staff—in cooperation with Mexican scientists—developed a series of wheats, corn, and other crops, which not only yielded more than local varieties, but were disease resistant, responded well to fertilizer, and were adapted to local conditions.

By 1963, Mexican wheat yields had tripled and corn yields had more than doubled: Mexico had become self-sufficient in both crops.

The program was extended to Colombia, Chile, and India. The Rockefeller Foundation, later joined by the Ford Foundation, helped establish graduate schools of agriculture in Mexico, Peru, India, and the Philippines. And a beginning had been made in research on increasing livestock production, first in Mexico and then in Colombia.

As the Mexican program became

Cooking on mud stove like one here is way of life for women in many developing nations. Attending a USDA workshop at National 4-H Center in Washington, D.C., these women drew plans and made their own improved smokeless mud stoves. Left to right, they are from Indonesia, Nigeria, the Philippines, and Malawi. Workshop was for trainees from foreign countries who will teach when they return home.

firmly established, the Rockefeller Foundation gradually withdrew its support and established, in 1966, the International Wheat and Corn Improvement Center (CIMMYT), as an autonomous research and training institute. CIMMYT, by 1969, was providing experimental wheat varieties to scores of nations, and supported production campaigns in Argentina, Pakistan, Tunisia, Morocco, and Afghanistan.

The Ford Foundation, in 1953, launched a community development program in India. Through contributions of leadership, capital, and specialists, it has sought to raise the level of living of India's 375 million people (now 550 million). It made large contributions to institutions for training local leaders, and established pilot farming projects and demonstration areas. Foundation specialists developed the concept of intensified effort applied to a limited area to move from traditional to modern agriculture.

The International Rice Research Institute (IRRI), established in 1962 by Ford and Rockefeller, assembled scientists of various nationalities to develop more productive systems of rice farming for the tropics. By 1965, they had produced new, short, stiff-strawed varieties, in one of the world's first uses of biological engineering—the breeding of plant varieties tailored to a preestablished and comprehensive set of specifications.

By 1968 the impact of IRRI's contributions was being felt throughout Asia. India planted high-yielding varieties on over 6 million acres—a dramatic achievement, even though only a small fraction of its rice acreage.

In 1967 the Philippines for the first time in decades achieved self-sufficiency in rice. Thailand's national rice breeding program, entirely supported by the Government, involves a network of 18 experiment stations.

Increased rice production in Asia, based on $15 million invested in IRRI, saved food-deficit countries some $300 million in foreign exchange in 1968 alone, according to George Harrar of the Rockefeller Foundation.

In response to the need for technical information, biological materials, and trained manpower to improve agriculture in the largely unexploited lowland tropics, two new institutes were launched in 1968. The Rockefeller and Ford Foundations helped to establish the International Institute of Tropical Agriculture (IITA) in Nigeria, to work on the crop and soils problems of the humid tropics.

In Colombia, the International Center of Tropical Agriculture (CIAT) was organized with initial support from the Ford, Kellogg, and Rockefeller Foundations. This institute will work on agricultural systems for Latin American tropics, with emphasis not only on crops but also the animal species that could convert the vast quantities of unused grasses and legumes into meat and dairy products.

Foundations have the advantage that they are not, like the U.S. Government, geared to an annual appropriation which is subject to constant review and change. Thus, a large foundation can commit support to an overseas institution for a decade or more if necessary. Long-term support is essential if an institution is to develop the skilled manpower required to achieve its objectives.

The foundations' research programs have brought about spectacular results in high-yielding grains. But their success could not have occurred without the many years of effort by the U.S. Agency for International Development (AID) and the developing countries themselves.

When the food crisis of the 1960's struck, AID increased its support for agricultural development from $200 million a year in the early sixties to $500 million in the late sixties. Direct assistance to agriculture became the largest item in U.S. foreign aid programs. Fertilizer was the largest single AID-financed commodity. The "War on Hunger" became a major U.S. policy objective.

AID increasingly used the services of land-grant universities and the U.S. Department of Agriculture in carrying out its agricultural programs. From 1966 on, each group supplied some 300 agriculturists to AID for foreign assignment each year. This represents about half of AID's total of 1,200 agriculturists, but still is less than one percent of all professional U.S. agriculturists.

By the end of the 1960's, teams from 30 U.S. colleges and universities were supplying technical agricultural assistance abroad. The AID university contracts in agriculture have been concerned principally with helping the developing nations to build institutions for agricultural education and research. These institutions have made progress: more people trained, more instructors, more useful research, and more technical knowledge passed on to the farmers.

About half of USDA's staff assigned to AID were on 2-year resident assignments in some 30 countries, usually located in the respective ministries of agriculture in the host country, as advisors to their counterparts. Their role was to quietly encourage local administrators to make decisions to stimulate agricultural improvements, suggesting policies hitherto untried in the Third World.

An equal number acted as short-term consultants—ranging from one entomologist who surveyed infestations of desert locusts in Ethiopia to a five-man conservation survey team in West Pakistan.

Most less developed countries' food policies favored consumers and kept food prices low. Such policies discouraged food production. The recent yield increases were as much due to the work of U.S. economists, who persuaded less developed countries to develop and implement price stabilization systems, as to the new seeds, fertilizers, and pesticides.

In the sixties, Americans committed some $700 million a year to people overseas, an estimated 5 percent of all U.S. private philanthropy. The main channels through which these private assistance funds flow are voluntary agencies (supported by individual contributions), foundations, religious groups, colleges and universities, and nonprofit businesses (such as cooperatives). The $700 million is the total for all philanthropy, not just for agricultural development, but does not include $200 million a year of U.S. Government support, mostly Food for Peace.

Voluntary organizations, operating both independently and in concert with government, represent the traditional humanitarian approach to assistance, but their emphasis in the decade of the 1960's has moved from relief to development. Larger groups such as CARE, Church World Service, and Catholic Relief Services, are well known. Some examples of lesser-known voluntary organization projects are:

• Action for Food Production started working in India in 1966. At AFPRO's headquarters in New Delhi, a former Swedish Lutheran missionary heads a development team consisting of a Philadelphia economist, an Australian journalist, an Indian poultry expert, a well-drilling engineer from New Zealand, a soil and water management expert from California, and three agriculturists from Canada, Australia, and New Zealand. AFPRO has 26 drilling rigs and other equipment working in eight Indian states, and nearly 1,000 Indians and foreign volunteers have been trained. Seven church agencies—from several countries—support the organization.

• Heifer Project, since 1944, has shipped a million animals to small farmers in 84 countries. Value of the animals, donated by 21 religious groups, foundations, and farm organizations, is close to $1 million a year. Each farmer who gets an animal is requested to give the first-born offspring to another farmer, who in turn gives his animal's first-born to still another.

• The Near East Foundation has been engaged in agricultural development since 1928. A 10-year development program of Ahwaz Agricultural College in Iran was completed in 1968. Facilities were expanded from four to 46 buildings, a small garden became a modern irrigated 1,000-acre farm, the faculty grew from three to 30, and the student body from 40 to 259.

U.S. cooperatives have helped in many countries, at first with their own funds and more recently under AID contracts.

Twenty-five U.S. farmers' cooperatives committed the equivalent of $1 million in technical assistance to help farmers in India build a $112 million nitrogen fertilizer cooperative. The plant, expected to be in production by 1972, involves a consortium including the Bank of America, AID, Indian cooperatives, and the Indian Government. It is expected to reduce fertilizer costs to farmers between 10 and 30 percent, and to save the Indian Government $350 million in foreign exchange each year.

U.S. private enterprise, until the mid-1960's, played a relatively minor role in agricultural development of the Third World. Before the 1960's, private investment produced enclaves of development; sugar, bananas, rubber, hemp, copra, pineapple—all export crops. Such investments provided employment and some foreign exchange, but low wages and low market prices minimized their contributions to development. Technologies were not transferable to domestic food output.

Many leaders of developing countries previously were not enthusiastic advocates of foreign investment. Some were actually hostile. Colonialism and capitalism were often linked in their minds simply as different forms of exploitation. Emphasis on public ownership in these countries made it even more difficult to attract U.S. private investment.

Beginning in 1966–67, attitudes in both the rich and poor nations began to change. Leaders realized that as a country runs out of accessible, acceptable land to cultivate, it must increase its productivity per unit of land by using large amounts of purchased inputs such as chemicals and machinery if it is to continue expanding food production. And, private enterprise could provide services such as research, credit, transport, and marketing facilities as well as the physical inputs.

Farmers in the developing countries found that the new wheat and rice seeds—yielding two and three times as much as traditional varieties—made the use of fertilizer, irrigation, and farm equipment not only profitable, but necessary. Government leaders began to encourage businessmen—local and foreign—to supply these inputs.

AID cooperates with U.S. firms planning to make preinvestment investigations in developing countries. AID can reimburse half of a firm's survey costs, if the firm decides not to invest. The firm pays the cost if it decides to invest.

From 1963 to early 1969, AID-sponsored investment surveys of agribusiness ventures resulted in 21 investments, totaling $22 million. In 1968, AID signed 10 agribusiness survey agreements, representing some $76 million in potential investments.

Since the United States hopes to relieve protein malnutrition worldwide, AID also has a special Commercial Protein Food Studies Program. This is designed to introduce high-protein, commercial foods—made from locally available, low-cost materials—into developing countries. U.S. firms are encouraged to pay for product development themselves. AID helps defray the costs of raw material surveys, food habit studies, and market testing. If an investment results, the company reimburses AID for the cost of the survey.

Of the 12 projects so far approved, one resulted in investment by late 1969: Monsanto apparently was marketing a successful protein soft drink in Guyana. On its own, the Coca-Cola Company was making and testing a protein drink in Brazil.

AID has also inaugurated a new program of assisting surveys in food marketing, processing, storage, and distribution. The survey program will be administered by the Agribusiness Council, Inc., a non profit organization which is comprised of leading U.S. companies, financial institutions, foundations, and research organizations. The Council was formed in 1967 to stimulate agribusiness investment in developing countries.

Surveying companies must have successful commercial experience, pref-

Left, garden type tractor used to power a simple machine to winnow rice on Taiwan. Such equipment becomes necessary as farmers produce more grain for sale in the cities. Right, winnowing rice—separating the grain from the straw—by hand in the Philippines. This time-consuming and often wasteful method is still common in most developing nations.

297

erably overseas, in owning and operating the kind of business to be surveyed. AID provides the survey funds and some administrative costs. Surveying companies reimburse survey funds to the Council if they invest.

Despite inadequate support for agriculture, and primitive farming methods, grain production (man's basic food) in the less developed countries has increased 71 percent during the two decades of 1948–1967. This compares with a 61 percent increase in the developed countries.

Unfortunately, population increased even more in the developing nations; as a result, the amount of food available per person has not increased, even though rising income, and rising expectations of a better life, have increased the demand for food.

The United States has contributed much toward increasing food supplies in the Third World, but the job is far from complete.

Uncontrolled population growth will apparently continue, even though many parts of the world have shown more interest in family planning than before. Current estimates are for a doubling of world population by the year 2000, almost wholly in the less developed countries.

This flood of human beings will, no doubt, present serious problems of unemployment and underemployment. The main burden of absorbing the increased labor force will fall inevitably on agriculture which, in most developing countries, occupies some 60 to 80 percent of the labor force.

New farming methods bring a vast array of new problems. Spending on agricultural research must continue and increase. More agricultural extension and massive investments in fertilizer and irrigation are needed. Governments in areas untouched by the high-yielding grains in Africa and Latin America, as well as Asia, must stimulate technological change.

It has also become quite clear that malnutrition, most notably protein deficiencies, can permanently retard both mental and physical growth, with severe implications for national development. The Food and Agriculture Organization (FAO) of the United Nations estimates that at least 20 percent of the population in developing countries (500 million people) are undernourished (receive too few calories), and about 60 percent (1.5 billion) receive diets that are "inadequate in nutritional quality" (commonly a protein deficiency).

Food production in the future must be geared to man's nutritional needs more closely than in the past, and adequate nutrition must be clearly established as the major purpose of food production.

NEW TECHNOLOGY: ROSE AND THORN

IF THE DEVELOPING NATIONS are to ever adequately feed themselves, the main thrust will have to be provided by new technologies. Recent advances in grain production in Asia—where yields of wheat and rice have been sharply increased through the use of new varieties and fertilizer—have highlighted the key role that technology can play in getting agriculture moving.

Technology, in its most simple form, is often considered the systematic application of scientific knowledge. Here we shall view it as the biological and/or physical means for carrying out agricultural production and marketing. Thus technologies include such things as new crops, varieties, cultivation practices, and tools and equipment.

While technologies can be of vary-

✦

AUTHOR DANA G. DALRYMPLE is an agricultural economist in the Foreign Economic Development Service.

ing degrees of complexity, the main result of a new innovation is increased output—or the same output at lower cost. In some cases the result may be a change in product quality.

The newness of a technology is often relative. What is new in one area may be accepted practice in another. More specifically, many technological changes in the developing nations may seem old hat to those familiar with agriculture in more advanced nations. But this does not diminish their importance.

How do new technologies come into being? The answer to some extent depends on their complexity. Simple innovations may well be created by peasants or local farmers. But as technologies grow more complex, the greater the likelihood is that they will be generated by some organized scientific research effort. The research may be conducted locally or brought in by transfer from another country.

American farmers are inveterate tinkerers and experimenters. Many mechanical or biological advances have grown directly or indirectly out of their efforts. Farmers in less developed nations do not have the same mechanical heritage, nor do they have the resources. Hence their innovations may be modest by American standards, yet they may make a significant contribution.

A recent example in Vietnam has been reported by Robert Sanson (*Oxford Economic Papers*, March 1969). Before 1963 the primary water-lifting device for irrigation was a foot pedal-operated water wheel with a low capacity. In 1962, however, a motor pump was initially devised by a technically trained Vietnamese farmer; a similar version was subsequently and independently designed by a mechanic (both individuals had at one time worked for a French dredging firm in Saigon).

There was no patent and the innovation spread rapidly; motor dealers, acting on descriptions from farmers, built similar models. Though the pump was inefficient by Western standards, it ". . . transformed the upper delta economy." Farmers began growing a second rice crop and cash crops such as vegetables. Production increased at least 40 percent.

Numerous similar stories could be told for other nations. They would include both mechanical and biological technologies. Given some training and resources, farmers themselves can be significant sources of technology. But there are limits as to how far they can go.

Scientific research may be required to develop appropriate new technologies. This research may be sponsored by public agencies, private firms, foundations, and cooperative efforts involving some combination of the three.

Agricultural experiment stations have been in existence in at least some less developed nations since the late 1800's. Government-sponsored agricultural research in the Ivory Coast began in 1888; a crop research station was established in Nigeria in 1899.

Many such programs were originally established by former colonial powers and were heavily oriented to plantation agriculture. Others are relatively new—the Malaysian Agricultural Research and Development Institute, for instance, was formally established in February 1969—and have a more general orientation. In any case, the governments of the developing nations spend only a fraction of the U.S. public investment on agricultural research.

In some developing countries, larger farmers have organized to sponsor research programs. This has been particularly true of sugar. Dr. Robert Evanson, formerly of the University of Minnesota, reports that the lack of alternative crops and the competitive situation on the international market have led "sugarcane growers in almost every country . . . to privately finance their own experiment stations." Sugar research began as early as 1887 in the British West Indies and in 1889 in Java.

Pump is assembled in Vietnam rice paddy, above, and put in operation, below.

Private firms in the developed nations have been an important source of technologies—particularly as related to farm machinery and farm chemicals. Some U.S. companies have vast agricultural research facilities; such facilities are particularly apt to be lacking in the developing nations.

Some multinational firms carry out significant research programs on export crops such as rubber and bananas. Dr. James Houck of the University of Minnesota notes that "much of the world's scientific and practical knowledge about bananas has been generated by these privately sponsored research programs."

Perhaps the most significant institutional advance in recent years has been development of international research programs sponsored by American foundations.

The Rockefeller Foundation initiated studies on crop improvement in Mexico in the early 1940's. This work gradually spread to other Latin nations. In 1966 it officially became international in scope with the establishment—in cooperation with the Ford Foundation—of the International Wheat and Corn Improvement Center (CIMMYT) near Mexico City.

The famed International Rice Research Institute (IRRI) was jointly established by the Ford and Rockefeller foundations in the Philippines in 1962. International research centers have subsequently been established in Colombia (the Kellogg Foundation has also provided funds for this center) and Nigeria.

In addition to doing basic research, the centers have close ties with national research programs in many countries. They help these nations to develop their own research efforts and to adapt the work done at the centers to local conditions.

The U.S. Agency for International Development (AID) has since 1967 helped fund various programs at IRRI including research training, assistance to other countries in Southeast Asia and India, and research on farm equipment.

These international research activi-

Agronomists inspect IR-8 at International Rice Research Institute in Philippines, while farmers feed rice from experimental plots into a combine for threshing.

ties are most important since relatively little work has been done in the past on increasing local food supplies. The research by international firms and by farm groups has largely been aimed at export (and in some cases nonfood) crops. Even the relatively small public-supported programs have tended to lead in this direction. Hopefully this balance will be righted in the future.

Not all technologies are home-grown. In the case of agriculture in the less developed nations, many may be imported in one way or another. An international transfer of technology has been going on for centuries.

The United States has both "borrowed" and "loaned" technology. There have been two phases to the loaning of technology: (1) direct outflow of technologies or technologists and (2) education of students from less developed nations.

One of the most striking early examples of the former approach occurred in 1871 when Horace Capron, then U.S. Commissioner of Agriculture, resigned his position to lead a mission to Japan. Among other things, the mission introduced new crops, livestock, and farm machinery.

As an outgrowth, an agricultural college was subsequently established on the island of Hokkaido with close ties to Massachusetts Agricultural College.

Religious groups also played a role. Missionaries trained in agriculture were sent to Japan and Africa as early as 1876. In 1904, James House established the American Farm School in Salonica, Greece. Mission agricultural colleges were first established in 1907.

Students in less developed nations have attended American colleges of agriculture since their early days. Japanese students were among the first. Then came other nationalities: For example, in the fall of 1906, seven Indian students were enrolled in agriculture at Cornell; from 1905 to 1911, 15 Russians studied at Michigan Agricultural College.

These small numbers have since grown into a virtual flood and have provided an important vehicle for the transmission of technological knowledge.

It is perhaps less well known that American industry has also played an important role. U.S. farm machinery has been exported around the world since the 1800's. During the 1920's and 1930's American agricultural machinery, particularly the tractor, was of vital importance in the development of Soviet agriculture. More recently, American private enterprise contributed to the growth of a highly advanced vegetable and small fruit industry in northwest Mexico.

All developed nations are to some extent involved—either formally or informally—in the transfer of technology. This is also true of some of the newer nations. Leopold Laufer reports (*Israel and the Developing Countries*, 1967) that in 1966, Israeli advisors were engaged in agricultural projects in at least 10 African, 5 Asian, and 8 South American countries.

Taiwan has been providing technical assistance since 1961: More than 20 teams have gone to Africa alone. In the fall of 1968 some 160 Taiwanese technicians were at work in the Ivory Coast helping to improve the rice industry.

There are problems to importing technology and limits on how much can be borrowed. Generally few technologies can be transferred without local adaptation. And as they grow in complexity there is a greater need for local research and modifications. Indeed with some technologies it may be possible to transfer only knowledge: the entire development of the technology may have to be done locally.

New technologies can take an infinite array of forms. Here we will cite examples of a few that might be considered relatively new to most of the less developed world. They apply to production, harvesting and marketing, and nutrition.

Perhaps the best known of the new technologies are the high-yielding dwarf varieties of grains. Through the efforts of CIMMYT and IRRI, new varieties have been developed which are now in widespread use, especially in Asia. The area devoted to Mexican type wheat and IRRI type rice has expanded as shown by the table.

These varieties have been referred to as high-yielding because output per acre may be increased 50 to 100 percent or more. It is, however, more appropriate to say the varieties are highly responsive—for in order to obtain increased yields it is necessary to have some measure of water control, to sharply increase the amount of fertilizer applied, and to give more attention to insect and disease control. A package of new technologies is required.

The original high-yielding varieties are quickly being replaced by new generations. The newer varieties developed at both CIMMYT and IRRI, as well as in individual nations, promise to be improvements on their forebears. They will be higher in taste and/or milling quality, besides being better suited for local growing and marketing.

In addition, nutritional levels will be improved: high protein quality is now being bred into wheat by CIMMYT and a high-lysine corn has been developed—with AID assistance—in Nigeria. Varietal improvement is, and must be, a continuing process.

Other less obvious technological improvements have aided adoption of the new varieties. Extension of electrification in Pakistan has facilitated the installation of water pumps for irrigation. New methods of fertilizer production in the developed nations have helped reduce the cost of fertilizer (and on the other hand, the new varieties have made it much easier to show farmers the value of fertilizers). Improved rural roads and communication have aided the distribution of both seed and fertilizer.

The new varieties have a shorter growing season than the traditional varieties. This means that in many cases two or three crops of rice can be grown instead of one or two. But to do so requires better timing of field operations. This in turn often increases the need for mechanization—greater use of garden or full-sized tractors. Furthermore, improved varieties of wheat should be planted at even depths rather than broadcast by hand; this in turn leads to a need for tractor-pulled mechanical drills.

While much recent emphasis has been placed on the payoff from wheat and rice, this should not obscure the fact that important advances have been made in other grains and indeed in other crops. Improvements in sugar-

Rice breeder makes a cross, bringing new selection into world.

cane and banana varieties, for instance, have played key roles in maintaining commercial production of these items. Concurrent improvements in insect and disease control have also been of great value. The future will probably see increased efforts in livestock breeding.

Technological changes in production usually lead to improvements in harvesting and marketing.

When, for instance, output of grains is increased, it is necessary to expand capacity to harvest, thresh, dry, and store the crop. Increased wheat crops may strain already seasonally short labor supplies; where a crop has been traditionally harvested by sickle, such as in India, it is increasingly necessary to use mechanical harvesters. Improved varieties of rice mature during the wet, rather than dry, season; this complicates the threshing process and increases the need for drying facilities.

In response, AID has helped sponsor development of a simple mechanical rice thresher at IRRI and the design of improved rice drying facilities in Vietnam.

New varieties of bananas have stimulated, as Prof. Houck has noted, the invention and application of new processing and handling techniques. Bananas formerly were shipped from producing areas in bulk on the original stem. New disease-resistant varieties were damaged by this system. To improve quality, a new system of cutting and boxing fruit in the producing nation was developed.

Many of the more striking technological improvements center about improving the product's nutritional levels. The greatest need in virtually every nation is more protein. Techniques have been developed for adding synthetic amino acids to grains in order to increase the protein level: a lysine-fortified bread is now being commercially produced in India.

High-protein beverages have been developed and are now moving into commercial use in Hong Kong, Brazil, and Guyana. It is also possible to utilize low-cost sources of protein such as those found in oilseeds or fish to fortify major foods or as ingredients of new foods. Work of this type is relatively sophisticated in nature and requires a high level of knowledge. Many efforts to date have been sponsored or encouraged through AID funding. Dramatic developments can be expected in this area in the future.

A promising start has been made on providing new technologies for grain production in some less developed nations. But many nations in Latin America and Africa remain relatively untouched by the "Green Revolution."

A great deal remains to be done in terms of supplying new technologies for (1) other grains, (2) other food crops, and (3) livestock. Moreover, much of the new technology, especially the grain varieties, are most suited for irrigated agriculture. Similar advances have not been made for dryland (or nonirrigated) agriculture.

Even where the high-yielding variety package has taken hold, gaps remain. Water management practices need improvement virtually everywhere irrigation is practiced (in the past, emphasis has been placed on the engineering of large waterworks rather than on the agronomic aspects of on-farm water management). And irrigation itself generally needs to be steadily expanded.

Fertilizer supplies in many areas are inadequate; the construction of domestic fertilizer plants has often moved slowly or is hampered by lack of local raw materials. Effective insect and disease control requires a never-ending struggle.

In all countries, there is a strong need for improving the marketing system. This involves both the provision of inputs such as fertilizer and pesticides to farmers as well as the more traditional role of handling farm production. The latter task is magnified by the fact that the new variety package has brought about an increase in both the quantity and share of farm production marketed.

Farm and warehouse storage must

"Maize is our best money-maker,"
India farmer, left, says. When he first tried
maize (corn), local extension service
brought farmers by busload to see cultivation
and harvesting of crop. Below,
bagging hybrid corn seed at depot of
National Seeds Corp. in India.

be expanded and improved if much of the increased production is not to be lost to spoilage, insects, and rodents. Transportation should be extended and upgraded to move produce from farm to city.

It is possible to get along without these improvements, but in their absence the people will not receive the full play of benefits from technological advance.

A less obvious need, but one which underlies all the above, is that of improving the public structure for research, education, and extension. The new wheat and rice varieties have gone a long way on a rather slim research base in most countries. We cannot count on being so lucky again.

Building the public sector effort in these areas is particularly important in the less developed nations. As we have suggested earlier, private industry has generally not advanced to the point where it can take over some of these tasks.

What do the technological advances which have been described, as well as the gaps which remain, suggest for public policies in agriculture?

To start with, the adoption of any technology depends on profitability. If the technology holds promise of significantly increasing income—increases which will more than offset the risks inherent in its use—it will tend to be quickly adopted. If it offers only marginal increases in return, it will be more slowly adopted. High grain prices in South Asia in the mid-1960's, brought about by poor weather, helped hasten the adoption of high-yielding varieties and improved cultural practices.

Profitability must be given priority consideration in future attempts to fill remaining technological gaps.

Technological gains tend to be unevenly distributed. In the case of the new varieties, the benefits have tended to fall more heavily to the larger grower with irrigation. Smaller growers without irrigation and landless laborers have often not benefited to the same degree. Thus income disparities within the population may have widened.

Restoration of some sort of balance will mean improving the lot of the smaller and disadvantaged farmers. Methods for accomplishing this are not altogether clear but might well involve increased emphasis on dryland crops, increased availability of credit, and expanded extension programs.

Another potential problem centers about the employment implications of certain new technologies. While the new varieties, if anything, seem to add to labor needs, other forms such as mechanization may sharply reduce the need for labor. Since most of the developing nations have abundant farm labor, except possibly during certain short seasons, the release of more labor may not be desirable. Increased attention will have to be given to employment effects in the future.

A problem which may be more familiar to those from the developing nations is the specter of surpluses—and their potential negative effect on farm prices. A few years ago this possibility would have seemed remote, but some Asian nations have quickly approached self-sufficiency in certain grains such as wheat and rice. What to do if supplies move beyond current needs? The first needed step in many countries is to build up a reserve or buffer stock.

Once this has been done, either exports have to be increased or production held back. Increasing the export of basic crops is a most difficult matter: competition from developed nations is apt to be severe and markets fade as other nations also increase their production capacity. Furthermore, comparative advantage constantly shifts.

Holding back production, as the developed nations have learned, is not an easy task either. Price support levels may be reduced and subsidies on fertilizer and pesticides removed. Or production capacity may be diverted to other crops.

Diversification of agricultural output is assuming expanded importance. It involves broadening production beyond one or two traditional crops ("monoculture"). Fruits and vegetables and livestock often are involved in diversification programs. Where diversification involves the production of labor-intensive crops, it is likely to absorb labor.

Such types of farming are often appropriate for small-scale producers. A further advantage is that nutrition may be improved. But to diversify properly usually requires a whole new set of technology, particularly with respect to marketing and food processing.

Thus technological changes in one area can unleash the need for a whole chain of further changes. These latter problems may be more sophisticated and difficult to solve than the initial production problem.

AGRICULTURAL DEVELOPMENT IN KENYA

THE DEVELOPMENT of Kenya since independence, in 1963, provides an encouraging success story. It is the result of pre-independence British policies, the determination and self-help of the Kenyans, and the effective use of external aid. The United States, certain Continental European countries, private foundations, and the International Bank for Reconstruction and Development have made significant contributions, although the British have provided the most assistance.

Kenya is located on the East Coast of Africa at the equator. It is slightly smaller than Texas and has approximately the same population. Climate of the coastal area is tropical but the highlands have a temperate climate. There are areas of high rainfall along the coast and in the extreme western parts near Lake Victoria. More than two-thirds of the area is too dry for crop production and is occupied by herdsmen with cattle, sheep, and goats, and by wild game animals.

British explorers and traders entered what is now Kenya late in the last century. With the building of the main railroad line westward across the country from Mombasa about 1900, agricultural development and the history of modern Kenya began.

The British policy of colonizing white settlers in the accessible fertile areas with a temperate climate and establishing a "reserve" of other areas for African farmers led to the development of a dualistic system. This consisted of a white commercial, export-oriented farming sector and a black subsistence, food-producing sector. Coffee, tea, pyrethrum, sisal, cattle, and dairying predominated in the commercial farming sector.

A system of supervising and controlling the production and marketing of the major commercial crops, through statutory marketing boards, was initiated after World War I. This continues to the present time.

Considerable agricultural expansion followed World War II when Britain adopted a policy of encouraging ex-servicemen to settle in the so-called White Highlands—mainly from Nairobi westward, into and beyond the Rift Valley. Most of these new settlers entered mixed or general farming with wheat, dairying, beef cattle, and pigs among the principal enterprises.

In 1946 the Government initiated a 10-year development plan covering all aspects of development and specifically directed at African agriculture. It is estimated that of the £11 million allocated to development of

✦

AUTHOR BENNETT S. WHITE, JR., spent more than 30 years in research and administration in the U.S. Department of Agriculture, interspersed with university teaching and research. He became advisor to the Minister for Agriculture in Kenya in 1968, under the AID program.

natural resources in the 1946–55 period, more than half was spent in African areas on land utilization and settlement, soil conservation, livestock improvement, rural water supplies, and tsetse eradication.

Nairobi, Mombasa, Nakuru, and other towns grew in size and became increasingly modern. Their growth was based mainly on the handling and processing of agricultural products and the sale of farm inputs and consumer goods to farmers and their employees.

During the colonial period a significant infrastructure associated with agricultural development was created. This included efficient railways and harbors, posts and telegraphs, customs and excises on a regional East African basis, and a regional agricultural research organization whose research program has become increasingly comprehensive. A generally efficient administration of Government contributed to development.

Many Africans found employment on European-owned and managed plantations, farms, and ranches and in European and Asian urban businesses. The great bulk of the African population, however, continued to live largely as self-sufficient farmers. Farming and closely related industries probably provided the major source of employment and livelihood for 80 to 90 percent of the population.

In 1963 there was a smooth transition of power from the colonial administration to the new African regime. Aim of the new Government was to rapidly increase opportunities for the mass of the African population in agriculture. At the same time it was desired to avoid serious injustices to the current European landowners, maintain overall production, and lay the basis for future increases in output.

It is mainly through the movement of the small, primarily subsistence, farmers and pastoralists into the commercial economy and increases in the scale and efficiency of their operations that the Government expects to raise employment and incomes in the agricultural sector.

Agricultural production in Kenya increased between 2.5 and 3.0 percent a year from 1963 to 1968. A severe drought in 1965 and depressed prices for some exports have held the rate of increase down.

Special interest attaches to the trend in marketed production and to the output of small farms. Coffee production on small farms rose from 26.3 percent of the total in 1962–63 to over 60 percent in 1967–68. The share of small farmers in tea production increased from less than 1 to more than 17 percent. For pyrethrum the share of small growers went from approximately 25 to nearly 90 percent.

Development of production of some commodities illustrates the course of agricultural development in Kenya.

Maize, or corn, is the most important staple in the diet of the population. Nearly all farmers, other than pastoralists in the most arid and remote areas, devote some part of their lands to maize.

A breakthrough in maize growing was achieved when research stations with both local and overseas support, including a USDA/AID Participating Agency Service Agreement, developed both high-yielding hybrid varieties for the higher rainfall districts and other varieties for areas not suitable for hybrids. These, promoted by vigorous extension efforts, have been readily accepted by both large and small farmers.

Since most maize is consumed at home without entering market channels, total output cannot be accurately estimated. Government supported prices are still above world prices although recently reduced.

It is now Government policy to encourage and expand maize output and to develop a modern system of bulk handling and storage. Kenya is one of the few developing countries that have recognized that a commercial agriculture requires developed marketing facilities.

Livestock is a developing industry with great potential for expansion. Since a large percentage of the livestock are kept by nomadic tribesmen for whom they serve as prestige symbols as well as sources of meat and milk, it has been difficult to bring modern technology to this industry. Improvement in livestock production is dependent on the control of disease, and improvement in breeding and in range and livestock management.

Dairying and the manufacture of dairy products is a developed industry but there is room for expansion if consumption can be increased. Lower prices could be achieved by improving the efficiency of production and marketing. This would lead to increased demand and improved nutrition in urban areas.

Horticultural crops include more than 80 products—pineapples, passion fruit, cashew nuts, macadamia nuts, and almost the entire range of temperate zone vegetables.

The Del Monte organization is vigorously developing the canned pineapple business.

Exports of fresh and frozen fruits and vegetables to Europe by air are growing, and it is believed that there are substantial opportunities for further expansion.

The Government looks to the horticultural crops as labor intensive enterprises which offer increased employment in agriculture, including opportunities for diversification in

Inflatable plastic warehouse built for Maize Marketing Board in Kenya. Warehouse holds 5,000 tons of bagged maize (corn). It is portable, moisture proof, and can be fumigated.

Sisal, formerly the second most important export of Kenya, has declined greatly as natural hard fibers have been replaced by synthetics in world markets, and further declines are likely.

Pyrethrum, used worldwide as a household insecticide, has been threatened in recent years by the development of synthetics in several industrial countries. The Pyrethrum Marketing Board is following a realistic policy of cutting prices, improving processing, and encouraging the growing of higher pyrethrin content flowers.

Sugar cane production is increasing upon the irrigation and settlement projects. A relatively low level of efficiency and a protected market make for comparatively high sugar prices to consumers.

coffee areas hard hit by the coffee berry disease.

In the past few years, prices for food crops domestically consumed as well as for the traditional export crops have fallen. In most cases, however, prices appear to be adequate to encourage production, providing that efficiency in production and marketing is maintained and improved.

For a small country, Kenya has a relatively large agricultural research establishment. The National Research Station at Kitale, source of the new corn hybrids, draws support from a number of sources including the British, the United States, the Rockefeller and Ford Foundations, and the Government of Kenya.

The Minister for Agriculture, an aggressive champion of development, is convinced that new research findings are essential if agriculture is to expand and to improve its competitive position in world markets. Efforts are being made to coordinate research and establish priorities.

Land ownership is a complex problem involving the transfer of land from British colonists to Kenya citizens. The farms are purchased by the Government of Kenya under the Land Purchase Program and Agricultural Development Corporation, and resold to Kenyan farmers as large or small farms on liberal, long term credit. Much of the financing for this has been from loans or grants from the British Government.

Extent of the transfer from European to Kenyan ownership is indicated by the decline in the number of European owners of mixed farms from between four and five thousand in 1963 to an estimated less than 800 in 1969. The general success in maintaining production on large farms and increasing output on small farms has already been noted.

Although not strictly a matter of expanding agricultural land, the irrigation schemes are designed to use land more intensively.

There are three major irrigation programs. Total areas cropped rose from about 7,000 acres to 9,750 acres between 1963–64 and 1967–68. Within the same period the number of plot holders increased from 1,966 to 2,296. Other irrigation projects are being developed. There are questions as to the favorableness of cost benefit ratios for the irrigation plans. Large projects require tremendous investments.

Land purchase loans are for a period of 20 years. Arrears in payments are high and many farmers are heavily in debt to the Government and also friends and relatives.

Future land transfer policy must take into account that there are comparatively few people with the personal financial resources, and technical and managerial skills, to manage large-scale mixed farms. In many cases investments were made hastily without proper regard either to the credit worthiness of borrowers or the likelihood of realization of sufficient additional farm profits to permit loan repayment.

Supervision of credit use is one means of compensating for the lack of managerial experience, which is necessarily characteristic of the farmers entering larger scale or commercial operations for the first time. Kenya is taking measures to reduce losses due to farm debt delinquency.

Much of Kenya's land area is still occupied, cultivated, and grazed on the basis of a variety of tribal, family, and hereditary rights. The extension of credit, however, usually requires that the borrower hold legal title to the land. Registration is being pushed vigorously, but the task is a formidable one and hindered by a shortage of necessary skilled personnel, local opposition in some areas, and the problems of a shifting population.

Of the perhaps 900,000 farmers in the small-scale sector, only about 50,000 have received any kind of public credit. With funds being made available by international agencies and other foreign sources, five programs for the extending of credit to small holders are to get underway by the early 1970's.

Lack of short term credit is one of the major deficiencies of the credit scene. The Government provides guaranteed minimum returns in the form of advances to wheat and maize farmers who meet certain specified conditions to aid them in paying planting and harvesting costs.

Kenya has a fairly well developed system of primary and secondary education, although it is not free. The payment of school fees is a burden on low income people. In line with experience in most developing countries, few who have attended school seek careers in agriculture. If unable to finance themselves or to qualify for a Government scholarship in technical or higher education, they prefer to join the ranks of job hunters in urban areas.

The Government is seeking to train farmers for modern commercial agriculture. In 1968 about 40,000 small-scale farmers attended one- to two-week courses in the 30 Farmers Training Centers, strategically located throughout the country. The college for training in large scale farming graduates about 100 per year. These training programs are useful and staffed by dedicated workers, but are small in relation to needs.

General extension covering the country as a whole is provided by the Ministry of Agriculture. The extension service faces serious problems of trained manpower. This is a typical problem of the developing countries, often intensified by the withdrawal of expatriates.

Fertilizer, seeds, agricultural chemicals, machinery, and other purchased inputs are generally available to the commercial agricultural sector, although there are exceptions. Handicapping development, however, are high costs of distribution due to the smallness of the total market, the thousands of small farmers, and the long distances. The Ministry of Agriculture is planning a study of costs and margins in the marketing of farm supplies.

Kenya has long had a railway system and extensive port facilities at Mombasa. Both are expected to be improved and extended in the future. For a developing country the road system is quite good, although farm to market roads in some areas leave much to be desired, especially during rainy seasons.

The Government is giving high priority to development of roads, but government revenues have been inadequate to maintain and improve all the road system. The World Bank is making a loan to Kenya for road improvement.

Overall responsibility for development planning is lodged in the Ministry of Economic Planning and Development. The initiation of proposals relating to agriculture, however, is a responsibility of the Ministry of Agriculture. In 1966, a Development Planning Division was established in the Ministry, staffed mainly by expatriate officers. USDA under an agreement with USAID has furnished from one to three economists for this planning activity.

Two major problems must be successfully solved if development is to continue. Population, increasing at 3.3 percent a year, already is pressing upon available supplies of high potential land. Only drastic reduction in rates of population growth can avoid further fragmentation of land holdings, and increased movement of people to the cities with their attendant social, economic, and political problems. Furthermore, population growth is a serious threat to Kenya's famous, but already seriously reduced, herds of great game animals—the basis for the important and growing tourist industry.

The second major general problem is reconciling social conflicts. Racial and tribal conflicts are a threat to political stability.

At the time of independence, most of the responsible positions in Government were held by Europeans and in business and trade by Europeans and Asians. During the past few years there has been considerable Kenyanization (in practice mainly Africanization), especially in the civil service.

Due to the shortage of skilled personnel, the important role played by expatriates is recognized. Yet there is continuing pressure to replace expatriates with Kenyans. The country also desires maximum economic development. Here are two objectives which are not entirely compatible.

Tribalism is also a major social problem.

The tribe or the clan was the first unit beyond the family which drew together for protection and advancement of group interests. With increasing population and widening interests, clans or tribes tended to band into confederations, usually of people of similar ethnic background.

In a strong national state, tribal

311

loyalties and interests must be subordinated to those of the nation.

Kenya is made up of more than 50 distinct tribes, ranging in size from a few thousand for the smaller up to more than 2 million for the largest. However, tribalism is weakened as a society becomes increasingly commercialized, urbanized, and interdependent, and as people move about more and more. In the meantime, it is a source of economic, social, and political rivalries and tensions.

Development has characterized Kenya's history, but it is still a poor country. The average per capita income is in the neighborhood of one hundred dollars a year. The people of Kenya are expecting rising levels of living and are working hard for them.

RICE REVOLUTION BRINGS PROGRESS FOR VIET PEASANT

THE WORD "REVOLUTION" must be one of the most commonly used nouns in the English language. We have revolutions in politics, in warfare, in economics, in technology. We have the Red Revolution, the Black Revolution, and now the Green Revolution in Asian agriculture.

Yet if by revolution we mean a rapid and fundamental change in a particular human institution or activity, it is not too strong a word to describe the changes in how farmers are growing rice in a number of Asian countries. Prominent among these is Vietnam.

Rice is Vietnam's "staff of life," filling over 80 percent of her cultivated land. In the late 50's and early 60's, the fertile Mekong Delta produced enough rice to meet Vietnamese needs and provide export averaging 200,000 tons a year.

Yields were above average for tropical Asia, but use of fertilizer and other modern inputs was very limited. This was understandable because the rice varieties used—though developed and selected through years of careful Vietnamese effort—did not respond well enough to fertilizer to make its use profitable at existing farm prices. It often just didn't pay farmers to modernize.

As long as the war remained limited this traditional technology met the needs of the Vietnamese people. But the war's sharp expansion in 196 reduced rice acreage by over 10 per cent, created a serious rural labor shortage, and inflated urban rice demand.

Vietnam dropped quickly from self sufficiency and became, in 1967, the world's largest rice importer. Most of these imports—one-sixth of the U.S. rice crop—were shipped to Vietnam as part of our food aid program.

Such rice imports were indispensable to Vietnam, providing needed food and preventing unmanageable price increases that could have destroyed the economy. But they were clearly not a long-run solution, and in that same year the government of South Vietnam and the United States agreed to place top priority on restoring Vietnam's rice output.

One reason for this decision was Vietnam's increasing rice deficit. But there was another, perhaps stronger motivation. Up to that point the economic benefits of the country's "war prosperity" had gone almost exclusively to urban areas. The Government of Vietnam sorely needed to do something for 11 million rural people if it was to deserve the alle

AUTHOR MAC DESTLER, now on leave from USDA, has served as Acting Asia Coordinator for the former International Agricultural Development Service.

312

Left, preparing rice seedbed. Right, transplanting rice.

giance of all Vietnamese. Moreover, a major achievement with rice—Vietnam's "staff of life"—would have overwhelming material and symbolic significance.

And a new and promising technology was available. As described by Robert Chandler in the 1968 Yearbook of Agriculture, the International Rice Research Institute in the Philippines (IRRI) had developed a "dwarf" rice variety—called IR–8—which was setting yield records at experiment stations throughout Asia.

In Vietnam, the average traditional yield had been 2 tons of rough rice (paddy) per hectare. IR–8, highly responsive to fertilizer use, showed promise of yielding at least 5 tons to the hectare, a net increase of 3 tons. By 1967 Filipino farmers were already planting IR–8 on a commercial scale.

IR–8 had also been tested under Vietnamese conditions, both at official experiment stations and independently by American provincial agricultural advisors and their Vietnamese counterparts. But the experimental evidence was scanty, though favorable, and the decision for a crash program was more than a small gamble.

Some Vietnamese agricultural officials were understandably skeptical, pointing to the threats of pests and disease as well as the lack of comprehensive adaptive research under Vietnamese conditions. However, the Vietnamese Minister of Agriculture was impressed by IR–8's promise and ordered his staff to proceed.

There had also been debate within the U.S. AID Mission—mainly on rice prices. In 1966 farm prices had been depressed, and agricultural specialists felt prices needed to be raised to make use of fertilizer and new varieties profitable to farmers. But others feared undue inflation might result. The issue was temporarily resolved when rice prices rose sharply in January 1967, thereby improving agricultural incentives without disastrous effects on the economy.

Implementation of the rice production program required intensive teamwork by a wide range of Vietnamese and American agricultural specialists. Fortunately, the U.S. agricultural assistance staff had the capability to do its part of the job.

A high-level advisory group headed by the U.S. Secretary of Agriculture had visited Vietnam in January 1966. Following its recommendations, the Department of Agriculture and the Agency for International Development recruited, trained, and sent to Vietnam experts in agricultural extension, credit, research, water management, program planning, and agricultural economics and statistics.

Total agricultural staffing increased from 21 at the beginning of 1966 to well over a hundred 2 years later. Per-

313

haps more important, over 50 of those newly arriving in 1967 had special training in rice production.

In the fall of 1967 these experts helped put together The Rice Goal Plan for 1968–71, which set forth production targets and outlined the range of supporting activities required to achieve them.

Adversity once again became a force for change. Just as Vietnam's declining rice output and increasing needs had spurred adoption of the new program, so September flooding which washed away the just-planted crop in the Vo Dat Valley offered an opportunity for planting several hundred hectares of IR–8 ahead of schedule.

Forty-five tons of seed were immediately purchased from the Philippines with AID funds, and they arrived within a month. Farmers planted the new seed readily, and its fine performance under difficult conditions convinced many a skeptic, whether in the rice paddies or in Saigon.

The target established for the 1968–69 crop year (June 1 to May 30) was 44,000 hectares (110,000 acres) planted to IR–8, or 2 percent of total rice land. The yield goal was 5 tons per hectare.

Management received top emphasis. U.S. specialists helped the Government of Vietnam program and meet the requirements of the various provinces and villages for seed, fertilizer, pesticides, and credit. Ten thousand IR–8 "kits" were prepared containing sufficient fertilizer, seed, pesticides, and planting instructions for a farmer to plant 1/10 of a hectare to the new varieties.

The campaign emphasized that farmers could double existing yields, and extension workers labored to make sure they did. This was not easy, for farmers could not just plant the new variety in the old way; they had to adopt a whole new package of inputs and practices.

Throughout the program the AID Mission and Vietnamese officials had to do much of the work handled routinely by the private sector in this country—ensuring that each farmer got the fertilizer and pesticides he needed. But at the same time, they sought to move responsibility for importing and distributing these inputs from government agencies to the private sector (including farmer organizations). This was substantially accomplished by the beginning of 1969.

The program received a setback from the TET offensive of January–February 1968. Though this hampered operations in various ways, perhaps the most important impact was on price.

Physical damage to roads and a sharp decline in security conditions caused rice deliveries from the Mekong Delta to the Saigon market to drop almost 90 percent in February from the already below-average January shipments. March saw a recovery to January's level, but from then through June movements remained sluggish and transport costs high.

Both of these factors meant lower returns to farmers. Delta paddy (rough rice) prices were 20 percent below those of the year before, at the very time that farmers were deciding whether they could buy fertilizer and count on getting their money back later in increased rice sales.

Doubtless many farmers shied away due to depressed prices. Yet the program still moved forward, as other farmers must have calculated that even with lower prices they would do far better with IR–8. The 44,000 hectare target was at least approximately achieved. An estimated 22,000 farmers planted IR–8, including some in all 44 provinces of South Vietnam, achieving an average yield at the targeted 5 tons per hectare.

Perhaps a greater measure of success was how eagerly Vietnamese farmers bought up the 1968 IR–8 crop to use as seed for 1969. As of mid-1969, IR–8 was selling at prices well above local varieties, despite the prevailing assumption that traditional varieties were preferred at the dinner table.

Encouraged by this progress, U.S.

advisors recommended a goal of 150,000 hectares for the 1969–70 crop. Vietnamese officials thought they could do better and upped it to 200,000 hectares—9 percent of the rice land.

IR–8 probably added 100,000 tons of paddy to Vietnam's 1968 rice output. But this contribution was more than offset by drought, which reduced total output to 4.4 million tons compared to the 1963 peak of 5.3 million. Thus until very recently the Vietnam program had not significantly affected total rice availability.

By early 1970, however, a substantial impact was evident. Accepting the program's yield assumptions, achievement of the 200,000 hectare target could be expected to increase production an additional 470,000 tons. This, supplemented by expanded fertilizer use on Vietnamese rice varieties and a more decent break from the weather, would bring the 1969–70 crop over the 5-million-ton mark.

Apparently this has happened. Official reports indicate that IR–8 plantings passed the 200,000 hectare mark by February 1970. The 1969–70 crop was estimated at 5.1 million tons, with some experts believing actual production was higher. Further advances of comparable magnitude could well accomplish the program goal of restoring rice self-sufficiency by 1971.

If ultimately successful, this production revolution will be a striking demonstration of the effectiveness of the "crop program" approach to agricultural development—organizing needed inputs and services around a specific crop production program, with clear acreage and input and output targets, and strong support of national political leaders from the top on down.

The achievement will be all the greater in the light of several serious program limitations:

• The technological base of the program has been very thin—with only two rice varieties, neither of them exhaustively tested in Vietnam before the general program dependent on them was adopted. Moreover, though other new varieties are rapidly being perfected by IRRI and various Asian national research agencies, virtually no effective high-yielding rice varietal development work is being done within Vietnam.

• The supply of trained manpower to carry out the program has been limited. Provincial technicians were substantially upgraded by the National Rice Production Training Center which began operations in April 1968 (500 were trained in a bit over a year), but the expansion of Vietnam's military draft pulled a large number of trained technicians away from agricultural work.

• Little effective work has been done to improve water control and management, a factor which will become crucial once the lands suitable to IR–8/5 are exhausted. There seems to be room to expand high-yielding rice plantings to at least 500,000 hectares, but most of Vietnam's rice land needs better water control and/or irrigation.

• Government price policy has not been a consistently favorable influence on the program to date. Rice prices rose sharply in early 1967 due to speculators' activities at a time when Vietnam had relatively low reserves. But in early 1968—one of the crucial periods for the program—paddy prices were depressed. They began to rise in August 1968, however, and the price in 1969 has become more and more attractive from the farmer's point of view.

Part of the price increase in 1969 was without a doubt encouraged by a movement of Vietnam Government policies away from exclusive emphasis on subsidizing urban consumers toward recognizing the importance of farm incentives. More recently it became to some extent a repeat of the early 1967 situation, with below-average stocks combining with speculators' activities to drive prices up quite sharply, so that the September 1969 level was virtually double that of the year's beginning. Prices continued to increase through the remainder of 1969, but dropped sharply early this year as the new harvest came in.

In late 1969 also, high-level Vietnam support seemed to be developing for a general rice price support and stabilization program which would guarantee farmers a minimum return.

The program thus far has been unusually effective through focusing on areas of immediate importance. Future progress will inevitably require more long-range planning. There will be need to broaden the research base, to expand the area amenable to high-yield agriculture through improved water control, and to strengthen Vietnamese extension and credit institutions to serve farmers who will grow ever more demanding as they further intensify their production techniques.

There will be also the problems of handling the increased amount of rice entering the market. Increased output will place a heavy strain on marketing machinery, including storage and drying facilities, and may well have unfavorable price effects in certain areas. Another question is how Vietnamese consumers will react to IR–8 when it enters their market on a significant scale.

A particularly crucial point will come if Vietnam moves past self-sufficiency and produces an exportable surplus. It is questionable whether she can compete in a world where other Asian countries are also exploiting IR–8's potential. The alternative is crop diversification—fortunately both the Government of Vietnam and the AID specialists are increasingly concerned with this problem.

The longer range political impact of the rice revolution is more difficult to judge. IR–8 is clearly popular with farmers, and to this degree the Vietnam Government is the gainer. Whether it will remain so when some of the "second generation" problems cited above are encountered is another question.

Much may depend on how well the Vietnamese Government can implement the sweeping "Land to the Tiller" bill enacted this year after 8 months of debate.

THE U.S. EXTENDS A HAND TO OUR BROTHERS SOUTH OF THE BORDER

THROUGHOUT THE 1960's, the U.S. Government gave substantial support to efforts to improve Brazilian agriculture. Scientists, administrators, technicians, and material and financial resources were provided through the Alliance for Progress, the Agency for International Development (AID), and the Food for Peace program. Their work shows, broadly, how the United States is helping other Latin American countries stimulate progress in rural areas.

The flow of ideas and help from the United States really began in the 19th century. It went on in a random manner but at an increasing rate through the first half of the 20th century. Migrant southern planters after the Civil War, agricultural scientists in the 1920's and 1930's, American firms which established branches in Brazil, and Brazilian youth coming to the United States for college and postgraduate training were some of the channels through which adaptable agricultural techniques were transferred.

After World War II, and especially in the 1960's, the flow of assistance increased greatly and was organized more purposefully.

Between the end of World War II and the beginning of the 1960's the Brazilian Government itself had established many programs of the kind

✦

AUTHOR LOUIS F. HERRMANN retired in 1970 as a staff assistant to the Administrator, Economic Research Service.

that have helped farmers so well in the United States. It had started new schools and colleges, experiment stations, extension services, agricultural credit agencies and assistance to farmer cooperatives, and was planning to expand these and establish others: new credit services, market news and economic information, land settlement and agrarian reform. The United States was asked to help.

The U.S. Department of Agriculture (USDA) sent a team in 1963 to study Brazil's needs. They found many problems, which had been recognized for a long time. Among them were low productivity of crops and animals; pockets of rural poverty, like Brazil's Northeast where too many people were crowded onto poor and periodically drought-stricken land; and a marketing system that was not keeping up with the population as it grew and crowded into industrial centers.

With these findings before them, officials of the Brazilian Government,

Brazilian farmers keep transistor radio tuned for market news reports as they work.

the U.S. AID Mission to Brazil, and USDA agreed on a number of things that the Agriculture Department could do to help. By early 1966 several teams of USDA specialists were in Brazil, working shoulder to shoulder with Brazilians in a variety of activities.

One of the first results of this Brazilian-U.S. cooperation was a market news service. Inaugurated in 1966, it gathers and disseminates price and other market information for farm products in Brazil's most important markets—Sao Paulo, Rio de Janeiro, and Belo Horizonte.

To help this market news service get started and staffed with skilled market reporters, two specialists of USDA's market news service went to Brazil, one for 4 years and one for 2 years. Brazilians were brought to the United States for training and to observe our market news system at work. They returned to apply what they learned in the United States to conditions in their own markets.

Along with these infusions of outside know-how, the Brazilian-American market news team quickly began to solve problems unique to Brazilian markets, enabling Brazil's market news system to serve and grow on its own momentum.

The Brazilian market news service was, by 1970, a sound and growing institution. Observing it, one might not suspect that it had passed through dark days, weeks, and months when its life hung by one thread or another.

Despite many obstacles, the service has grown. Financial problems were resolved and facilities enlarged. By 1969 three more major markets had been added to the network—Curitiba, Porto Alegre, and Recife—and two were being readied for service— Fortaleza and Salvador.

Market reports from the service were reaching users through many of Brazil's some 200 daily newspapers, 1,000 radio stations, and 100 television stations. The news covers fruits, vegetables, grain, cattle, hogs, poultry, and meat.

Producers and merchandisers of these products now have timely information about prices and market conditions to help them decide what, when, and where to plant, harvest, and sell.

At the marketing stage, especially, such information helps shippers to take full advantage of the flexibility afforded by Brazil's improving highway and railroad networks. Fewer producers receive less, and fewer consumers pay more, than is reasonable in relation to general supply and demand conditions.

Assistance to cooperatives was another important field in which USDA's know-how was made available to Brazil, and where rapid advances were achieved.

USDA's Farmer Cooperative Service provided four men to help full time in the Brazilian effort. Others went to Brazil to give spot help for a few weeks or months at a time. Principal goal of this work was to improve the organization, operation, and services of cooperatives, and to improve the capability of Federal and State institutions so they could assume more aggressive leadership in developing stronger programs of assistance to cooperatives and their members.

The USDA team coordinated its work through INDA (National Institute for Agricultural Development) and State governments such as the Department of Assistance to Cooperatives. In addition, team members working with Brazilian technicians contacted hundreds of individual cooperatives and helped them solve many pressing problems.

At the time this program started in 1965, very few projects were being conducted in Brazil to help cooperatives in educational, technical assistance, and research problems. In fact, Federal and State governments had few technicians qualified to plan and conduct programs of assistance to cooperatives.

Thus, it was necessary to impress upon government institutions the importance that properly organized and operated cooperatives could play in agricultural and community development, and the need for action and leadership in providing and coordinating educational, technical, and research services to cooperatives during their early developmental years. Cooperatives not only needed such services to develop more rapidly and soundly but they had no other place in Brazil to obtain them.

The Brazilian institutions responded well to new ideas and challenges and, with the advice and assistance of the USDA advisors, accomplished many worthwhile projects. Some of the most important are:

• Comprehensive cooperative training courses of from 2 to 3 months were developed, and more than 100 technicians from Federal and State agencies and cooperatives trained. In addition, some 35 government workers and cooperative officials were brought to the United States to observe and study how our cooperatives are organized, financed, managed, and operated— and to gather ideas from seeing the many ways cooperatives serve their members in the United States.

• A permanent center for cooperative studies and training was established in Campinas.

• About 800 managers, directors, accountants, and other leaders from cooperatives were given 1 to 2 weeks training.

• Five coordinating councils of agencies that serve cooperatives at State levels were organized to help coordinate and strengthen the activities of the several agencies and avoid undue duplication of efforts.

• About 450 agricultural youth received training for 1 year in agricultural production, marketing, and cooperatives.

• Members of 35 cooperatives received full-time veterinary and agronomy services through contractual arrangements with INDA.

• A cooperative journal was established and printed monthly by INDA in the State of Parana, and numerous campaigns promoting cooperatives were conducted at State and local levels.

As a result of these and other projects, INDA generated considerable enthusiasm over co-op activities and had a strong desire for continued assistance from USDA through USAID/Brazil. As such, it requested that the USAID/USDA cooperative project not only be continued but expanded into other States by requesting a total of 10 cooperative advisors to assist in planning and executing cooperative activities in the future.

Brazil asked for help in improving credit services to farmers. Here again, the U.S. experience had been impressive: that of starting a specialized system of credit for farmers with capital supplied by the Government, and transforming it into a largely farmer-owned system with all the Government capital repaid. This had a special appeal in Brazil, where there is a desire for individual freedom and independence not unlike that in the United States.

U.S. advisors helped plan for wider use of supervised credit in Brazil. Many farmers there are sadly handicapped for lack of education, and supervised credit helps them use their loans more productively.

Brazil is encouraging all its banks to make more loans to farmers. At least 10 percent of their deposits must be loaned to farmers, or redeposited with the Central Bank for discounting other agricultural loans.

The task of defining loans which would meet this requirement was difficult, and U.S. credit specialists helped. Also, many banks began lending to farmers for the first time, and their officers had much to learn about financing agriculture. Training schools with 2-week sessions were held throughout the country so officers of rural banks could improve their ability to serve clients.

The activities just described— market news, cooperatives, and credit—are only part of the story. One could write similar accounts about USDA help with Brazil's minimum price program; the survey of land resources in Brazil's vast interior which to date is largely untapped for its rich resources for agriculture and industry; crop estimates; and economic analysis and improvement of marketing facilities.

From 1964 to 1969, 26 technicians each worked 2 years or more in Brazil, and 37 had one or more shorter assignments in the country. Hundreds of Brazilians were brought to the United States to study or to get ideas which might help them solve their country's problems.

Food for Peace, administered jointly by the Agriculture Department and AID, sold Brazil more than half a billion dollars worth of wheat, fats and oils, and dairy products between 1954 and 1968 on more liberal terms than commercial sources offered. Another $140 million worth of food was donated for relief and economic development.

Brazil paid for most of the purchase in its own currency. Much of this currency was then loaned to the Brazilian Government or given as grants for economic development. Some was kept by the United States for paying its own expenses in Brazil.

Food for Peace feed grains helped farm supply cooperatives establish mixed feed departments. This in turn gave farmers better feeds and encouraged increased production of livestock products needed to upgrade the Brazilian diet.

Funds from Food for Peace sales were lent to Brazilian credit agencies, and from them to farmers. One such loan was made especially to help farmers use more fertilizer.

Another Food for Peace loan provided capital for special credit programs through selected banks in the commercial banking system. The banks in turn made loans to farmers under strict rules to keep the cost of credit within farmers' ability to pay. Some of the credit was earmarked for medium- and long-term loans, which, because of inflation, farmers had been unable to get for several decades.

One of the most significant donations under the Food for Peace program helped Brazil start one of the largest and most successful school lunch programs in the world. Food for Peace commodities in 1968 helped feed nine million children in more than 90,000 schools.

What has been exciting about school lunches is the way Brazil has made the program its own. It began with 40,000 tons of nonfat dry milk from the United States in 1962, and ran at first as a small, centrally organized operation.

By 1969 it had grown to involve national officials, mayors, educators, State governors, private businessmen, and the military, not to mention innumerable enthusiastic parents in all 22 States, three territories, and the Federal district.

Food for Peace commodities for the school lunch program in 1968 amounted to 105,000 tons, worth some $7 million, but food purchases by Federal, State and local Brazilian governments came to about $55 million. Many Brazilian firms donated equipment and supplies.

Throughout the country, towns and villages were encouraged to improve local warehouse and transportation facilities, engage in community activities with school lunch and nutrition themes, adopt laws and administrative codes to establish uniform local programs and expand local contributions, increase local purchases of foods and serving equipment, take part in training programs, and improve local planning.

Long after the last shipment of Food for Peace has been distributed in Brazil, the National Campaign for School Feeding will go on contributing to the health and educational achievements of Brazilian youth.

American universities joined in the effort to help Brazilian agriculture, at the request of the Brazilian Government and USAID.

North Carolina State University helped establish a system of soil testing laboratories in Brazil as in other Latin American countries. Because Brazil's soils frequently respond poorly to applications of fertilizer, soil testing to tell the farmer what and how much fertilizer he can afford to use is doubly important.

Mississippi State University took part in a program to assure farmers a more dependable supply of high quality seeds. Michigan State University looked into marketing problems in the Northeast, and Auburn University advised on fish production.

Several American universities supplied professors to Brazilian universities, and worked alongside Brazilian colleagues to bring that country's teaching and research to new peaks of serviceability to students and farmers. Arizona State, Ohio State, Purdue and Wisconsin Universities paired off with Brazilian universities in the States of Ceara, Sao Paulo, Minas Gerais, and Rio Grande do Sul.

The work of USDA and the universities is helping Brazil achieve long-range goals. It is equipping institutions to provide a continuing flow of highly trained scientists and administrators to work in schools, on farms, and in government positions. It is preparing institutions and people to develop the new knowledge that is needed if Brazil is to achieve its full potential for progress.

A Look into the Future

TECHNOLOGIES FOR TOMORROW

AGRICULTURE in the United States, in fact in all of North America and in many other parts of the world, has historically served two purposes. It has primarily served as a way of life; secondarily it has served as an enterprise with a profit motive.

In recent years the emphasis has changed. In the upcoming years of the 1970's and beyond, changes will continue more rapidly toward making agriculture and its many specialized forms into increasingly profitable businesses.

These enterprises will have many of the characteristics of nonagricultural business operations. They may be independently owned or managed units or they may be parts of large and diverse product businesses.

Some may specialize in certain crops, as for instance wheat on acreages from Texas to Canada, to reduce hazards of weather and to increase use of highly productive equipment. Others may enter all phases of production, processing, and marketing as in the production of feed for dairy cows and the processing of milk and the various products of milk for consumer markets. Their major objective will be rapidly increasing productivity of all the related essential resources.

Achievement of this objective will be measured primarily in profits from producing and distributing the foods, fibers, and products basic to processing for further industrial and consumer uses in response to continually growing demands throughout the world.

Profits will be the main criterion of these businesses but they will also increasingly measure their success in terms of socially healthful operations and other forms of social good that go well beyond their immediate self interests.

For most of the history of the United States, and still reflected in our Federal and State governments, agriculture has been considered as a single, monolithic industry. Nothing could be further from the truth.

The diversity of our agricultural legislation and regulations and the numerous farming operations have made clear that agriculture represents many interests—many industries—with many competing products whose producers obviously have competing or dissimilar interests.

This diverse and internally competitive nature of agriculture is nowhere more apparent than in the impacts of newer, better, or more economical products, practices, and forms of organization. This was sharply focused a few years ago in the butter-margarine contest. Such contests are now more frequent and take many forms due to new findings related to our human, social, and economic health.

Meat and dairy product producers, for example, have been challenged by controversial findings indicating the damaging effects of high levels of cholesterol in contributing to the incidence of heart attacks.

Users of some chemicals, both fertilizers and insecticides, are finding them socially undesirable and humanly detrimental.

Agricultural producers who are imaginative and responsive are altering their products and practices to meet new findings.

Those who are not responsive are following the defensive and undoubtedly losing path so common in the butter-margarine contest.

✦

AUTHOR LESTER S. KELLOGG, a consulting economist, is former Corporate Economist for Deere & Company. He resides at Tryon, N.C.

COAUTHOR BERNARD A. EVERETT is an economist in the Market Economics Department at Deere & Company, Moline, Ill.

Development of synthetic or non-agricultural substitutes for agricultural products may also have reduced the monolithic character of agriculture.

Manmade fibers, for instance, have taken a large share of cotton's former market, forcing new developments in the processing of the natural fiber and freeing land once used for this fiber for use of other crops.

Not only crop geography but livestock geography as well has been affected. There is, for instance, an increasing amount of successful feeding of cattle in areas of the South formerly used for cotton.

The shifting geography of soybean production along with its important intraagriculture competitive impacts—including the development of high protein substitutes for meat and drying oils for industrial products—give further evidence of the increasing diversity of interests represented by what we call "agriculture."

These types of developments will continue to occur, probably with an increasing frequency and with a wider range of impacts upon previously established agriculture: its products, its practices, and its technologies. Such developments naturally raise many new uncertainties and hazards for agriculturists.

Major readjustments in crops produced and resources used require more capital and new product and market knowledge than is quickly available to a traditional multicrop operator. Such impacts require broad-scale decision making, financial planning, long-range forecasting and projections, and even market research, seldom used by even the medium to large size agricultural units in the past.

In this broad sense there is scarcely any limit to the technologies with which the producer of products from and on the soil must be acquainted. The impacts of this responsibility will themselves provide the foundation of many of the changes that will and must take place in agriculture. Basic characteristics of these changes have in recent years become fairly obvious.

• The number of agricultural business units will continue to decline during the 1970's—from just under 3 million today to perhaps little more than 1.5 million. There will be fewer opportunities in agriculture for individuals to own and operate their own businesses. But there will be increased opportunity to participate as specialists in broadly based business units with agricultural interests.

• Agricultural business units will get larger in acres used—probably nearly doubling in average size during the decade. Increases in physical output, value of production, and capital used will keep pace with the increase in size. Many more units will gross in the hundreds of thousands to millions of dollars.

• Employment in agricultural business units directly will continue to decline to perhaps one-half of the approximately 4 million workers at present. This will be offset in part by increased employment in supportive supplying, servicing, marketing, and distributing industries.

• Agricultural enterprises, such as beef or corn production, will become more highly specialized. But such businesses may actually become more diversified functionally by bringing specialized producing, distributing, servicing, and research enterprises together under one management.

• Management abilities will become more important for heads of agricultural businesses than knowledge or training in specific agricultural fields.

• Productivity per man-hour of employment in agriculture will probably increase during the decade to more than double the present level, with provision of more capital per worker, new breeds, new and better practices, and more efficient and less dangerous chemicals.

• Avenues of financing will broaden, leaving further behind the old country lane that led to the local bank and traditional roads of debt financing. Financing through sale of shares to the public will become increasingly common.

In the 1970's, the changes suggested above will continue at greater speeds than in the past.

The speed of change will vary by crops, areas, types of ownership, age, and other characteristics of agricultural leaders, excellence of management, and access to necessary capital. They will also vary depending upon whether future legislative policies are forward looking and adaptive or protective and restraining.

The agricultural industry emerging from these changes will differ greatly from that which characterized the birth and formative periods of our country's growth.

Now for the developing technologies with which the changing agriculture of tomorrow must deal:

Land and Water. The United States is a favored nation in the whole world for the extent and quality of its agricultural "green belt."

To retain this favored position requires both new technologies and the practice of those already proved beneficial.

To improve the fertility of our soils without at the same time increasing the pollution of our water supply will require special attention to current practices of "responsible" agricultural producers.

Larger area operating units may lead to larger and more compatible soil and water conservation technology and practice.

There is something to be said for getting "big enough," in terms of business size, to be able to assume citizenship responsibilities beyond the self-interests of the business.

Manpower. "Farmwork" historically has involved long hours, with uncertain seasonal schedules, and drudgery to the point of enslavement to an enterprise, at lower rates of pay than any other employment. In a modern "full-employment" economy, agricultural enterprises must develop means of paying wages—direct and fringe benefits—and providing working conditions competitive with or better than other industries in order to have a dependable and better than submarginal work force.

Labor must be held responsible, with the increased capital provided, for obtaining increasingly greater output per man-hour of work.

The nature and value of capital equipment furnished by agriculture, already higher than in any other industry, must increase to take full advantage of old technologies and adapt to new ones. Manpower to operate this more sophisticated capital equipment must be better educated and better managed. Managers must learn the technologies involved in working with trade unions—collective bargaining, strike strategy, grievance procedures.

Capital Equipment. As the production of food and fiber becomes more specialized and is profitable, the necessary new capital equipment including special purpose equipment employing the many facets of new knowledge and technology will become available. Simultaneously there will certainly be interacting developments by plant breeders and machine and equipment designers which will save labor, improve products, and also increase productivity.

The trends in these directions have been apparent for a number of years—tomato harvesting is one of the most widely recognized examples.

Potential profits are essential, however, to guarantee development of such equipment.

Some crops, traditionally requiring a high labor input per unit of output, must be increasingly mechanized or automated and new strains of plants permitting easier cultivation and harvesting developed or these crops will disappear from our country.

Decision Making. The new era of electronic data processing (EDP) is a godsend—a natural for agricultural enterprises. There is scarcely another industry in which the number of variables to be taken into account in decision making is as great as in agriculture.

Since many of the variables are

similar for a wide range of crops, although they may differ in dimension, large computer programs may be widely applicable.

To utilize fully the potentials of EDP, however, individual farm businesses must develop much better and more detailed data pertaining to their production and marketing activities. The output of computers can be no better than the information inputs.

With the rapidly expanding variety of hardware (computing equipment) and software (computer programing services) in prospect, such resources are becoming increasingly accessible to small, medium, and large agricultural enterprises at reasonable rates.

Agricultural enterprises offer great potentials for the future by making effective use of the rapidly developing management skills, and the opportunities for obtaining necessary operating capital through share ownership. The ownership of shares and debts, through bonds and debentures, outside the immediate membership of a single family will add economy and financial stability.

Even the increasing inclusion of agricultural enterprises in conglomerate business structures may become both financially possible and cconomically desirable.

Systems Approach. The term "system" means the taking into account simultaneously and continuously, as situations change, of all of the steps of a productive process, from the initial and simplest input to the finished product, including sale, marketing, and storing, plus the knowledge and information gained in carrying out the process.

The recent emphasis on "systems" approaches largely results from the capacity of computers to aid in analyzing feedback information of large and complex systems and to yield the kinds of information that decision makers need to control them.

Decision making has always involved consideration of many variables, usually more than the capacity of the human mind.

The major contribution of the computer is its built-in capacity to handle very large numbers of variables and extensive information about each of them, well beyond human capacity. For example, linear programing solutions involving thousands of variables and hundreds of restrictions are now possible.

This unique characteristic of the computer makes possible the analysis of a whole system at one time. The system can be as broad as the ability and imagination of the decision maker to conceive it. This has not previously been possible.

Among illustrations related to systems the following two may be suggestive.

In a recent advertisement one of the old and highly productive corporations in the United States said:

"(We) realize that today, machines have reached a point of diminishing returns. Refinements to existing designs can still be made. But major breakthroughs are increasingly difficult. So instead of building individual machines to perform individual tasks, (we) decided to concentrate on an exciting new approach: The Productivity System.

"The system would include not only machines to do the work, but also the materials handling; chemicals, fasteners, and adhesives to be used in the process; as well as the computers to control the overall complex. Ultimately, the system will take basic materials in one end and feed finished products out of the other.

"That in essence, is the idea behind the second industrial revolution. To help you manufacture more or less by means of a complete productivity system.

"It won't happen all at once. But it will happen."

It's easy for you to react by saying "maybe this can happen in manufacturing but it can't happen in agriculture." The fact is that it is already happening in agriculture; specifically in the production of eggs, broilers, and pork.

Appropriate systems of processes will be extended and initiated in other parts of agriculture as fast as imagination, ingenuity, and capital can be combined to attain an economical "complete productivity system."

The second brief illustration adds another dimension to the "systems" approach.

Ray F. Smith, in his article on "Integrated Control of Insects," published in Agricultural Science Review, Vol. 7, No. 1, First Quarter 1969, at page 2, says:

". . . it should be clear that all aspects of the agro-ecosystem must be considered simultaneously in the development of sound protection."

By way of definition he says:

"The term, agro-ecosystem, refers to a unit composed of the total complex of organisms in a crop area together with the overall conditioning environment and as further modified by the various agricultural, industrial, recreational, and social activities of man.

"Thus, agro-ecosystems are a part of the man-altered landscape modified and controlled for the production of agricultural and forest crops. Man and his civilization are dependent upon reaping a harvest from these systems."

Don't stop here and say "This is pretty far out and not for me." It is for you, if you are an agriculturist. It is for all leaders and participants in agriculture in a responsible, competitive, free enterprise economy. It is for everyone who is seeking highest returns in terms of least total economic and social cost, reasonable profits, and who operates as nearly as possible according to a complete productivity system.

Technologies touching many facets of business activity are already developed well beyond those now widely used in the agricultural industry. Technologies applied to many facets of agriculture as a modern industry are well advanced for use in the 1970's. They will be developed further ahead for great productivity as fast as the industry will make use of them.

BETTER CEREALS SOUGHT IN FIGHT AGAINST WORLD HUNGER PROBLEM

PRODUCTIVE CEREALS with more and better protein are on plant breeding drawing boards. Some agricultural research teams are betting that such cereals will be a key to solution of the world's hunger problem.

Two billion or roughly two-thirds of the world's people depend upon rice and wheat as their basic food. Add to these the millions who rely upon maize (we call it corn), sorghum, rye, or millet and you have some idea of the importance of the food from this group of crop plants.

At least one of the cereals can be grown successfully anywhere in the world where the climate will support crop production. Rice, maize, sorghum, and millet are found from the tropics to the temperate regions. Wheat, rye, barley, and oats extend from the subtropics to the northern latitudes. Wheat has a particularly broad range of adaptation.

Cereal grains are an inexpensive source of both carbohydrate and protein. Their importance as a protein source is not well recognized by people in developed countries where meat, animal products, and a wide array of other foods are readily available. Yet more protein and essential amino acids can be produced from wheat on an acre of land than from livestock on the same land. Meat and animal products to satisfy the major portion of protein needs of people may be a luxury that few developing countries can afford.

The cereals, particularly wheat and rice, have been prized as food since early in recorded civilization. They are well established in the eating habits of people. Substitution of new unfamiliar foods, however nutritious, encounters a strong resistance, even among the malnourished. Cereals with improved nutritional value, then, would have distinctive acceptance advantages over unfamiliar replacement foods.

There are acute shortages of both carbohydrates and protein on a world scale. The protein problem is considered the more serious, although it cannot be treated independently.

Carbohydrates can be considered fuel for the body. They provide the energy needed for work and physical activities. In contrast, protein is necessary for tissue synthesis and body growth.

Protein malnutrition has particularly serious implications for the very young because of its effect on early brain development.

Unfortunately, the protein requirement of a person cannot be satisfied without also providing his minimal carbohydrate needs. This is because protein will be utilized for energy instead of growth if there is insufficient carbohydrate in the diet. Improved productivity of the cereal grains, therefore, is basic to their nutritional improvement.

Breeders have achieved spectacular successes in increasing yields of the cereal crops. The impact of hybrid maize and sorghum on the productivity of these cereals is a matter of record. In the United States the average corn yield rose from 28 bushels per acre in 1940 to 78 in 1968. Sorghum yields jumped from 20 bushels per acre in 1954 to 60 in 1968.

Maximum wheat yields now have been pushed above the 200 bushel per acre mark in the United States.

✦

AUTHOR VIRGIL A. JOHNSON is Research Agronomist, Crops Research Division, Agricultural Research Service, and Professor of Agronomy, University of Nebraska, Lincoln.

Average wheat yields in Mexico rose from approximately 11 bushels per acre in 1945 to 41 bushels per acre in 1967. Mexico has been self-sufficient in wheat production since 1956.

New highly productive dwarf wheat and rice varieties that respond to fertilizer, water, and improved farming practices are revolutionizing production in India, Pakistan, Iran, Iraq, and Turkey. It is predicted that these countries, where population long ago overran food production, can become self-sufficient in wheat as did Mexico.

Cereal breeders and production specialists are demonstrating that enough cereal grains to feed hungry people can be grown. Many are now turning their attention to the job of improving the nutritional quality of cereals. It is a significant development and a logical second step to the production advances. There have already been some notable successes.

Protein consists of many amino acids which serve as building blocks for the body. All proteins are not the same for they may vary in number and quantity of amino acids.

Of the known amino acids, eight are considered essential in human diets because they must be present in the food eaten. The body cannot synthesize these amino acids as it can the others.

Maximum utilization of protein by a person can occur only when the eight essential amino acids are present in the protein consumed in approximately the relative amounts required by the body. Protein also varies in digestibility according to source as well as composition.

The high nutritional value of meat and animal products stems from the fact that the essential amino acids are present in approximately the required ratio, and digestibility of the protein is high.

Cereal proteins contain all eight essential amino acids but not in the amounts needed for maximum utilization of the protein. The amino acid lysine is in shortest supply in all cereals and has received the most attention thus far by cereal researchers. Some other amino acids also are a problem. In ordinary maize tryptophan is in short supply, while in wheat and rice it is threonine and methionine.

The question confronting cereal breeders is whether different strains or varieties of a cereal are inherently different in the amount of protein they produce or in amino acid composition of the protein. In order to breed varieties with more or better protein, such genetic or inherited differences must be present in the cereal species.

Little was known in 1950. Investigators at the University of Illinois had conducted long-time selection experiments beginning near the turn of the century with open pollinated maize to see if they could increase its protein content. They were successful in increasing crude protein from the usual 11 percent to about 20 percent, but the extremely poor quality of the protein and low productivity of the high protein selections discouraged others from pursuing the work.

Concerted efforts to increase the protein content of wheat by breeding trace to 1954. At that time, Gordon K. Middleton, Charles E. Bode, and Burton B. Bayles reported that the soft wheat varieties Atlas 50 and Atlas 66 released by the North Carolina Experiment Station in 1949 were significantly higher in protein than other soft wheat varieties. Evidence pointed to the Brazilian variety Frondoso, a parent of the Atlas wheats, as the donor of genes for high protein.

This finding stimulated Agricultural Research Service (ARS) and State wheat researchers at the University of Nebraska to embark upon a cooperative wheat protein research project in 1954 that has continued without interruption since that time.

Only limited laboratory facilities were available for wheat protein research at the university. The Nebraska Wheat Commission comprised of wheat farmers provided needed initial financial assistance. Not only did the commission support the research but it provided funds to establish and equip a wheat quality laboratory that has since been the focal point of the research.

Our cooperative ARS-Nebraska effort helped clarify several wheat protein questions. We now know that higher protein in wheat is heritable and can be transferred readily from one variety to another. The Atlas 66 genes promote two to three percent more actual protein in most production and soil fertility situations.

We have not found it possible to fix wheat protein at a predetermined level by breeding because of the strong effect of growing conditions on level of protein. High protein can best be achieved by the use of high protein varieties combined with timely heavy applications of nitrogen fertilizer.

We also determined that amino acid balance in high protein lines from Atlas 66 crosses was not adversely affected. The relative amounts of essential amino acids in the protein of several lines remained about the same as in other varieties. This meant that lysine, threonine, and methionine could be increased merely by making the protein content of wheat higher.

Other sources of high protein in wheat have been uncovered. In 1965, Harry McNeal, ARS wheat breeder at Montana State University, tentatively identified three wheats from the World Collection as high protein types. One of these, the Brazilian variety Frontiera, probably possesses the same protein genes as Frondoso. The other two varieties were from Africa and India.

In 1963 we crossed the spring variety Aniversario from Argentina with a hard winter variety and identified high protein lines among the progeny of the cross. A fertility-restoring experimental wheat used in the Nebraska hybrid program also appears to possess high protein genes.

Crosses among these different high protein wheats may push the grain protein level even higher than is now possible with Atlas 66.

A tremendously significant breakthrough in the improvement of the nutritional quality of cereal protein occurred in 1963. The Purdue University research team of Oliver E. Nelson, Edwin T. Mertz, and Lynn Bates produced the first evidence of large genetic differences in amino acid composition of cereal protein.

They discovered that an old maize strain known to breeders as opaque-2 because of its chalky textured grain was twice as high in lysine and tryptophan as ordinary maize. For the first time, a maize that possessed protein with relatively well balanced amino acid composition had been identified. Was it actually as good nutritionally as chemical analyses indicated? The answer was soon forthcoming.

Opaque-2 stocks were quickly distributed to researchers in several countries and nutritional experiments organized. When diets in which opaque-2 was the only source of protein were given to children suffering from Kwashiorkor, a serious protein deficiency disease in Latin America, the disease symptoms disappeared. Ordinary maize had been the main food for many of the afflicted children.

The high lysine opaque-2 maize was comparable to skim milk in nutritional value. No cereal had ever rated so high before. Here was a grain that held out hope of life and health for countless millions of people in Latin countries for whom maize is the most common food!

The high lysine find triggered further intensive nutritional research efforts in maize as well as in the other cereals. The Purdue team soon identified a second maize strain called floury-2 as also having high lysine properties. The search of germ plasm collections of other cereals was begun. There have already been some exciting finds.

Discovery of a high protein wild oat species from the Mediterranean region was reported by the U.S. Department of Agriculture in 1967. It produces grain with 30 percent protein, compared to 18 to 19 percent in the best commercial oat varieties. It is not yet known whether the high protein content can be bred into plump-seeded commercial varieties.

The Swedish Seed Association of Svalof, Sweden, and USDA jointly announced in 1969 the discovery of a high protein-high lysine barley variety. It has been appropriately named "Hyproly". The lysine content of Hyproly, a hull-less, wrinkled-seeded variety, is 20 to 30 percent higher than ordinary barley varieties. It is already being studied extensively in barley breeding programs throughout the world.

The ARS-Nebraska research team is screening the USDA World Collection of wheats. Since 1967 we have measured the protein and lysine content of 15,000 strains. This work is supported in part by funds from the Agency for International Development, U.S. Department of State.

Wide differences in both protein and lysine have been detected. Lysine ordinarily constitutes about three percent of wheat protein. We have analyzed samples with over four percent lysine. Our wheat effort is closely coordinated with the International Wheat and Corn Improvement Center (CIMMYT), Mexico City.

An international winter wheat performance nursery was organized by the ARS-Nebraska group in 1968 to evaluate winter wheats with unusual yield and nutritional properties on an international scale. It is grown in 26 different countries. A similar international nursery in spring wheat, initiated by Norman E. Borlaug of the Rockefeller Foundation in 1960, was instrumental in early identification of the varieties that are now revolutionizing wheat production in India and Pakistan.

Work on nutritional improvement of rice is underway in several countries. The International Rice Research Institute (IRRI) in the Philippines has utilized worldwide germ plasm in a concerted effort to improve rice agronomically and nutritionally.

As with wheat, new stiff strawed varieties that can tolerate heavy fertilization and produce high yields are making an impact in the rice producing countries. Protein and lysine differences have been identified which are being evaluated for their usefulness in rice breeding programs.

A sorghum research program directed by Robert C. Pickett at Purdue University has uncovered substantial variations in protein level and amount of lysine among the sorghums. This work has financial support from the Agency for International Development. Potentially useful variations in sorghum protein also are reported by the Rockefeller Foundation and from India. Yellow endosperm sorghums from Africa have been found to be high in vitamin A.

Development of a new cereal crop called Triticale has aroused worldwide interest since 1967. Triticale was created from two different cereals, wheat (*Triticum aestivum* L. or *T. Durum* Desf.) and rye (*Secale cereale* L.). Its name is based on the names of the parent species.

Triticale was initially a biological curiosity but chromosome juggling in university laboratories around the world resulted in a new crop type that may be superior to either parent species.

New lines emanating mostly from research at the University of Manitoba at Winnipeg, Canada, and CIMMYT have given new hope for success of this new crop. The lines show promise of high yields of grain with protein content equal to or higher than wheat.

There is no longer much question that large differences in amount and composition of protein exist in all cereal species. Opaque-2 maize, Hyproly barley, and Atlas 66 wheat provide ample evidence. Now it remains for cereal breeders to build new varieties that are nutritionally better than the old ones. The task is not easy but the stakes are high. The past record of accomplishments would indicate that cereal breeders can and will meet the challenge.

330

ORGANIZATIONAL AND CONTROL TRENDS IN FOOD SYSTEM

THE NUMBER OF HOURS worked on farms in the United States was reduced by half from 1950 to 1967. If this trend were to continue, there would be *no* work on farms by 1984.

No one expects this to happen, but it does dramatize the changing nature of U.S. food production. At one time, food production was an activity of the farm and household. This is no longer true.

Food production and distribution today make up a complex system involving the combined effort of a very large number of specialists. Farming has become only several steps in an extended sequence of specialized activities.

The farmer acquires a complex set of inputs—seeds, fertilizers, herbicides, machines, technical advice, etc.—and transforms them into products. These products are in turn usually further processed, packaged, and distributed by other specialists.

My intent in this brief discussion is to identify some of the trends and pressures which might give an insight into the future direction of change in the organization and control of the food system. I will concentrate on the vertical relationship between functions in the sequence of production and distribution.

Vertical integration refers to the extent the coordination of a vertical sequence in production and distribution is administrative. Some examples of vertical integration are: feed companies expanding their operations to control broiler and egg production; meat packers and retail food chains engaging in cattle fattening; and vegetable canning companies controlling production of the vegetables they process.

Economic activity is coordinated administratively and through markets. The coordination within a firm is administrative while, in our economy at least, most of the coordination between firms involves some kind of market or bargaining relationship.

Bills have been introduced in Congress limiting vertical integration by large firms in some parts of the agricultural economy. The concern regarding vertical integration seems to be that it threatens to alter the existing economic organization of agriculture, reducing freedom or effective competition.

Perhaps the most significant trend in American agriculture is the increasing scope and complexity of U.S. food systems. The central idea of a system is interdependence. A system is an assemblage of objects or actions united by some form of regular interaction. Agriculture consists of both biological and socio-economic systems.

The central concept of ecology is that the physical environment is a system; that is, a change in one part of the biological environment will affect other parts. In the same sense, economically interdependent activities make up a system.

A combination of science-based technology, with the associated investments in capital goods and specialization of labor, stimulates large scale vertically integrated systems. And it is the development of vertical integration by large firms which creates policy issues. Policy is concerned not directly with vertical integration, but rather with potential concentration and misuse of economic power.

The completely self-sufficient subsistence farm is an example of a fully integrated food system. All steps

✦

AUTHOR JAMES DUNCAN SHAFFER is Professor of Agricultural Economics, Michigan Agricultural Experiment Station, Michigan State University, East Lansing.

in the production and use of food are controlled by a single management. The inputs for every farm enterprise originate within the firm. While fully integrated, the subsistence farm is clearly not what concerns us in terms of economic regulation.

Several decades ago many dairy farms extended their operations to milk processing and delivery. They were, in modern terms, integrated systems. However, they were in no sense fully integrated systems, for many of their inputs were purchased. And, being small scale, no one considered this to be an undesirable combination of activities.

Both specialized labor and equipment create situations whereby, for some combination of economic activities, the costs of production per unit decline as the size of the operation increases. For example, development of machines and equipment for processing and bottling milk enabled large dairy plants to be more efficient than small ones. The result was that processing and retailing by dairy farmers was not competitive with larger specialized firms. In this case, technology reduced the level of vertical integration.

Introduction of the bulk tank into the dairy system illustrates both the impact of a technological change on a system and the fact of interdependence in such systems.

Development of the bulk tank for cooling and holding milk on farms and during transportation offered an opportunity to significantly reduce assembly costs for milk. However, switching from milk cans to a bulk tank system required many changes.

Dairy plants found it necessary to receive large quantities of bulk milk in order to make bulk handling equipment at the plant profitable. Specialized bulk tank trucks had to be used for transportation, again necessitating large volumes for economical use. Thus the system was economical only if large numbers of farmers could convert to farm tanks. Also, a system using both cans and bulk added to the processing and transportation expenses. Small dairy farms could not justify the expense of a bulk tank.

Thus, introduction of the bulk tank required changes in equipment and operating procedures on the farm, in transportation, and in the processing plant. One consequence of this change was a significant reduction in the total number of dairy farms and their related increase in size.

Modern science has introduced the possibility that much more efficient and complex food systems will be designed in the future. Current illustrations indicating possible future directions include the development of new varieties with characteristics compatible with new handling technology.

For example, efficient mechanical harvesting of both pickling cucumbers and processing tomatoes depended upon the development of varieties which produce a uniformly maturing fruit, making a once-over harvest profitable. A significant adjustment in the growing-processing system was required to use this new technology.

Recent development of the cherry harvester is another example of a technical change requiring a significant adjustment in a much larger system. The harvester is a machine which shakes the cherry tree. In order to preserve the quality of the cherries it is necessary to cool them from four to eight hours, immediately after harvest.

This requires that (1) expensive cooling facilities be installed on farms, (2) timing of harvesting and processing be coordinated, and (3) specialized transport methods be used, for the cherries must be shipped in cold water.

A coordinated system has not yet been completely developed. Mechanically harvested cherries are not easily shipped the distances from farm to processor as was common for hand-picked ones. Scheduling has not been worked out, and bottlenecks exist because of a lack of pitting capacity close enough to the areas of production served by suitable transportation.

Cherry processing equipment is relatively inexpensive and is adaptable to small scale operations. An electronic sorter and two pitters will process about what can be harvested by one mechanical harvester.

Since the equipment is highly specialized, it appears feasible to shift the processing to the farm unit. Several large cherry growers have done this, and many more contemplate it because of their inability to adequately coordinate the existing system. An additional incentive is that an expensive scale is required to weigh-in cherries delivered in water, whereas the scale is not required if title to the cherries is not transferred between the farm and processing.

Introduction of the new system is having a very significant effect on the number and size of cherry orchards, greatly increasing the average size.

Large firms, which manufacture farm inputs and process and distribute food, require long-term planning and financing. They have a high incentive to reduce risk. They attempt to reduce risk and expand their sales through promotion.

Successful mass promotion requires that products of highly consistent specification be available in large quantities at predetermined times. Controlling product characteristics and timing between industrialized processes also is necessary to reduce costs. Thus, as the economy becomes more industrialized and productive, we can expect the demand for specification in product characteristics and timing in food production and distribution to increase.

Many firms in the food system extend the scope of their control through contracts. The contract offers a means of coordinating activity between two firms.

Many believe the hog-pork subsector will be integrated through contracts in the not too distant future. A hog-pork system of the future may be designed to specify product characteristics and timing at each step in the production-distribution sequence.

Contracts would control the number and types of hogs bred each period, the feeding practices, weights and age of hogs delivered to the packing plant, and specification on cuts and packages to be delivered on a predetermined schedule to the retail store. Each firm would meet narrow specifications.

Such a system could result in savings in feeding, processing, and storage, and could more accurately reflect consumer preferences and reduce the cyclical variation in pork supplies.

I recall a conversation with the owner of a retail food chain whose image of the future food system was one coordinated by a purchasing organization operated by food retailers. His idea was that all steps in the production and distribution of food would be controlled by contracts specifying product characteristics, timing, prices, etc.

He believed the buying organization could specify every detail from development of the seed to the consumer package. Every factor known to affect quality would be specified. He did not want the buying organization to own the system, but did believe the system could be improved if the retailers controlled it through contracts.

PUTTING WINGS
ON YOUR FOOD

JUICY PINEAPPLES and papayas flown from Hawaii to New York. Red-ripe strawberries and freshly cut flowers, flown from Florida to Chicago. Vine-ripe melons and crisp lettuce, flown from California to Boston. All delivered by air almost overnight.

With the coming of the jumbo jets in the decade ahead, so aptly dubbed the soaring seventies, this vigorous and growing transport technique will help spark a distribution revolution that will give consumers more farm-fresh food at lower cost than ever before. These changes can be expected to enhance the diets of rural and urban consumers alike, while at the same time creating new world-wide marketing opportunities for producers in many rural areas.

Plans for the coming of the big cargo jets are well advanced. The passenger version of the Boeing 747 transport is already flying the airline routes, while the Lockheed L–500, a larger commercial all-cargo version of the U.S. Air Force's C5–A military transport, is in the advanced design stage.

New cargo handling systems are being developed to speed loading and unloading of the huge air freighters and to hurry the shipments through the air cargo terminals. Plans for computerization of the shipping paperwork, and the design of insulated and refrigerated containers to protect the products, are well underway.

Speed, the primary advantage of air transport, greatly reduces transit time—a vitally important factor in the marketing of many agricultural products.

Products shipped by air include commodities which benefit from reduced transit time, either because of their high perishability or because of highly fluid marketing situations. These products are generally high in value in both normal supply and seasonal short supply and can, therefore, bear higher transport costs. Among the products having these characteristics are fruits and vegetables, flowers and nursery stock, poultry and baby chicks, hatching eggs, meat, seafood, some dairy products, and live animals.

Most of these products arrive at their destinations in much better condition and with less loss of quality, lower spoilage rates, and, consequent-

+

AUTHOR PHILIP L. BREAKIRON is Investigations Leader, Transport Techniques, Transportation and Facilities Research Division, Agricultural Research Service.

ly, longer shelf life when shipped by air instead of by surface transport. In many instances, shipment by air is the only way distant shippers can get their products to markets when supplies are scarce and prices high for short periods of time.

Increased speed in transit has opened up new, distant markets to many shippers that were not previously accessible to them by slower surface transport. With faster delivery of their products, shippers and receivers have less capital tied up in products in transit and the shipper's returns from his marketings are speeded. Such savings and flexibility afforded by air transport justify its extra cost in marketing many perishables.

In 1968, domestic airfreight of all types totaled about 1,900 million ton-miles (a ton-mile is 1 ton carried 1 mile). Agricultural products accounted for about a third of this amount, or about 600 million ton miles. Projections show total ton-miles increasing to about 14 billion by 1980. If the proportion of agricultural products shipped by air remains about the same during the coming decade, these commodities will make up almost 5 billion ton-miles of the total annual domestic airfreight by 1980.

Even this projection of future air shipments may be too conservative. Although domestic airfreight of all types is increasing at about 20 percent a year, air shipments of agricultural products have been growing at least twice as fast. All predictions point to continuing dramatic increases in air cargo in the future.

Domestic shipments of fruits and vegetables by air in 1968 totaled 1,161 million pounds, or about 2,904 rail carload equivalents. In terms of traffic volume, this total amounted to about 128 million ton-miles. California alone shipped more than 50 million pounds of fruits and vegetables by air in 1969—an increase of almost 150 percent over the 1965 volume.

It is estimated that about 40 percent of the cut flowers marketed in the United States, or about 63 million bunches valued at $67 million, moved by air in 1968. The bulk of this moved from Hawaii to the mainland or from California, Colorado, and Florida to large eastern and midwestern cities.

Growth of international air traffic in food and other agricultural products is even more impressive than the growth of domestic air traffic in these products. International airfreight of all types totaled about 3,300 million ton-miles in 1968—a sevenfold increase in 10 years. The average annual growth rate has been more than 20 percent in the past 5 years. International air traffic in agricultural products during the past 2 years has increased at a rate of about 45 percent a year.

Major commodities exported from the United States by air include strawberries from California and Florida to European destinations; and hatching eggs, baby chicks, nursery and floral stocks, and some meat products to Europe, South America, and the Far East. Air shipments of strawberries from California to markets in seven European countries in the first 6 months of 1968 totaled almost 2 million pounds. Precut and packaged beef is being shipped by air from the Midwest to European destinations.

Livestock for herd improvement programs abroad also moves by air; 100,000 head of veal calves were shipped from one U.S. air terminal to Italy in one 4-month period. Livestock exported by air from the United States in 1968 was valued at $18 million, 72 percent of which was live poultry and 15 percent live cattle. Even horses are exported by air; shipments valued at $2,184,222 were moved by air in 1968 compared with $421,556 worth by ship.

Imports of agricultural products to the United States by air totaled more than 47.5 million pounds in 1968. Some of the major imports are grapes, mangos, bananas, papayas, plantains, and fish and other seafood.

Most agricultural products being shipped by air possess a favorable weight-to-volume ratio (or density).

Small van containers being loaded through rear cargo hatch of prop-jet air freighter.

Packaged meats, for example, have twice the density of auto parts. Also, most agricultural products are shipped from southern and western winter garden areas to large cities in the industrial Northeast and Midwest. They provide backhauls for planes carrying shipments of industrial products from these cities to the west and south. For these reasons agricultural products have enjoyed favorable airfreight rates.

Since many agricultural products move in fairly large quantities, they lend themselves to containerization for air shipment. Because this technique reduces ground handling expenses, the airlines now offer shippers a 10-percent discount on container shipments. Some shippers save as much as 30 percent by containerizing their cargos.

The first 10 years of the jet age have seen the level of airfreight rates reduced about 20 percent. Further reductions can be expected as the larger jets with greatly increased cargo capacities come into use in the decade ahead. This development will, in turn, generate further increases in air shipments as field-fresh products are placed within reach of more and more consumers.

The new jet cargo planes that will speed these products to market in the 1970's are so huge they stagger the imagination. The cargo compartment in the L–500 is 176 feet long and 19 feet wide; and in the 747, it is 161 feet long and 19 feet, 5 inches wide. Both planes will be able to carry containerized cargo, with the L–500 having a capacity of 30,300 cubic feet, almost 15 times that of a 40-foot-long rail refrigerator car. The cargo compartment of the L–500 can hold 58 large automobiles or 120 compact automobiles.

Weight-carrying capacities of the new planes are also impressive. Payload capacity of the L–500 is 160 tons and that of the 747 is 137 tons— or the equivalent of 8 to 10 truck trailer loads of cargo.

The new air freighters will be not only larger but also faster than today's cargo jets. Average speed of the big jets will be 515 miles per hour, compared with about 473 miles per hour for the largest of the cargo jets in use today. Flying range of the huge planes with maximum payloads will be about 3,000 miles.

With greater speed, range, and cargo capacities, the jumbo jets will have lower ton-mile costs (cost of carrying 1 ton 1 mile). The new planes are expected to produce almost

800,000 ton-miles a day, compared with about 240,000 ton-miles for today's jets and only 46,000 ton-miles for the propeller-driven cargo planes of 1950. Total operating cost per ton-mile for the big jets is expected to range from 5.2 to 5.4 cents, compared with a cost of about 8.6 to 9.8 cents for today's jet freighters and from 20 to about 31 cents for the piston-driven aircraft in use about 15 years ago.

It is estimated that more than 30 percent of total jet freight costs today are incurred in ground handling of the cargo. Further, the airlines know from bitter experience that savings in transit time gained in flight can be lost on the ground because of delays in cargo handling. U.S. Department of Agriculture studies of air shipments of strawberries from California to eastern markets revealed that only 34 percent of the transit time was spent in the air, whereas 45 percent was spent at airports and 21 percent in trucks going to and from the airports.

Ground handling delays are being attacked on several fronts. New sophisticated ground handling devices are already in service. These devices are, in effect, huge portable elevators on wheels that can lift pallet loads and containerized shipments to the height of the plane's cargo compartment.

New cargo terminals, planned or already under construction, will have their floor areas at plane height for direct movement of cargo into the planes. By the mid-1970's, domestic air carriers are expected to have almost $6 billion invested in air cargo terminals; and $8.5 billion by 1980.

Aircraft makers also are in the cargo handling act. The L–500 air freighter, for example, is designed for straight in and out movement of cargo and containers through huge openings into the main cargo compartment, 19 feet wide and 13½ feet high. The plane will have built-in, power-driven roller conveyors in the cargo compartment floor to allow 20- and 40-foot long van

Van container is moved into place in 747 jet freighter by built-in powered conveyors in cargo compartment floor.

containers to be rolled in and out in a few minutes.

Intermodal containerization is another technique that will cut air terminal delays and handling costs. The loading of refrigerated and insulated van containers at the shipper's plant allows his products to be carried direct to the receiver's loading dock without any rehandling or transfer of individual packages.

Controlled temperatures, humidities, and atmospheric makeup will be maintained inside the containers. This controlled environment puts many perishables to sleep to keep them at the peak of freshness. Handling damage, spoilage, and quality losses will be minimized.

Special types of containers such as those for livestock, with food and water in each of several compartments, will allow live animals to be carried with the same comfort and care as airline passengers.

All transportation, especially international shipments, requires paperwork. Paperwork can be more time consuming and costly than cargo handling, and sometimes the movement of shipments is delayed until the necessary paperwork can be completed.

Plans for cutting through the paperwork jungle cover many fronts. They include simplification of shipping documents, and computerization and automation of many steps in handling and processing. Computers also will process reservations for cargo, days and weeks in advance, thereby assuring the shipper that a plane will be waiting for his shipment when it reaches the airport.

Ground transport of shipments to and from the airports is also receiving attention. Mathematical simulation and systems analysis techniques will be used to find the fastest, lowest cost routing for trucks picking up and delivering air shipments. Such sophisticated analytical techniques also will be used to coordinate cargo flight schedules and pick-up and delivery schedules with the shipper's and the market's requirements.

These are but a few of the many steps which will be taken to speed shipments of agricultural products to market by air in the 1970's. But what about the decade beyond?

Already in the planning stage are such developments as the SST (Supersonic Transport); a six-engine giant subsonic air freighter capable of carrying half a million pounds; a new type of jet freighter made lighter with helium gas; and helicopters with lifting capacities of 25,000 pounds, which could be used to pick up and deliver containers in a few minutes.

MORE AND BETTER, BUT HOW? A RECAP OF OUR NATURAL RESOURCE CHOICES

AFFLUENT AMERICANS will demand more and higher quality natural resources in the future. Provision of more natural resources or their products will present difficult but not insurmountable problems. Meeting the probable demand for higher quality natural resources will require greater technological and social adjustments—and may, in fact, require substantial modification of popular attitudes and prevailing life styles.

So much popular discussion concerns "natural resources" that the term has come to have many meanings, and hence sometimes to be ambiguous. I use it, in this chapter, to include literally any attribute or characteristic of Nature that Man can and does use to his profit or enjoyment.

Thus, I include not only such obvious candidates as minerals and fuels, and forests, land, water, but also such aspects of Nature as a favorable

337

climate which attracts a labor force which in turn is the basis for an electronics industry. I include also the beauty of a natural or man-made scene and clean water and clear air.

The arguments to support my assertion that more natural resources will be demanded in the future are easily stated. In fact, implicitly they have been provided in earlier chapters. For one basic fact, there will be more Americans in the future than there are today. In every year of our national history, total population has risen; barring some catastrophic war, it will continue to rise in every foreseeable future year.

The instinct to reproduce and the fundamental desire to have a family are basic to the whole of our society. More people will demand more natural resources—it is as simple as that.

But the average citizen of the future will also have a higher real income than his mythical counterpart of today. We older folk need only recall the conditions of life in our youth to realize how dramatic has been the increase in living standards during our lifetimes. Younger people demand today as their rightful due articles of consumption of which we did not dream in our youth. They in turn are going to discover how quickly their standards of living and of consumption get out of date.

If real incomes per capita in the next generation are double those of the present—as many sober economists think probable—then consumption patterns will differ substantially from those of today. And as a result the demands upon natural resources of nearly every kind will increase.

Partly as a result of higher real incomes, but perhaps partly as a result of new standards and concepts, the life

✦

AUTHOR MARION CLAWSON is Director, Land Use and Management Program, Resources for the Future, Inc., Washington, D.C. RFF is a nonprofit research organization supported by the Ford Foundation. Mr. Clawson is former Director of the Bureau of Land Management, U.S. Department of the Interior.

style of the average American is changing and will change. For instance, more and more families will possess a second or a third home. It will be increasingly difficult to say where they "live," for some parts of their lives will be in one place, other aspects elsewhere. Some of these additional homes will be mobile.

On Labor Day 1969, my son and I drove through the mountains of Utah and Colorado. Fully half of all the many cars we met on the road were campers—marvelously compact and convenient houses in pickup trucks, for vacation and other second home living. As recently as a decade ago, such campers were relatively uncommon. In another decade or so, nearly every family in the middle and upper income brackets, located near enjoyable outdoor country, will own one, I think.

Or, to take another instance, ownership of high quality sound reproduction equipment (stereos, hi-fi's, tape recorders, etc.) will become nearly universal for every *individual*, not merely for every family. Millions of teenagers today possess such equipment; one need only visit a record shop to see how much it is the young people who buy such equipment and the necessary records or tapes.

At the same time, there are some counter forces which will diminish the need for natural resources, at least relative to the gross national product (GNP). That is, though average incomes may double, average per capita demand for natural resources of all kinds may increase only by half or some other fraction. For one thing, increasingly our total national output is made up of services of many kinds, rather than goods. The beauty shop requires a lot less natural resources than does the manufacture of radios.

It is also true that the average unit of natural resources is processed today to a far greater degree than was the average unit a generation or more ago. Consider, for example, the difference between the iron used for steel rails to build the railroads a century or more ago, and the machined and finished metals in present-day space rockets. The one had a very high content of natural resources with a modest complement of labor and capital; the other has a limited component of resources and a very large input of highly skilled labor and of complex machines.

Moreover, the sheer efficiency of natural resource use has risen. This is perhaps most marked in the case of fuels; a pound of coal today produces far more electricity, or far more productive energy at the factory machine, than did a pound of coal a generation ago.

These trends toward more emphasis upon services and less upon goods, toward more processing of average units of natural resources, and toward greater efficiency in resource use will continue in the future. They will temper, but not fully offset, the increasing demands for natural resources growing out of more people, higher incomes, and changing life styles.

It is here that modern technology plays such a large role. Ours is clearly the age of Man most influenced by technology—up to now; but the future will almost certainly be increasingly technological.

One of the major effects of rising technology has been to develop substitutes for scarcer or more expensive resources. The development of a wide variety of versatile plastics, to serve many needs, has taken much of the pressure off of the supply of many minerals and also of some agricultural commodities, such as cotton.

Using coal, oil, limestone, and other common materials, a great variety of plastics has been developed for clothing, packaging, and numerous other uses. In my memory, artificial rubber has developed from an impractical suggestion to a vast industry; and the natural rubber-producing lands of the world have surely felt the impact of this technological development.

Technology can make a previously unusable natural resource usable and valuable. Geologists and others have known for many decades of the vast oil shale deposits of the Western United States and of the vast deposits of tar sands in Canada. The latter have begun to be used commercially; the oil shales are still on the horizon, but constitute a vast reservoir of potential oil for the inevitable day when other deposits of oil and gas are inadequate to meet the demand.

Technology underlies the increases in efficiency of natural resource use described earlier. Indeed, the greatest asset of our country, or any other, is likely to be its institutions of higher learning and research laboratories. With them, adequate natural resources can be found, or invented, or developed; without them, an otherwise generous natural resource endowment may have dubious usefulness.

My colleagues at Resources for the Future and I for 15 years have conducted intensive research on these problems of natural resource supply and demand. We have drawn upon the research of government agencies, universities, and industry; and we have, I think, stimulated some such research by others.

The results of our research can be summarized, somewhat over-simplified, by saying that for the foreseeable future the material well-being of the American people will not be jeopardized by absolute scarcities or seriously rising prices of raw materials. There will be problems in providing enough natural resources of the kinds sought in the time and place demanded, at what seem to be reasonable prices; but the problems are far from insurmountable.

This is a comforting conclusion, in sharp contrast to the viewers-with-alarm who have predicted famine and disaster, from the time of Malthus on down. There is no reason to relax, to assume that the apples will fall from the tree into our laps or our mouths, but no reason to predict doom. These are the bases of my opening statement about the supply of natural resources being sufficient to meet our needs.

Left, signs along highway in a suburban county. Right, after lecture from a State trooper for littering highway, these motorists were given chance to retrieve litter.

But the quality of the available natural resources is something else again. There will be enough water (at a price), but how polluted? There will be as much air as there has ever been, but how polluted? There can be an adequate park acreage, but how littered will be the parks and how cluttered with billboards will the highways be? And so on, one could go through the whole range of natural resources, contrasting the quantity and quality aspects of the situation.

I think it clear that people are going to demand higher quality natural resources in the future. There has been a mounting tide of criticism about air pollution, for instance. Whereas 30 years ago, in the Great Depression of the 1930's, almost any city would have been delighted to have a factory pouring smoke into the air, for that would have evidenced some jobs, to-day many cities are beginning to enact ordinances and otherwise to control air pollution. Once a stream was looked upon as a cheap outlet for industrial and municipal wastes; today we have Federal, State, and local legislation to control waste discharges and to maintain or improve water quality.

In my youth, we thought it natural to dump our tin cans and other garbage at some convenient spot at the edge of town and were not concerned if a little spilled onto the streets as we hauled our garbage to the dump; today, every State has highway litter laws, with stiff penalties for those who litter the roads. Once upon a time, we felt little demand for parks, depending upon the natural countryside to supply our limited outdoor recreation demands; today, there are National, State, and local programs to acquire and develop more park acreage.

"Beauty" has become a national program or issue, and many persons have become conscious of the scars and blots upon the natural landscape. A Wilderness Act has been passed, and many areas have been or likely will be designated as wilderness, to have no commercial development. These and other recent actions or popular outcries are evidence of powerful public attitudes which will condition natural resource use in the future.

Much of the concern over natural resource quality of the past decade has been more notable for the indignation it has expressed than for the action it has produced. Thus, though every State has a highway antilitter law, most highways are lined with beer and soft drink cans, and facial tissue has been described as our national weed.

Everybody fulminates about air pollution, yet mighty little effective

340

action to control pollution has yet been taken. The demand for more parks is very vocal, and indeed the voters in many States have approved bond issues to increase park acreage, yet Federal and other commitments to expend funds for this purpose have repeatedly been postponed.

I do not wish to sound cynical. The first step is to arouse people to the need for action; this has been, at least partially, achieved. The problems are stubborn; they did not arise yesterday, and they cannot be solved quickly and cheaply. Persistent action will be called for, and costs must be met some way. One can admire the progress made, and yet be realistic about what is yet to be done.

There is a fundamental inconsistency between our demands or requirements for *more* natural resources, and our rising demand for *better* resources. If we are to have more electricity for myriad consumption uses in our homes then in some way the smoke, or nuclear radiation, or excess heat "pollution" inevitable in generation of electricity must be absorbed, discharged, or dissipated somewhere. If we are to have an automobile per person, and if each of us is to drive to work or to shop when and as he pleases, then air pollution is inevitable with present technology.

The whole range of consumption goods that flows into a city must somehow flow out again, as "waste" or "residuals." Thus, the water, fuel, food, building materials, and scores of other production or consumption goods must show up as air, water, or solid waste residuals. The tonnage of the outflow must be equal to the tonnage of the inflow; this is the law of the conservation of Nature which scientists long ago formulated and which most of us learned in our youth but overlooked in our concern with some specific form of pollution.

We can scrub the stack gases from the electric power plant, and thus reduce the air pollution; but do we dump the ash in the streams, thus creating water pollution, or do we

bury it, thus creating a solid waste disposal problem? We can burn household trash, thus adding to air pollution; or we can run it through the disposal, thus adding to water-borne wastes; or we can have it hauled to the city dump, thus increasing the solid waste disposal problem.

The inconsistency in our demands for natural resources runs still deeper than the foregoing illustrations suggest. Life is, in many ways, an inconsistency. Birth itself implies death; if people are born but no one ever died, an inexorable accumulation of human beings would result. We wish to preserve and lengthen life, and to enrich its quality; and, in this as in nearly every other country, we also wish to have more children and to increase population, as families and as a nation. Yet one cannot have both more people and a higher level of living per person, without paying a price of some kind.

Our accumulated knowledge, our research, our accumulated material resources, our government and other institutions, the energy and skill of our people—all these, and other aspects of our modern life can be mobilized to cope with the resource problems inherent in a rising demand for both more and better natural resources. But let us not delude ourselves that the answers will come easily or without some sacrifices.

Like the fairy tale that ended with "they were married and lived happily ever after," we have assumed that delivery to the consumer was the end. Every young married couple has to wake up to the fact that marriage is just the beginning of a long series of adjustments and changes, many pleasurable and some less so. Likewise, those of us concerned with national production and consumption are just beginning to realize that delivery to the consumer is not the end but only the first step in a new round of processes.

Our manufacturing industries have designed autos, refrigerators, washing machines, and a thousand other consumer goods to meet the needs of the consumer; no one has yet designed an auto or a refrigerator that would be efficient to scrap and from which the metal and other production materials could easily be salvaged.

Our food processing industries have concentrated on getting food and drink to the consumer in an unpolluted, hygienic, and attractive condition; but little concern has been directed to the ultimate disposal of the containers in which that food and drink was packaged. We need a faster rotting beer can, for instance, which will at the same time preserve the beer adequately until it is consumed.

It seems clear to me that Americans in the future must learn a great deal more about production, consumption, and residual management processes than we have generally known in the past. We will be, I think, forced increasingly to choose among or between essentially incompatible desires and demands. Costs will have to be incurred to dispose of wastes in acceptable ways; one cannot have both the lowest cost electricity or other goods or services and also the purest air and cleanest streams.

If we choose a degree of improved resource quality, then we must restrain those productive mechanisms which would produce cheaper products at the expense of more pollution, or we must provide new incentives for producers to reduce pollution as well as to produce more cheaply. The competitive business system has put great rewards on efficiency in production, but few or no rewards to minimizing pollution. Government action has increasingly intervened, to provide new controls or new incentives. I see no reason to expect that public action will not be necessary in the future.

We can do a great many things to preserve or create a world we want, but we cannot have everything—some situations or outputs are mutually incompatible. What do we, as a people, really want?

342

THE YEARS AHEAD IN AGRICULTURE

FARMING OPERATIONS will be increasingly coordinated with related industries into a broad and dynamic food and fiber industry. By 1980–85 farms may number at least a third fewer than today. And a larger share of them will be the more specialized and highly commercialized operations.

These projections reflect prospects for continued advances in technology, rising costs for labor and land, demand growth, and extensive demand shifts among commodities. They also reflect the prospects that farming will become more factory-like and coordinated in a complex of related agribusinesses.

Today's food and fiber industry is made up of a group of closely related industries. They produce and move to the final users, mostly consumer households, a volume of food and fiber products valued at nearly a fifth of the total value of goods and services produced (Gross National Product) by the economy.

Expected growth in economic activity and population provide a basis for appraising demands on farming and the agricultural industry. Although economic growth will continue small in 1970, growth potential is favorable for the decade, in view of prospects for a rapid increase in the labor force and continued advances in production technology.

Population of the United States totaled more than 205 million in 1970. The projected rise to about 230 million people by 1980 probably will not quite match the 14 percent increase in the 1960's.

During the seventies the most vital and fertile 25-to-34-year age group will increase by 50 percent. The number of people 45 to 54 years old will decline.

This changing age mix will result in rapid growth in the labor force among the younger and most vigorous workers. They will be establishing new families and demanding all manner of goods and services. Marriage rates will increase, and the number of children under 5 years may rise by 30 to 40 percent in the decade.

Combining the major elements of growth—labor force, hours worked, and productivity—suggests an economic growth potential of more than 4 percent per year in the 1970's. This would increase the output of goods and services by around 50 percent in the decade.

With a much less inflationary rise in the general price level, the Gross National Product may increase at an average annual rate in excess of 6 percent. This would add up to a rise of 85 percent in the decade, or to around $1.8 trillion by 1980 compared with the $980 billion estimated for 1970. Such economic growth would materially expand domestic markets for the agricultural industry.

Consumption of food and fiber products as they come from the farm changes little in response to changes in income and prices. Per capita use may increase only 1 to 2 percent with a 10 percent advance in income or a 10 percent reduction in prices.

The small increase in per capita use during recent years is due mainly to upgrading the diet to higher valued meats and convenience foods. Consumption of foods in pounds and calories has trended downward. However, today's housewife desires quality, variety, and convenience in her foods, textiles, and clothing. Accordingly, her demand is strong for related processing and services.

Consumer demand for these services is possibly 5 times as responsive as the raw farm product to changes in

✦

AUTHOR REX F. DALY is Director of the Economic and Statistical Analysis Division, Economic Research Service.

prices and incomes. A 10 percent increase in income may step up the demand for processing and marketing services, including eating out, by possibly 8 percent or more.

Combined consumer expenditures for such final products as food, beverages, clothing, shoes, and tobacco, both for the farm product and related services, usually increase about two-thirds as much as consumer income. Thus, expenditures for food are a declining percentage of consumer income as the economy grows.

In 1970 consumers will spend around $190 billion for food, beverages, clothing, footwear, and tobacco. Food and beverage outlays, projected to 1980 on the basis of their relationship to income, may increase about 65 percent to more than $205 billion. Combined expenditures for clothing, tobacco, and shoes are projected to rise nearly 85 percent to around $112 billion.

Expenditures for products of the agricultural processing industries increased nearly 80 percent in the decade 1958 to 1968 compared with an increase of about 25 percent in the value of farm output. Value of the major final consumer products originating in agriculture increased about 60 percent.

In 1968, around two-thirds of the value of consumer expenditures for food represented purchases from processing industries. Small direct purchases from agriculture and outlays for trade and transportation services accounted for the balance. The value of farm products sold to the processor plus direct consumer sales by farmers equaled around a fourth of total consumer expenditures for food and beverages.

Demand for the processing and marketing services purchased with basic farm products, including eating out, will increase in coming years perhaps about as rapidly as consumer income. In response, the output of the processing and marketing industries may increase 80 to 90 percent in the 1970's.

Domestic markets for raw farm products will likely increase only a little faster than population in the 1970's—perhaps 15 to 18 percent. Most of the increase will come in red meats and poultry and in the feed crops needed by livestock.

Export markets will remain important for grains, soybeans, fats and oils, some fruits, and perhaps for cotton and tobacco. Although growth in exports may not match the fast pace from 1950 to 1965, expected increases greatly exceed the rate of growth in the domestic market.

Domestic and export markets for food and fiber products largely determine a projected 20 percent increase in farm output. Purchased materials and goods used in production, which in recent years accounted for around two-thirds of farm output, will increase possibly half again as much as output. These purchased inputs include such farm products as livestock, feed, and seed, as well as fertilizer, chemicals and petroleum, agricultural processing, transportation, trade, and business services.

Recent industry input-output tables, which show deliveries of products to the final consumer as well as sales and purchases among some 370 other industries, suggest that an increase of $1 billion in deliveries to consumers of food from livestock products would require an increase in total economic activity of almost $2.7 billion.

Perhaps the most rapid changes in agriculture will continue to be in resource adjustment and associated changes in productivity and farm numbers.

Shifts in resource use, largely in response to advances in technology and changes in the relative cost of inputs, have resulted in the replacement of labor and, to some extent, land with machinery and equipment, fertilizer, chemicals, and other nonfarm resources. These inputs will continue to substitute for increasingly dear labor and land.

Yields will continue to increase and gains may be rapid enough in the 1970's to match demand expansion without an increase in the use of land.

The volume of resources used in agriculture has changed little in the past two decades despite big changes in the capital-labor-land mix. In view of prospects for further moderate growth in demand and continued advances in productivity, total resource use in agriculture may change little in the next 10 to 15 years.

Farms now contain more than a billion acres of land, some 450 million acres of which are classified as cropland. Around 300 million acres have been harvested in recent years. The remaining cropland has been pasture, fallow, idle, or diverted acreage under Government programs. In recent years, 50 to 60 million acres of cropland have been so diverted.

In addition to the 450 million acre cropland base, possibly 250 million acres are suitable for regular cultivation and could be brought into use if demand expansion or incentives were strong enough.

Crop yields per acre will continue to increase, possibly about as fast as in the past. The growing concern about contamination of our environment could operate to moderate chemical inputs and to slow yield advances. Moreover, as agriculture approaches an industry of large commercial units, yield advances due to structural change will be slower.

Nevertheless, crop yields probably will continue to increase about as rapidly as growth in demand for crops in the next 10 to 15 years.

The stock of productive assets in agriculture—consisting mainly of land, buildings, and livestock—increased less than 5 percent in real (adjusted for price level) terms during the past decade. Although outlays for purchased inputs will continue to increase more rapidly than output, combined use of productive assets may increase only modestly, particularly if the pace of farm consolidation continues.

The projected rapid rise in labor productivity will require increased use of capital per farmworker. But if

Advanced farm of future may have high-rise livestock feeding houses with connected feed mills, controlled environment fields, remote controlled combine-tillers, rapid transportation and control towers equipped with computers, instantaneous market and weather reports, plus analytical techniques for gearing production to markets. (Illustration © National Geographic Society)

agriculture is made up of fewer farm-workers as well as fewer and larger farms, overall capital requirements may grow relatively slowly.

Labor employed in agriculture will decline further in coming years. In 1969 farm employment was about 4.6 million, and only 1 million of these were hired workers. Total employment was about 60 percent of what it had been a decade earlier.

Projected labor requirements for 1980 suggest around 3 to 3½ million workers. And farm population, as now defined, may total around 7 to 8 million by 1980 compared with 10.3 million in 1969.

Technical possibilities exist for an accelerated combination of farms into large efficient units. Production technology and the feasibility of more interindustry coordination of operations will continue to be a major force in farm consolidation.

Projections of recent trends in farm numbers by size of operation suggest

around 2 million farm units by 1980. The fewer than 3 million farms in 1969 compares with over 4 million in 1959 and 5.7 million in 1949.

The size distribution of the 2 million farms projected for 1980 would look about as follows:

• Around a fourth of the farms would have cash receipts above $20,000 per farm. They would account for 85 to 90 percent of total cash receipts, 75 percent of net farm income, 75 percent of productive assets, and possibly 60 to 70 percent of the land and labor employed in agriculture.

• Some 25 to 30 percent of the farms would fall in a group with cash receipts per farm ranging from $2,500 to $20,000. These farms may account for around a tenth of cash receipts, a fourth of the labor, and perhaps 15 to 20 percent of the land and productive assets used in agriculture.

• Possibly 40 to 45 percent of the farms would be largely rural resi-

345

dences. They may account for less than 2 percent of total cash receipts, around 10 percent of the land and other assets, and possibly 15 percent of total labor used. Most of their income would continue to come from off-farm sources.

Although the organization of agriculture projected above appears reasonable based on recent trends, technical possibilities exist for an even greater shift to larger commercial farm units. U.S. agriculture in 1980 could be made up of farms of the size and general organization of today's Class I commercial farms having sales above $40,000 per farm. Perhaps around 400,000 such farms could produce the farm output projected for 1980.

It is equally reasonable to assume an even greater consolidation into units much like today's large-scale farm units with sales above $100,000. These farms are increasing in number the most rapidly of all size groups. Possibly fewer than 200,000 of today's large-scale farms could produce the farm output projected for 1980.

Such farms could average gross income around $375,000 to $400,000 per farm in 1965 prices. Net income may run $70,000 to $80,000 per farm.

Farms this size, organized as today, would use productive assets of perhaps $1 million or more per farm and average around 4,000 acres per farm. Total acreage of land in farms probably would run well below the billion acres now in farms, but there might be little change in total acreage of land planted to crops.

Farms this size may average 7 or 8 men per farm, but total employment in farming could drop to 1½ to 2 million workers, including family labor.

Farm and related marketing and processing operations will become more highly coordinated for some commodities even though the farm operating unit does not become huge. There is widespread evidence that the agribusiness industry is extending its technical and managerial skill into the production and marketing of some foods. But the process is selective and so far involves mainly poultry, eggs, citrus, and a few other crops.

The mix of farm types that may evolve by 1980–85 can be only roughly indicated, partly because even specialized farms will produce more than one commodity.

However, if the farms of 1980 were organized much like today's large-scale farm, the following numbers could provide projected output for selected commodities:

• Possibly 60,000 to 70,000 livestock farms.

• Some 20,000 to 30,000 poultry farms and a similar number of dairy farms.

• Only 10,000 to 15,000 cotton farms.

• Probably no more than 5,000 tobacco farms.

• Perhaps around 100,000 large-scale grain farms.

Farming by 1980 probably will not be as much of a two-sector farm-nonfarm split as it is today. Farming operations will become more highly integrated into the food and fiber industry.

Many production and marketing processes will be even more factory-like, with output geared to consumer demand. This will involve greater coordination between producers and processors, integrated planning and management, and close orientation to market demands.

The food, beverages, tobacco, clothing, shoes, and other products of the agribusiness industries, which now amount to a third of total consumer outlays, will continue to be of primary importance to the consumer.

A more highly coordinated industry of large farms very likely would operate more like the large nonfarm manufacturing industries. Accordingly, planning of capital outlays, production schedules, and pricing of food and fiber products may be more closely tailored to market demand and to the income goals of the agricultural industry.

INTERNATIONAL AGRICULTURE IN THE SEVENTIES

THERE ARE SEVERAL bright spots as international agriculture enters the 1970's. International trade in farm products is at an all time high. The developing countries have emerged from a decade of near stagnation in per capita food production and can reasonably expect a modest improvement in their food situation. New and higher yielding seeds, cheaper and more abundant fertilizers, and the required herbicides and pesticides are now a reality.

In the developed countries the average economic well-being of farm people is at an historic high and has been increasing at least as rapidly as for the rest of the population. Thus farm people are sharing fully in the fruits of economic growth.

These are significant accomplishments, indeed. But there are other facts, both actual and potential, that bode little good for the decade unless appropriate action is taken.

Due in large part to the agricultural and trade policies of the developed countries, the output of farm products is increasing faster than demand. This fact would have been evident in the 1960's had it not been for three quite unrelated events that temporarily put heavy pressure upon the world's supply of food grains: poor wheat crops in the Soviet Union in 1963 and 1965 resulting in large-scale wheat imports over a four-year period, lagging grain production in India and Pakistan through the early 1960's followed by serious drought in 1965 and 1966, and the emergence of Communist China as a major importer of wheat.

The sharp increase in international trade in feed grains, which has now tapered off, also helped to engender a feeling of optimism.

As the 1960's ended, world stocks of grain were once again on the increase and they were built up at a more rapid rate than they had declined earlier in the decade.

The Kennedy Round of Trade Negotiations had accomplished relatively little reduction in the barriers to trade for farm products. One of the outcomes of those negotiations, the International Grains Arrangement, had been largely nullified before the decade ended.

As the 1970's began there was little evidence that most developed nations were concerned about the impending consequences of more rapid growth of supply than of demand at prevailing prices.

If the developing countries increase their own food production faster than demand increases due to rising incomes and population growth, the need for—and willingness to accept—food aid will clearly be less than in the 1960's.

It should be remembered that before World War II the developing regions of the world were net exporters of grain. For the first half of this century South America exported more grain than North America. Even Asia, with its huge population, was a small net exporter of grain until World War II.

It appears unwarranted to expect a significant increase in food grain imports by the developing countries during the decade of the seventies. In fact, the Indicative World Plan of the Food and Agriculture Organization projects a small net export of grains by the developing countries in 1985.

Of equal, or perhaps greater, significance is the conclusion of the Indica-

+

AUTHOR D. GALE JOHNSON is Professor of Economics at The University of Chicago. He is author of *Trade and Agriculture: A Study of Inconsistent Policies*, and *The Struggle Against World Hunger*.

tive World Plan that the developed countries have the potential for increasing grain output much faster than the growth in demand. Thus, unless policies are changed, a huge surplus capacity will emerge by the end of the 1970's.

Two other recent studies, one by the Economic Research Service of the U.S. Department of Agriculture and the other by the Organization for Economic Co-operation and Development, come to the same conclusion. The OECD study concludes that the developed (non-Communist) regions "have the potential to expand food production well beyond their own needs."

While the above has emphasized grains, the same general situation is likely to prevail for dairy products, sugar, tobacco, fats and oils, and cotton.

I hasten to note that the cautiously optimistic view of food production potentialities in the developing coun-

Left, healthy child in Malawi. Below, bringing in the grapes by motor scooter in Italy.

348

tries should not lead them or the United States to relax their efforts to increase food production *in* the developing regions.

The recent trends and projections of food availability in the developing regions imply only a very modest improvement in per capita food consumption during the seventies. Diets would still be largely grain or root oriented; animal products would have only a minor role. Perhaps most important, the deficiency of high quality protein would remain in many parts of the world.

Thus while U.S. aid programs will need to be adjusted to anticipated changes, such programs should not be abandoned. In fact, the U.S. support for research efforts within the developing countries should be strengthened and greatly expanded.

The basis for cautious optimism concerning the food situation in the developing countries is due primarily to the availability of new varieties of wheat, rice, and other grains. These varieties are responsive to fertilizer and improved cultural practices. But two facts must be remembered.

First, a great deal of research will be required to maintain the productivity of the new high yielding varieties. As all farmers know, plant varieties become susceptible to insects and diseases as time goes by. We must never ignore the possibility that unforeseen developments may result in near crop failure of one of the new varieties as its acreage expands. Our own experience indicates how much vigilance is required to win the continuous "battle with nature."

Second, the new high yielding varieties are now available for only a relatively small part of the cultivated area of the developing countries. Africa and Latin America, especially the tropical areas, have gained little from the recent developments.

Except for rice, very little research has been undertaken on food products grown in the tropics. Substantial investment in research may be required to develop high yielding varieties for all of the major tropical areas, especially those areas relying on food crops other than grains.

If the U.S. governmental aid programs are to make a major contribution to the vastly expanded research effort, there must be a major change in our aid efforts. Up to the present our governmental research programs for agriculture in the developing regions have been less successful than the much smaller programs undertaken by private foundations.

Much of the limited success of the governmental efforts has been the result of our impatience—our hope of quick results. As a nation we have been unwilling to underwrite the necessary long run commitment to research for the development of new varieties and new cultural practices.

One of the challenges of the 1970's is to reorganize and expand our research contribution. There is no doubt that we have the capacity to do so. Most of what is required is patience and long-term financial commitment.

While the need for food aid on a continuing basis probably will decline during the decade, it would be a mistake for the United States to dismantle the effective machinery it has developed to meet emergency conditions almost anywhere in the world.

For several years the food situation in many parts of the world will be precarious even if there is considerable success in increasing food production. Most developing countries have inadequate storage facilities and limited amounts of uncommitted foreign exchange. Thus a crop disaster could lead to human distress or could substantially slow up progress in improving conditions.

In this situation the provision of food aid on a temporary and emergency basis could prevent human suffering and permit the progress being made to continue with little adverse effect from crop disaster.

The United States has an unparalleled ability to transport food under emergency conditions to virtually any point in the world. That ability has been called upon many times in recent years and I can see no good reason why this capacity should not be maintained. It is an instrument of goodwill and humanitarianism; it has prevented much human suffering. It makes the world a little better place for millions of very poor people.

Capacity of the developed countries to produce more farm products than they can export and consume, at satisfactory prices, is a major impediment to a reduction in the barriers to trade in agricultural products during the 1970's.

The excess capacity in the developed countries has not come about primarily as a result of certain inexorable natural forces or rapid technological change. It is primarily the creature of farm and trade policies that have induced farmers to produce more and more, even though there is no satisfactory market for the additional production.

The United States is the only country that has programs designed to limit production of major farm crops. Programs have removed about 50 million acres of cropland from cultivation. But our agricultural policies have never been known for their consistency.

While limiting cropland, we have had other programs that increase farm production. And in the case of some farm products we follow a price and production policy that is similar to what we criticize others for. Our dairy prices are significantly above world prices, due to import quotas and export subsidies, and we make no effort to restrict production.

In fact, we have no evidence to show that on balance all of the U.S. farm programs actually reduce production below the level that would prevail in the absence of governmental programs.

Unless a concerted effort is made by the governments of the developed countries, trade in farm products will be more managed at the end of the decade than at the beginning. The market for the increased output of the developing countries probably will be more circumscribed than it is now.

A developing country that is successful in increasing its output of a grain above its domestic use will be confronted with artificially depressed world prices. The prices will be depressed by high import levies and export subsidies, which are the reactions of governments of the developed countries to excess productive capacity.

It is relatively easy to say what should be done in a new round of negotiations, if the objective is to achieve a reduction in trade barriers. Such negotiations must be concerned with all aspects of the agricultural policies of the participating nations. It is quite clear that little is gained by binding a tariff duty or even by reducing it if domestic subsidies are increased to keep the returns to farmers at the same level as before.

It would be utopian to believe that during the 1970's governments will not attempt to increase the incomes of their farm populations. But in accepting this there is room for meaningful negotiations. The negotiations could emphasize the elimination of all domestic measures that increase farm production and the development of means to assist farmers to adjust to changing conditions. A search for farm income support measures with minimum effects upon production should also be a part of such negotiations.

As long as the governments of the developed countries claim that it is only their own business how high their farm prices are or how much and what kind of subsidies are paid to farmers, international trade in farm products will continue to be subjected to trade barriers that greatly restrict the advantages of specialization.

The United States would have a very special and delicate role to play in such negotiations. In a number of cases it would greatly expand its exports if trade barriers were reduced. On the other hand, most of Western Europe would significantly increase imports. But it must also be recognized that the United States would have to accept more imports of several farm products.

We could certainly not anticipate gaining access to other markets for our low cost products and at the same time exclude imports of the farm products that we are currently protecting, especially sugar, dairy products, peanuts, and long staple cotton. And the United States would also have to be willing to discuss a number of its politically popular farm programs that increase farm production, such as the Agricultural Conservation Program, irrigation, watershed developments, and the form in which it pays subsidies to its producers of cotton, wheat, and feed grains.

As noted in my earlier chapter, what the United States does with its agricultural, aid, and trade policies is important to the world. But believing this we should not overestimate the importance of our efforts at limiting farm output, either to ourselves or to the rest of the world.

It has been assumed that if one of the major export commodities gets into enough trouble, the United States will make an effort through acreage limitation and storage to try to set things right. Such a course of action is no longer meaningful for the United States. We are not so important in the production of any given farm product that we can for long have a significant effect upon the world price for that product. Nor would successful restriction of our production of major export crops have any significant effect upon farm incomes.

Almost all the income gains from our present farm programs come from direct payments plus the marketing certificates on wheat. The price effects of the programs are very small. And if we attempt to increase the price effect, we will clearly see a major loss of export markets.

Unless other industrial countries take steps to limit the growth of farm production, we may well find there is little or no good purpose in our engaging in output limitation programs for the major export commodities. At a minimum, we can make the case that there is little point in our limiting production of the commodities whose output is encouraged by others.

Most of the farm programs of the industrial countries fail to attack the real causes of the income disparities suffered by farm people.

These disparities are not due to the level of farm prices or to the presence or absence of subsidies, but to certain conditions that exist in all industrial countries.

Policies and programs of industrial societies seldom recognize a fundamental and irrefutable truth, namely that one of the major consequences of economic growth is a continuing decline in the number of farm families. Yet government policies do little or nothing to assist the necessary and often quite painful adjustments that are required.

It is a social and political tragedy that in no society are farm people provided with the same educational opportunities available to the rest of the population. This failure is one of the main reasons for rural-urban income disparities.

The greatest challenge to international agriculture in the 1970's will be to meet the legitimate needs and aspirations of farm people in the industrial countries while achieving a reasonable balance between the growth in supply and demand for farm products. Such a balance should not be narrowly conceived in terms of the circumstances of a given country or a small group of countries, but should also reflect the legitimate aspirations of the developing countries to find export markets for their farm products.

This challenge will be difficult to meet. Yet if it is not met, a considerable part of the potential that agriculture has for contributing to the welfare of all mankind will be lost. This would be a tragedy. But such a tragedy is not inevitable and one can hope that the 1970's will prove that it can be avoided.

AND MILES TO GO . . .
WELL-BEING OF
PEOPLE MUST BE
OUR FINAL GOAL

THE VAST ABUNDANCE of food and fiber in the United States is the result of investments in research and education to develop and use improved technology in the production, processing, and distribution of farm commodities. The progress that has been made during the last 30 years is phenomenal.

Despite this progress, it is clear that currently known technology will not be sufficient to meet future needs. So it is imperative that our efforts to enhance the productivity of our agricultural resources be continued. But I shall argue that although the research to improve technology remains essential, we must give more attention to the side effects of changes in technology.

New technology may affect both the methods of production of a commodity and how much of it is produced. In most cases, though, when a new technology is introduced the effects extend quite far beyond the commodity.

As an example, the production of other commodities also may be changed. These effects may spill over into the farm supply, marketing, processing, and distribution firms. They, therefore, may affect greatly the level of economic activity throughout a community.

In total, the changes in technology that have been made during the last 30 years have altered the entire system of production, processing, and distribution of food and fiber. In many instances, the effects have been evi-

dent throughout communities and in some cases geographic regions.

There is no question that changes in technology have increased greatly the efficiency of production of farm commodities. However, many side effects that were unanticipated have emerged and constitute major problems for some people and some communities. Let us look at a few of these.

All people have not shared in benefits of the new technology. In fact, technological improvements in production resulted in hardships for farms which were too small to adopt profitably the new technology. These farms were placed at a greater disadvantage.

Many people who depended upon farm labor for a living suffered hardships as a result of adoption of the new technology. Those who depended upon farm employment as a source of livelihood found the demand for their services decreasing sharply. Whether the technological improvements were biological, chemical, or mechanical in nature, they almost invariably increased the productivity of capital and provided incentives to use more capital and less labor in the production of farm commodities. Many persons have found that they were no longer needed. They were left behind.

The net effect of changes in technology was to increase production and to increase the number of large, high-income farms, but to decrease the number of small, low-income farms and the number of farmworkers.

The structural reorganization of agriculture also extended far beyond farm boundaries. Changes in technology usually involve creation of new forms of capital. For example, the tractor replaced the mule. When this happens, old forms of capital such as mules are made obsolete while markets are created for the new forms, such as tractors.

The marketing firms created to

✦

AUTHOR C. E. BISHOP is Vice President for Research and Public Service Programs, University of North Carolina, Chapel Hill.

Shack is home to this rural South Carolina family.

supply these new capital forms usually serve a larger area than the old firms. Consequently, technological improvement may be accompanied by an extensive relocation of economic activities.

When this takes place the small towns and villages that are highly dependent upon forms of capital and methods of distribution that have been rendered obsolete experience an eroding away of their economic base. They too are left behind.

Technological and organizational changes of the kind referred to above have had major impacts upon many industries in the United States. These impacts have been so extensive in the natural resource-based industries such as farming, mining, and forestry, that there has been a large-scale reduction in the employment of people in these industries.

In most rural areas the employment created in other industries has not been sufficient to employ those released from the natural resource-based industries. The result has been one of the most massive migrations of people in history as millions left the small farms and villages of the United States in search of better employment opportunities elsewhere. Migration from rural areas has been so heavy, particularly among young adults, that many counties in the United States now are experiencing a decline in their population.

353

Small towns and villages have been particularly hard hit by the changes in technology. During the decade of the 1950's more than half the towns with 500 or fewer inhabitants suffered losses in population. On the other hand, more than 83 percent of the cities with 25,000 or more inhabitants gained population.

Between 1940 and 1960 the changes that took place in production technology and transportation technology encouraged concentration of production of farm and nonfarm products and concentration of people in urban centers. During this period, the growth of major metropolitan centers was quite pronounced.

Although the total rural population has been stable since 1950, the location of it has continued to change, with growth occurring in the suburbs near the cities and with population declining in the more isolated counties.

The changes in economic structure and location of population have altered relationships between rural and urban areas. Many of the functions that formerly were performed in the small villages in rural areas now are performed in cities. The changes in technology, therefore, ultimately have resulted in a transfer of functions from rural areas to urban areas and have strengthened the ties between rural and urban areas.

Neither the rural nor the urban areas are self-sufficient. Many of the services needed by farmers and others living in rural areas come from urban

Grass grows along street in main business section of southern town. About half the shops are closed down.

Kentucky rural school.

centers. Urban centers, on the other hand, depend upon farmers and people from the rural areas for food, fiber, labor, and other resources.

Because of the shifts in economic activity and the migration of people, many of the villages, towns, and counties in rural areas face stagnant or declining economic conditions.

Many counties, especially in the sparsely populated areas, are finding it increasingly difficult to provide schools, libraries, health services, and roads that constitute an environment conducive to rapid economic growth and development. Even more important, when the education and health services of an area are inferior, the residents of the area become handicapped.

Few would contend that the pattern of growth and development in the United States today is optimal. Although it has been shaped considerably by the development of technology, the pattern largely reflects adjustments to technological change rather than changes in technology designed to create any particular pattern of growth and development of the Nation.

Indeed, so far as the agricultural sector is concerned, the goals in the development of new technology have been to increase the efficiency of production of crops and livestock. Sufficient attention has not been given to the fact that production technology, the structure of the industry, and the pattern of growth of employment and population are interrelated.

Neither have the linkages between rural and urban areas received sufficient attention. In much of U.S. history the rural and urban areas have been treated as if they were separate and distinct. People living on farms and in rural areas were presumed to have different tastes and different needs than people in urban centers.

For example, it was assumed that

355

young men were quite likely to enter the same occupations as their fathers. Therefore, those who were born on the farm were offered an education oriented toward the training of farmers. Consequently, as the number of opportunities in farming dwindled and as young men who were born on farms turned in increasing numbers to non-farm employment, they found that their training and skills did not match the requirements of the occupations they were seeking to enter.

Many of those who migrated to urban centers became disillusioned and returned to their rural residences. Others who remained on farms and sought nonfarm employment have shifted back and forth between non-farm and farm employment, often unable to fulfill their expectations.

These facts illustrate the need for organizing society in such a way that people living in sparsely settled areas are able to obtain education, health services, and other services comparable to those available to people living in urban areas. Unless and until this is done, many of those who migrate from the rural areas will continue to be disillusioned.

There should no longer be any question that the vast majority of the people of the United States will live in metropolitan areas. Social organization in the United States cannot be treated adequately in an urban versus rural context. When there was less interdependence of economic and social activities of urban and rural areas, and when the political strength in the rural areas was greater, many organizational problems could be treated adequately by viewing the rural areas as an entity.

The technological and economic changes that have occurred during the past 30 years have rendered the urban-rural differences virtually meaningless from the standpoint of economic and social organization. Factor and product markets in rural areas are very much dependent upon conditions in the cities.

Furthermore, changes in the polit-ical arena have forced the rural population to become virtually dependent upon the urban population. It is imperative that the sparsely populated areas be related to their metropolitan counterparts if the people in those areas are to have access to adequate health services and other institutional services in the contemporary society.

Sound planning for the future dictates that rural areas be related to metropolitan areas in a system embracing the entire Nation. The task is to develop a settlement pattern that will focus simultaneously upon efficiency in the production and distribution of goods and services in both the private and public sectors.

Industrial plants should not be located in areas where costs will be excessive. Neither should government be expected to provide services under conditions where costs are excessively high. The location of industrial plants and the location of population affect the costs of producing and distributing both goods and services.

We need a comprehensive plan for development of the Nation that gives consideration to efficiency of production of goods in the private sector. Special consideration should be given to the number, size, and location of cities and how they are related. But consideration also must be given to how the people living outside the cities and beyond the metropolitan areas are to obtain access to the goods and services supplied through the private and public sectors.

A great deal of discussion is taking place concerning the possibilities of developing new towns and subsidizing the development of industry in special locations. Some nations are endeavoring to guide the settlement pattern on the land. The United States has done so in the past, and through various purchase and subsidy programs exerts an important influence upon the location of economic growth and the location of population currently.

But the necessary research has not been done to determine the benefits to the Nation from the creation of new towns and growth centers. Until the necessary research is done, public policies must be made on the basis of scanty information, and economic and social organization will continue to be determined largely in response to changes in the technology of production and marketing of material goods.

On the other hand, if the settlement pattern that is desired can be determined, perhaps technology can be developed that would enable that pattern to operate efficiently.

Although agricultural scientists have contributed greatly to economic growth through development of improved production technology, insufficient attention has been given to structural and organization implications of the technology developed.

In like manner, while production possibilities have been expanded greatly for many commodities, the opportunities for a large number of families have not expanded accordingly. Although many of the improvements in agricultural production technology have resulted from public investment in research and education, little attention has been given to distribution of the gains and the losses from technological change. The assets of some have been enhanced in value by the changes. The assets of others have been rendered obsolete.

Those who have incurred losses have been given little assistance in developing their resources or in finding alternative employment. Special assistance often is needed in making the adjustments necessary to establish profitable farms or in transferring to nonfarm employment. Without such assistance, many must continue to depend on public assistance and other forms of income transfers.

In summary, research is needed to obtain additional increases in the productivity of farm resources. This will be essential to meet the demand for food and fiber in the future. Research also is needed to improve the quality of life in rural areas. More emphasis should be placed upon distribution of the benefits of farm programs and of the gains from improvements in farm production technology.

Agricultural research has come a long way. The progress that has been made in increasing the output of farm crops and livestock products has been phenomenal. But—there are miles to go . . .

A balanced program of development must give consideration to improving the well-being of the people and to improving conditions in the communities, as well as to increasing the efficiency of production of crops and livestock. Enhancement of the well-being of the people is and must remain the ultimate objective.

357

Most of the photography in this Yearbook is the work of U.S. Department of Agriculture photographers. Prints of USDA black and white photos may generally be obtained from the Photography Division, Office of Information, U.S. Department of Agriculture, Washington, D.C. 20250. These are free to news media; others may obtain prints for a nominal charge. News media may obtain free duplicate color slides of many of the color photos from the Photography Division. These slides may also be purchased. In ordering prints or slides, please refer to the 1970 Yearbook and give the page number.

The Editor is indebted to the farm and food trade magazines, the State land-grant universities, the individual photographers, and the companies and organizations that helped provide additional photos for the Yearbook, and which in most cases are credited on the opposite page. USDA photos are not listed in the credits.

Please note that the first 32 pages of the Yearbook carry no page numbers. However, Page I is the page on which the first photo in full color appears. In the photo credits, pages are numbered consecutively with Roman numerals from this page on through the initial photo section. Credits with Arabic numerals indicate photos further back in the book.

Index